Core Connections, Course 3
Second Edition*, Version 5.0

Managing Editors / Authors

Leslie Dietiker, Ph.D., Director of Curriculum (Both Editions)
Boston University
Boston, MA

Evra Baldinger (First Edition)
University of California, Berkeley
Berkeley, CA

Michael Kassarjian (2nd Edition)
CPM Educational Program
Kensington, CA

Barbara Shreve (First Edition)
San Lorenzo High School
San Lorenzo, CA

Misty Nikula (2nd Edition)
CPM Educational Program
Bellingham, WA

Contributing Authors

Elizabeth Baker
Zane Middle School

Tara Bianchi
American Canyon Middle School

Bev Brockhoff
Glen Edwards Middle School

Clanci Chiu
Santa Barbara Junior High School

Mark Coté
Beaver Lake Middle School

Suzanne Cisco Cox
Turner Middle School

Kathleen Davies
Rincon Valley Middle School

Josea Eggink
Bloomington Public Schools

William Funkhouser
Zane Middle School

Lori Hamada
CPM Educational Program

Brian Hoey
CPM Educational Program

Janet Hollister
La Cumbre Jr. High School

Carol Jancsi
CPM Mentor Teacher

Rakesh Khanna
Hotmath, Inc.

Judy Kysh, Ph.D.
San Francisco State University

Sarah Maile
CPM Educational Program

Bruce Melhorn
International School Bangkok (ISB)

Chris Mikles
Post Falls Middle School

Bob Petersen
CPM Educational Program

Tom Sallee, Ph.D.
University of California, Davis

Lorna Thomas Vázquez
Neillsville, WI Math Consultant

Stephanie Whitney, Ph.D.
DePaul University

Program Directors

Elizabeth Coyner
Christian Brothers High School
Sacramento, CA

Leslie Dietiker, Ph.D.
Boston University
Boston, MA

Lori Hamada
CPM Educational Program
Fresno, CA

Brian Hoey
CPM Educational Program
Sacramento, CA

Michael Kassarjian
CPM Educational Program
Kensington, CA

Judy Kysh, Ph.D.
Departments of Education and
Mathematics San Francisco
State University, CA

Tom Sallee, Ph.D.
Department of Mathematics
University of California, Davis

Karen Wootton
CPM Educational Program
Odenton, MD

*Based on *Making Connections*: *Foundations for Algebra, Courses 1 and 2.*

e-book Manager
Carol Cho
Director of Technology
Martinez, CA

e-book Programmers
Rakesh Khanna
Daniel Kleinsinger
Kevin Stein

e-book Assistants
Debbie Dodd
Shirley Paulsen
Wendy Papciak
Anna Poehlmann
Jordan Wight

Assessment Manager
Karen Wootton
Director of Assessment
Odenton, MD

Assessment Assistants
Elizabeth Baker
Zane Middle School
Eureka, CA

William Funkhouser
Zane Middle School
Eureka, CA

Assessment Website
Elizabeth Fong
Michael Huang
Daniel Kleinsinger

Illustration
Kevin Coffey
San Francisco, CA

Jonathan Weast
Sacramento, CA

Homework Help Manager
Bob Petersen
CPM Educational Program

Homework Help Website
Carol Cho
Director of Technology

Parent Guide with Extra Practice
Elizabeth Coyner
Christian Brothers High School

Brian Hoey
CPM Educational Program

Bob Petersen
CPM Educational Program

Based on the Skill Builder materials created for Foundations for Algebra (2003), created by:

Heidi Ackley	Steve Ackley	Elizabeth Baker
Bev Brockhoff	Ellen Cafferata	Elizabeth Coyner
Scott Coyner	Sara Effenbeck	William Funkhouser
Brian Hoey	Judy Kysh	Kris Petersen
Robert Petersen	Edwin Reed	Stacy Rocklein
Kristie Sallee	Tom Sallee	Howard Webb

Technical Managers
Sarah Maile
Sacramento, CA

Aubrie Maze
Sebastopol, CA

Technical Assistants

Stephanie Achondo	Robert Ainsworth	Bethany Armstrong
Rebecca Bobell	Delenn Breedlove	Jason Cho
Hannah Coyner	Mary Coyner	Carmen de la Cruz
Matthew Donahue	Bethany Firch	Dana Kimball
Leslie Lai	Michael Li	Jerry Luo
Eli Marable	James McCardle	Nyssa Muheim
Alexandra Murphy	Wendy Papciak	Atlanta Parrott
Juanita Patian	Ryan Peabody	Iris Perez
Steven Pham	Anna Poehlmann	Eduardo Ramirez
John Ramos	Ali Rivera	Andrea Smith
Rachel Smith	Claire Taylor	Christy Van Beek
Megan Walters	Sarah Wong	Alex Yu

8 9 10   18 17 16 15

Version 5.0

Printed in the United States of America

ISBN: 978-1-60328-091-4

A Note to Students:

Welcome to a new year of math! In this course, you will learn to use new models and methods to think about problems as well as solve them. You will be developing powerful mathematical tools and learning new ways of thinking about and investigating situations. You will be making connections, discovering relationships, figuring out what strategies can be used to solve problems, and explaining your thinking. Learning to think in these ways and communicate about your thinking is useful in mathematical contexts, other subjects in school, and situations outside the classroom. The mathematics you have learned in the past will be valuable for learning in this course. That work, and what you learn in this course, will prepare you for future courses.

In meeting the challenges of this course, you will not be learning alone. You will cooperate with other students as a member of a study team. Being a part of a team means speaking up and interacting with other people. You will explain your ideas, listen to what others have to say, and ask questions if there is something you do not understand. In this course, a single problem can often be solved several ways. You will see problems in different ways than your teammates do. Each of you has something to contribute while you work on the lessons in this course.

Together, your team will complete problems and activities that will help you discover mathematical ideas and develop solution methods. Your teacher will support you as you work, but will not take away your opportunity to think and investigate for yourself. Each topic will be revisited many times and will connect to other topics. If something is not clear to you the first time you work on it, you will have more chances to build your understanding as the course continues.

Learning math this way has an advantage: as long as you actively participate, make sure everyone in your study team is involved, and ask good questions, you will find yourself understanding mathematics at a deeper level than ever before. By the end of this course, you will have a powerful set of mathematical tools to use to solve new problems. With your teammates you will meet mathematical challenges you would not have known how to approach before.

In addition to the support provided by your teacher and your study team, CPM has also created online resources to help you, including help with homework, and a parent guide with extra practice. You will find these resources and more at www.cpm.org.

We wish you well and are confident that you will enjoy this next year of learning!

Sincerely,

The CPM Team

Core Connections, Course 3
Student Edition

Chapter 3 Graphs and Equations   91

Chapter 4 Multiple Representations   149

CHAPTER 1 Problem Solving

Welcome to math class! This initial chapter will introduce you to many of the big ideas you will explore and the ways in which you will be working. You will apply your current mathematical knowledge to solve problems, some of which you will revisit later in the course using new algebraic tools.

In the second part of this chapter, you will develop methods for solving problems that involve proportional relationships. For example, if you want to know how many people at your school are left-handed, how can you use the information from your class to make a prediction? Questions like these will rely on your understanding about proportions.

Finally, this chapter is about problem solving. During this chapter, you will use a variety of problem-solving strategies that will remain useful throughout this course, including:

Guiding Questions

Think about these questions throughout this chapter:

How can I solve a problem that I have never seen before?

How can I organize my work?

How can I describe my process?

What is the relationship?

Collecting Data	Finding Patterns	Writing and Solving an Equation
Drawing a Graph	Working Backward	

Chapter Outline

Section 1.1   This section includes several problems and activities that use many of the big ideas of algebra. Each problem or activity requires your study team to work together and use various problem-solving strategies.

Section 1.2   In this section, you will use what you know about proportional relationships to solve proportional problems.

1.1.1   What stories can a graph tell?

. . . .

Interpreting Graphs

In this first section, you will focus on several challenges that will require you to use different problem-solving strategies. All of the problems are solvable with your current math skills. Some of them will be revisited later in the course so that you can apply algebraic tools to solve them more efficiently at that time. Each problem also introduces you to an important concept that you will study in this course.

1-1.   GETTING TO KNOW YOU, Part One

How can a graph tell a story? Today you will meet your team members and then work together to write a story for a graph.

Your Task: Your teacher will give you one part of a graph. Find the students in the class who have the other pieces of the same graph. When you find all of the students whose graph parts belong with yours, sit down together around a table or with your desks facing each other.

As a team, come up with a story that could be represented by your team's graph. Think carefully about each part of the graph. Once your team agrees on a story, make sure every member of the team can describe each part of the story. You should also be able to explain its connection to the corresponding part of the graph.

To help you and your team work together today, each member of your team has a specific job. Your job is assigned by your first name (or last name if team members have the same first name).

Team Roles

Resource Manager: If your name comes first alphabetically:

- Make sure that the team has tape.

- Ask the teacher when the *entire* team has a question. *"No one has an idea? Should I ask the teacher?"*

- Make sure your team cleans up by delegating tasks. You could say, *"I will put away the _____ while you _____ ."*

Facilitator: If your name comes second alphabetically:

- Start the team's discussion of the graph by asking, *"What could this graph be about? What are some ideas?"*

- Help the team agree on a story: *"Do we agree on all of the parts of our story?"*

Recorder/Reporter: If your name comes third alphabetically:

- Tape the graph pieces together on a piece of paper to form the graph.

- Take notes for the team. The notes should include phrases like, *"For part one…"* and explanations like, *"Because part one is not so steep…"*

Task Manager: If your name comes fourth alphabetically:

- Remind the team to stay on task and not to talk to students in other teams. You can suggest, *"Let's move on to another part of the graph."*

- Listen for reasons and challenge your teammates to justify their thinking. *"But why do you think that?"*

1-2.   GETTING TO KNOW YOU, Part Two

Suppose the graph at right represents something about the four students in your team. But what is the graph about? Decide what information the *x*- and *y*-axes could represent so that each point represents a different member of your team. Justify your statements.

METHODS AND **M**EANINGS

Fraction⇔Decimal⇔Percent

The **Representations of a Portion web** diagram at right illustrates that fractions, decimals, and percents are different ways to represent a portion of a number. Portions can also be represented in words, such as "four-fifths" or "twelve-fifteenths," or with diagrams.

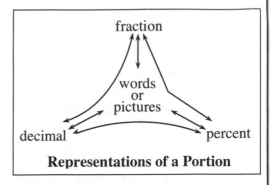

Representations of a Portion

The examples below show how to convert from one form to another.

Decimal to percent:
Multiply the decimal by 100.

$$(0.34)(100) = 34\%$$

Percent to decimal:
Divide the percent by 100.

$$78.6\% = 78.6 \div 100 = 0.786$$

Fraction to percent:
Set up an equivalent fraction using 100 as the denominator. The numerator is the percent.

$$\tfrac{4}{5} \cdot \boxed{\tfrac{20}{20}} = \tfrac{80}{100} = 80\%$$

Percent to fraction:
Use 100 as the denominator. Use the digits in the percent as the numerator. Simplify as needed.

$$22\% = \tfrac{22}{100} \cdot \boxed{\tfrac{1/2}{1/2}} = \tfrac{11}{50}$$

Terminating decimal to fraction:
Make the digits the numerator. Use the decimal place value as the denominator. Simplify as needed.

$$0.2 = \tfrac{2}{10} = \tfrac{1}{5}$$

Fraction to decimal:
Divide the numerator by the denominator. If sets of digits repeat, then write just one of the repeating sets and place a "bar" over it.

$$\tfrac{3}{8} = 3 \div 8 = 0.375$$

$$\tfrac{70}{99} = 70 \div 99 = 0.70707... = 0.\overline{70}$$

1-3.   MATHOGRAPHY

Write a letter about yourself that will help your teacher get to know you as an individual. Address each of the general topics below (in bold). Choose a few of the suggested questions to get you started.

About You: By what name do you like to be called? What are your interests, talents, and hobbies? What are you proud of? With whom do you live? What languages do you speak? When is your birthday? What are you like as a member of a team? In what ways are you excited about working in a team? In what ways are you nervous about it?

You as a Math Student: Describe your memories as a math student from kindergarten until now. What experiences in math have you liked? Why? How do you feel about taking this math class? Have you ever worked in a team in a math class before? What kinds of math do you imagine yourself doing in this class?

1-4.   DIAMOND PROBLEMS

Finding and using a pattern is an important problem-solving skill you will use in algebra. The patterns in Diamond Problems will be used later in the course to solve other types of algebraic problems.

Look for a pattern in the first three diamonds below. For the fourth diamond, explain how you could find the missing numbers (?) if you know the two numbers (#).

Copy the Diamond Problems below onto your paper. Then use the pattern you discovered to complete each one.

a.   b.   c.   d.   e.

Core Connections, Course 3

1-5.   In this course, you will need to be able to work with numbers, words, and geometric representations. Use each of these representations to answer the following problems.

   a.   Draw and shade a figure that represents 100%. Label your figure "100%." Then describe the figure in words.

   b.   Similarly, draw and shade figures that represent 50%, 25%, and 150%. Label each figure and describe it in words.

   c.   Write another fraction that is equivalent to $\frac{4}{5}$. Draw diagrams to show that they are equal. Then find the equivalent decimals for both fractions and write the equivalent percent.

   d.   Draw and shade a figure that represents "one-third." How can this figure be represented with a number?

   e.   Describe what the diagram at right represents using words and numbers.

1-6.   Susan's apartment is shown at right. Assuming that all rooms are rectangular, find the areas described below. All measurements are in feet.

   a.   Find the area of her living room.

   b.   Find the area of her entire apartment.

   c.   How much larger than her bedroom is her living room?

   d.   Find the perimeter of the kitchen.

1-7.   CAR COMPARISON

The following three graphs describe two cars, A and B.

Decide whether each of the following statements is true or false. Explain your reasoning.

a.   The newer car is more expensive.

b.   The slower car is larger.

c.   The larger car is newer.

d.   The cheaper car carries more passengers.

1.1.2 How can I generalize a pattern?

Finding and Generalizing Patterns

Often, mathematics is described as "the study of patterns." Today you will preview later work with patterns by studying two tile patterns and using them to make predictions. As you work on these patterns, consider these questions:

How do I see the pattern?

How is it changing?

Is there another way to find a solution?

1-8.   When you are working with your team to answer questions and solve the problems in this course, it is important to work effectively with other people. Effective math conversations are a valuable part of the learning process throughout this course. Choose a member of your team to read the "Collaborative Learning Expectations" below out loud.

COLLABORATIVE LEARNING EXPECTATIONS

Working with other students allows you to:
- Develop new ways of thinking about mathematics,
- Learn to communicate about math, and
- Understand ideas better by having to explain your thinking to others.

The following expectations will help you get the most out of working together.

T	Together, work to answer questions.
E	Explain and give reasons.
A	Ask questions and share ideas.
M	Members of your team are your first resource.
S	Smarter together than apart.

1-9.   GROWING, GROWING, GROWING, PART ONE

Copy the tile pattern shown below onto graph paper.

Figure 2   Figure 3   Figure 4

a.   Draw the 1st, 5th, and 6th figures on your paper.

b.   How is the pattern changing?

c.   What would the 100th figure look like? How many tiles would it have? How can you justify your prediction?

1-10.   GROWING, GROWING, GROWING, PART TWO
Examine this new tile pattern. Copy it onto your paper.

Figure 2   Figure 3   Figure 4

a.   Draw the 1st, 5th, and 6th figures on your paper.

b.   Michael knows that one of the figures in this tile pattern has 79 tiles. What is its figure number? There are *many* ways to figure this out, so be sure to listen to each person's ideas about how to find a solution. Be prepared to explain how you answered this question.

1-11.   For the pattern that your teacher assigns to you, from either problem 1-9 or problem 1-10, prepare a team presentation or poster with your description of the pattern and your prediction. Every team paper or poster should include:

•   Clear drawings of figures from your pattern.

•   An explanation of the pattern you found.

•   Your prediction. (Make sure your reasoning is clear!)

METHODS AND MEANINGS

Axes, Quadrants, and Graphing on an *xy*-Coordinate Graph

Coordinate axes on a flat surface are formed by drawing vertical and horizontal number lines that meet at 0 on each number line and form a right angle (90°). The *x*- and *y*-axes help define points on a graph (called a "Cartesian Plane"). The **x-axis** is horizontal, while the **y-axis** is vertical. The *x*- and *y*-axes divide the graphing area into four sections called **quadrants**.

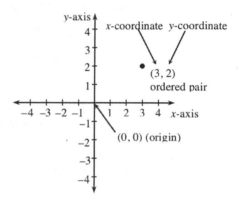

4-quadrant graph: 1ˢᵗ-quadrant graph:

Numerical data can be graphed on a plane using **points**. Points on the graph are identified by two numbers in an **ordered pair** written as (x, y). The first number is the **x-coordinate** of the point, and the second number is the **y-coordinate**. The point $(0,0)$ is called the **origin**.

To locate the point $(3,2)$ on an *xy*-coordinate graph, go three units from the origin to the right to 3 on the horizontal axis and then, from that point, go 2 units up (using the *y*-axis scale). To locate the point $(-2,-4)$, go 2 units from the origin to the left to −2 on the horizontal axis and then 4 units down (using the *y*-axis scale).

1-12. Examine the tile pattern at right.

a. On your paper, sketch Figures 4 and 5.

b. How does the pattern grow? Explain how you know.

Figure 1   Figure 2   Figure 3

c. How many tiles will there be in Figure 100? Explain how you know.

1-13. Copy the axes below onto your paper. Add an appropriate scale and then place and label a point on the graph for each of the products listed below.

a. Dog-Eat-Dog has a supreme hotdog that weighs 80 grams and has 40 grams of fat.

b. Hot Doggies has a diet hotdog that weighs 50 grams and has only 9 grams of fat.

c. Dog-alicious has a cheap hotdog that weighs 40 grams and has 30 grams of fat.

1-14. Copy and complete each sequence below. Using words, not numbers, describe how the patterns work. (For example, write, "Double the previous number.")

a. $1, 3, 6, 10, \underline{\quad}, \underline{\quad}$

b. $1, \frac{1}{2}, \frac{1}{4}, \frac{1}{8}, \underline{\quad}, \underline{\quad}$

c. $1, 3, 9, 27, \underline{\quad}, \underline{\quad}$

d. $8, 7, 5, 2, \underline{\quad}, \underline{\quad}$

e. $49, 47, 52, 50, 55, \underline{\quad}, \underline{\quad}$

Core Connections, Course 3

1-15.   Recall the Diamond Problem pattern that you found in
         problem 1-4, which is represented in the diamond at right.
         Copy and complete the Diamond Problems below using the
         same pattern.

a.   b.   c.   d.

1-16.   Use the graph at right to answer the following
         questions about quadrants and coordinates of
         points. Read the Math Notes box in this lesson if
         you need to review these concepts.

         a.   What are the coordinates of the two
               points in Quadrant II?

         b.   What are the coordinates of the two
               points in Quadrant IV?

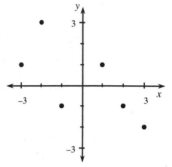

1.1.3 Can I graph myself?

The Algebra Walk

Today you will use a **xy-coordinate system** to refer to the locations of specific points in the form (x, y). By the end of this lesson, be sure you and your teammates know the answers to the following target questions.

How can you plot a point using its (x, y) coordinates?

How can you name a point on the graph?

How can you describe a pattern formed by points?

1-17.   ALGEBRA WALK*

The Algebra Walk is an exercise in "human graphing" where people represent points on a graph. Your teacher will give the class instructions for how to form human graphs. Then you will work in study teams to complete the problems below.

For each of the following rules, copy and complete the table. Then neatly graph each point. Use the resource page provided by your teacher.

The x-values in the table are sometimes referred to as **input** values, since they are the values used with the rule for x. The y-values are the **output** values, since they are the result of what happens to the input (x) value.

IN (x)	–6	–5	–4	–3	–2	–1	0	1	2	3	4	5	6
OUT (y)													

a. $y = 2x + 1$ b. $y = -2x$ c. $y = x + 4$

d. $y = -x + 4$ e. $y = x^2$

1-18.   Describe what you did and what you observed in today's classwork.

    a.   Compare the graphs in 1-17. How are they similar? How are they different?

    b.   Using words, express each symbolic rule in parts (a) through (e).

    c.   Did you notice any patterns? Why was it easy to spot someone who was out of place?

METHODS AND MEANINGS

Writing Equations using the 5-D Process

The 5-D Process is an organized method to help write equations and solve problems. The D's stand for Describe/Draw, Define, Do, Decide, and Declare. An example of this work is shown below.

Example Problem: The base of a rectangle is 13 centimeters longer than the height. If the perimeter is 58 centimeters, find the base and the height of the rectangle.

Describe/Draw: The shape is a rectangle, and we are looking at the perimeter.

height

base

Define		Do	Decide
Height (trial)	Base (height + 13)	Perimeter 2(base) + 2(height)	58?
Trial 1: 10	10 + 13 = 23	2(23) + 2(10) = 66	66 is too high

Use any trial value.

Use the relationships stated in the problem to determine the values of the other quantities (such as base and perimeter).

Now use the trial to create an equation by defining and adding a variable line.

Let x represent the height in cm	x	$x + 13$	$2(x) + 2(x + 13)$	$2(x) + 2(x +13) = 58$

$$2x + 2x + 26 = 58$$
$$4x + 26 = 58$$
$$4x = 32$$
$$x = 8$$

Now use your algebra skills to solve the equation.

Declare: The base is 21 centimeters, and the height is 8 centimeters.

If you do not write an equation, you can solve the problem by making more trials until you find the answer.

1-19.   Use your graphs from problem 1-17 to answer the questions below.

    a. How can the graph for the rule $y = 2x + 1$ be used to predict the result for an input (x-value) of 7? How can the graph be used to predict the output (y-value) associated with an input of $3\frac{1}{2}$?

    b. If you wanted an output of 7 for the rule $y = -x + 4$, what would you need as an input?

    c. For each of the rules in parts (a) through (e) of problem 1-17, where does the graph cross the y-axis? Describe any patterns you notice.

1-20.   Solve the problem below by defining a variable and then writing an equation. If you find this too challenging, then use the 5-D Process described in this lesson's Math Notes box to help you get started. State your solution in a sentence.

    Jabari is thinking of three numbers. The greatest number is twice as large as the least number. The middle number is three more than the least number. The sum of the three numbers is 75. Find the numbers.

1-21.   Latisha's friend Brandee forgot to take a make-up test and had these scores: $80\%, 92\%, 91\%, 75\%,$ $89\%, 84\%, 0\%,$ and 85%.

    a. Calculate Brandee's mean. (Refer to the glossary if you do not remember how to do this.) Does this mean score really represent her abilities? Why or why not?

    b. Brandee persuaded her teacher, Ms. Juarez, to allow her to make up the missed test. Brandee's score was a 78%. Calculate her new mean.

    c. What difference did the 0% score make? Does this new mean represent Brandee's ability more accurately?

1-22.   The area of a rectangle is 24,396 square centimeters. If the width is 38 centimeters, what is the length? How do you know?

1-23.   Copy the number line below onto your paper. Locate the following numbers by placing the lowercase letters a through f on the number line corresponding to the values given below. Part (a) is done for you.

$$\xleftarrow{\qquad} \underset{-5\ -4\ -3\ -2\ -1\ \ 0\ \ 1\ \ 2\ \ 3\ \ 4\ \ 5}{\overset{a}{\bullet}} \xrightarrow{\qquad}$$

a. $2\frac{1}{3}$

b. -2.7

c. $0.9 - 0.04$

d. -0.2

e. $33\frac{1}{3}\%$ of 12

f. $\frac{7}{10} + \frac{2}{3}$

1.1.4 How can I use data to solve a problem?

Collecting, Organizing, and Analyzing Data

Computing batting averages, performing scientific experiments, and polling people during elections are just a few examples of how data can provide useful information when it is collected and analyzed. In this lesson, you will be collecting and organizing data to determine the potential danger of riding a roller coaster.

1-24. NEWTON'S REVENGE

Have you heard about Newton's Revenge, the new roller coaster? It is so big, fast, and scary that rumors about it are already spreading. Some people are worried about the tunnel that thrills riders with its low ceiling.

The closest the ceiling of the tunnel ever comes to the seat of the roller-coaster car is 200 cm. Although no accidents have been reported yet, it is said that very tall riders have stopped riding the roller coaster.

Your Task: Consider how you could determine whether the tunnel is actually safe for any rider, no matter how tall. Discuss the questions below with your team. Be ready to share your responses with the rest of the class.

Discussion Points

What is this problem about? What is it asking you to do?

What information can help you answer this question?

How can you get the information you need?

1-25.   One way to determine if the roller coaster is safe is to collect and analyze data.

a.   Collect data from each member of your team.

Each member of the team needs to be measured twice. First, have one team member stand and have another team member measure his or her height. Second, have the same student sit in a chair or desk, raise his or her arms so that they are stretched as far as possible above his or her head, and measure the distance from the seat of the chair to his or her fingertips (called "the reach"). All measurements should be in centimeters.

Student Name	Height (cm)	Reach (cm)

Each person should record the team's data in a table like the one above.

b.   Send one person up to record your team's data on the class table. Then add the rest of the class data to your own table.

c.   Each person should put his or her initials on a sticky dot, then graph his or her own *height vs. reach* point on the class graph.

1-26.   Use the class graph to answer the questions below.

a.   Are there any dots that you think show *human error*? That is, are there any dots that appear to be graphed incorrectly or that someone may have measured incorrectly? Explain why or why not.

b.   Is a person's reach related to his or her height? That is, what seems to be true about the reach of taller people? Explain.

c.   Since a person's reach depends on his or her height, the reach is called the **dependent** quantity (or variable) and the height the **independent** quantity (or variable). Examine the class graph of the data from problem 1-25. On which axis was the independent data represented? On which axis was the dependent data represented?

d.   Is there a trend in the data? How can you generalize the trend?

Core Connections, Course 3

1-27.   Everyone is complaining about how the teacher made the class graph.

   a.   Jorge is confused about how the teacher
         decided to set up the graph. *"Why is it a 1st-
         quadrant graph instead of a 4-quadrant
         graph?"* Answer Jorge's question. In
         general, how should you decide what kind of
         graph to use?

   b.   Lauren is annoyed with the *x*-axis. *"Why didn't the teacher just use the
         numbers from the table?"* she whined. *"Why count by twenties?"* What do
         you think?

   c.   Hosai thinks that the graph is TOO BIG. *"The dots are all mashed
         together! Why did the teacher begin both the x- and y-axes at zero?
         Anyone that short would never be allowed on the roller coaster. Why not
         just start closer to the smallest numbers on the table?"* she asked. What
         do you think?

   d.   Sunita says the graph is TOO SMALL! *"If we're supposed to be using
         this data to check if the coaster is safe for really tall people, the graph has
         to have room to graph tall people's dots too."* Do you agree? If so, how
         much room do you think is needed?

1-28.   Using all of your ideas from problem 1-27, make your own graph that will help
         you determine whether the ride is safe for very tall people. An example of a
         "very tall" person is Yao Ming, who retired from the NBA in 2011. He was one
         of the tallest NBA players in history, measuring 7 feet 6 inches (about
         228.6 cm) tall. Is the roller coaster safe for him? Explain.

1-29.   Is the roller coaster safe for all riders? Prepare
         a poster that shows and justifies your team's
         answer to this question. Every team poster
         should include:

   •   A large, clear graph.

   •   A complete, clear, and convincing
        explanation of why your team thinks the
        ride is or is not safe for all riders.

1-30.   Kerin discovered that a human's height is related to his or her reach. Kerin is curious if the same thing is true for foot size.

   a.   It was not practical for Kerin to measure her classmates' feet, so Kerin collected the following shoe-size data from some of her classmates. Make a graph with appropriately scaled axes.

Shoe Size	Height (cm)
6	153
8	160
7.5	155
8.5	161
8	168
8	166
8.5	164
6.5	156
10	170
9.5	167
7.5	158
7.5	156
8	161

   b.   Is there a relationship between shoe size and height?

1-31.   One important statistical display is a box plot. If you need help remembering what a box plot is, refer to the glossary before you complete parts (a) through (d) below.

   a.   What is the median shoe size in problem 1-30? The minimum shoe size? The maximum?

   b.   What are the quartiles (the median of the upper half, and the median of the lower half)?

   c.   Above a number line, plot the five numbers you found in parts (a) and (b) and then create a box plot.

   d.   Where does your own shoe size fall in the distribution of Kerin's classmates?

1-32.   Latisha is determined to do well in school this year. Her goal is to maintain at least an 85% average (mean) in all of her courses.

    a.   Latisha started her history class with two scores on tests, 72% and 89%. Confirm that the mean of these two scores is 80.5%. Show your work.

    b.   Latisha's third score was 90%. Use her scores from part (a) to figure out her mean now. Be sure to show your work.

1-33.   On your paper, copy the Diamond Problems below and use the pattern you discovered earlier to complete each of them. The pattern is shown at right. Some of these may be challenging!

  a.   b.   c.   d.

  e.   f.   g.   h.

1-34.   Compute *without* using a calculator.

    a. $-15+7$ b. $8-(-21)$ c. $6(-8)$

    d. $-9+(-13)$ e. $-50-30$ f. $3-(-9)$

    g. $-75-(-75)$ h. $(-3)+6$ i. $9+(-14)$

    j. $28-(-2)$ k. $-3+(-2)+5$ l. $3+2+5$

1-35.   The area of each rectangle below is shown in the middle of the rectangle. For each figure, find the missing length or width.

a.

A = 60 in.²

8 in.

b.

A = 180 m²

15 m

c.

A = 231 cm²

14 cm

1-36.   Without using a calculator, compute the value of the following expressions.

a. $\frac{3}{7} \div \frac{2}{3}$

b. $1.2 \div 0.04$

c. $\frac{11}{4}$ of $\frac{3}{7}$

d. $4.16(0.2)$

1-37.   Latisha earned an 85% on her test today. Her previous scores were 72%, 89%, and 90%. Calculate her new average (mean).

1-38.   Consider this data: 22, 15, 30, 51, 27, 33, 19.

a.   Arrange the data into a stem-and-leaf plot. (Refer to the glossary if you need a reminder of what a stem-and-leaf plot is.)

b.   Find the mean and median.

c.   If the value 51 was replaced with 33, which measure(s) of central tendency would change and which would not? Explain.

1-39.   Estimate the areas of Montana and California using the grid below. Which state has the greatest area? Compare the area of Montana to the area of California. Explain how you estimated the area of each state.

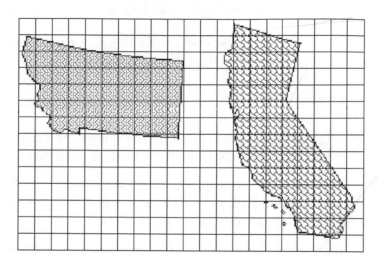

1-40.   The pattern below is composed of nested squares.

a.   Draw the next figure in the pattern.

b.   Find the area of the shaded region for the figure you drew in part (a).

1.2.1 How do they compare?

. . . .

Proportional Relationships with Graphs and Tables

You may recall studying about proportional relationships in a previous course. Today you will investigate proportional relationships in graphs and tables.

1-41.   Make a table and a graph to represent each of the situations below.

   a.   Parvin often cleans the dishes for her mother. She can clean 17 plates in 10 minutes. How many plates can she clean in different amounts of time?

   b.   Yasmin's puppy, Maggie, weighed 14 ounces at birth. She doubled her birth weight in 10 days. Assuming her growth is constant, how much will she weigh at various times in the first year?

   c.   Angel saw an Internet pop-up advertisement for an investment that doubles your money every year. If Angel invests the $20 her grandmother gave her for her birthday, how much money will she have in various years?

   d.   Which of the situations in parts (a) through (c) describe a proportional relationship? How do you know if a relationship is proportional by looking at the table? What about by looking at the graph?

1-42.   Doug regularly mows his neighbor's lawn. Last month, Doug's neighbor paid him $55 for 6 hours of mowing.

Doug	
Time (hr)	Earnings ($)
6	55

   a.   Is this situation most likely a proportional relationship? How do you know?

   b.   Make a table that shows how much Doug earns for various numbers of hours of mowing.

   c.   Johnny brags that he is getting paid more than Doug to mow lawns. Johnny gets paid according to the graph below right. Who is getting paid more? How do you know?

   d.   At what unit rate do Johnny and Doug each get paid? How do you know? Remember that a unit rate compares the change in one quantity to a one-unit change in another quantity, so in this case you would compare dollars to one hour.

   e.   If it is not already there, how could you show the unit rate in Doug's table? How could you show the unit rate on Johnny's graph?

Core Connections, Course 3

1-43.	Ferroza's pet ferret eats so much that Ferroza has to buy ferret food in bulk. Five pounds cost $17.50, and 30 pounds cost $105.00.

a.	Make a graph of the cost of ferret food for various sizes of bags.

b.	Calculate the value of y at the point $(1, y)$ on Ferroza's graph. Why would Ferroza want to know what the value of y is?

1-44.	Toby wrote the equation $t = \frac{7}{10} m$ to represent the relationship between the number of tubes of toothpaste (t) he uses in any number of months (m).

a.	How much toothpaste does Toby use in 5 years? Show how you found this.

b.	Toby's sister kept track of her toothpaste use in the following table.

Who uses toothpaste faster, Toby or his sister?

Toby's Sister	
Time (months)	Tubes (#)
14	9
28	18

c.	If you have not already done so, find the unit rate (in tubes/month) for both Toby and his sister. Do the unit rates confirm your answer to part (b)?

1-45.	The larger bag of ferret food is on sale at the SuperPetMart for $89. Ferroza made the following table. Explain to Ferroza why the cost of food at SuperPetMart is not a proportional relationship.

Ferret Food	
Weight (pounds)	Cost ($)
0	$0
5	17.50
30	89

1-46.　LEARNING LOG

In this course, you will often be asked to reflect about your learning in a Learning Log. Writing about your understanding will help you pull together ideas, develop new ways to describe mathematical ideas, and recognize gaps in your understanding. Your teacher will tell you where your Learning Log entries should go.

For your first entry, explain in your own words what you know about a proportional relationship. Write a reflection in your Learning Log that addresses the following questions:

- How do you recognize a proportional relationship in a table?

- How do you recognize proportional relationship in a graph?

- How can you find the unit rate in a table and in a graph?

Be sure to include examples to support your statements.

Title this entry "Proportional Relationships" and label it with today's date.

Methods and Meanings

Proportional Relationships

A **proportional relationship** can be seen in a table: if one quantity is multiplied by an amount, the corresponding quantity is multiplied by the same amount. On a graph, a proportional relationship is linear and goes through the origin.

Proportional example: Three pounds of chicken costs $7.00. Below, other values are shown in the table and plotted on the graph.

Pounds	0	3	6	9	12
Cost ($)	0	7	14	21	28

The relationship between pounds and cost is proportional.

Non-proportional example: The video arcade costs $5.00 to enter and $1.00 per game.

Games	0	1	2	3	4
Cost ($)	5	6	7	8	9

The relationship between games and cost is *not* proportional. For example, someone who plays four games ($9) does not pay twice as much as someone who played two games ($7). There is no multiplier for the relationship. The graph does not go through the origin.

Chapter 1: Problem Solving

29

1-47. Decide whether each of the following situations represents a proportional relationship. Explain why or why not.

    a. Karim is ordering video games. Each game costs $39.99, and there is a $4.85 shipping charge per order. How much will it cost him to order any number of video games?

    b. A given rectangle has an area of 20 square feet. What is the length for various widths?

    c. Oleg ran 8.8 miles in 1 hour 20 minutes. Assuming he continues at a constant rate, how long will it take him to run any number of miles?

1-48. Jerome is keeping track of how many books he and his friends have read during the first 100 days of school. To help Jerome present the data to his teacher, make a box plot of how many books each person has read. The numbers of books are 12, 17, 24, 18, 31, 17, 21, 20, 14, 9, and 25.

1-49. Simplify the following expressions.

    a. $-0.75 - 0.4$ b. $\frac{7}{8} - \frac{2}{3}$ c. $0.65 - 0.89$

    d. $\frac{11}{12} + \frac{4}{9}$ e. $\frac{9}{10} \cdot 2\frac{1}{3}$ f. $12 \div \frac{7}{8}$

    g. $1\frac{2}{3} + (-\frac{2}{5})$ h. $\frac{4}{7} - (-\frac{3}{8})$ i. $-4.05 + 3.18$

1-50. Look at each graph below and write a story or description about what each graph shows.

    a.   b.   c.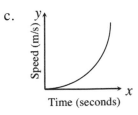

1-51.   Riley was monitoring the growth of his favorite tomato
         plant and collected the data shown in the table at right.

Time (days)	Height (cm)
10	3
14	4.3
18	7
21	8.9
23	11.4

    a.   Graph Riley's data.

    b.   What can you tell Riley about his plant based on
         the data?

1.2.2 How can I solve the proportion?

• •

Strategies for Solving Proportional Relationships

Proportional relationships can be identified in both tables and graphs. In the last lesson,
you also used both of these representations to make predictions about proportional
situations. Today you will continue to develop strategies for solving proportional
situations using an equation.

1-52.   Kenny can make seven origami (folded-paper) cranes in ten minutes. He read a
         story about a girl who made 1505 cranes, so he was curious how long it would
         take him to make that many without stopping.

    a.   Complete Kenny's table below, and then explain how you did so. How
         many minutes would it take Kenny to fold 1505 cranes? How many hours?

Origami Cranes	
Cranes (#)	Time (minutes)
0	0
7	10
1505	?

    b.   Instead of solving this problem using a table or a graph, Kenny represented
         seven cranes in ten minutes as the ratio $\frac{10 \text{ minutes}}{7 \text{ cranes}}$. Then he wrote an
         equivalent ratio as follows:

$$\frac{10 \text{ minutes}}{7 \text{ cranes}} = \frac{? \text{ minutes}}{1505 \text{ cranes}}$$

         Use two different strategies to find the missing value in the equivalent ratio.

1-53.   MULTIPLE STRATEGIES

Kenny's class found several ways to solve $\frac{10}{7} = \frac{x}{1505}$. Three of the strategies that they used are presented below. Some of these strategies might be the same as what your class did in problem 1-52. However, others may be new. Work to understand each strategy so that you could use it to solve a new problem.

a.   Giant One Method:

Multiplying a ratio by 1 does not change the value of the ratio. You can write 1 in many forms, such as $\frac{3}{3}$ and $\frac{14}{14}$. In this course, this kind of fraction is called a "Giant One." Find a value to use as a numerator and denominator in a Giant One, and then find the value of x in the equation below.

$$\frac{10}{7} \cdot \boxed{} = \frac{x}{1505}$$

b.   Undoing Division Method:

In this ratio, x is divided by 1505. You can undo the division by multiplying each side of the proportion by 1505 like this:

$$\left(\frac{1505}{1}\right)\frac{10}{7} = \frac{x}{1505}\left(\frac{1505}{1}\right)$$

Work with your team to explain how this strategy works. Are the two ratios still equal? Why are both sides multiplied by 1505? Simplify each side of the equation and find x.

c.   Fraction Buster Method:

If multiplying both sides by 1505 gets rid of the denominator of the x, then you can use the same strategy to get rid of the 7 in the other denominator. Discuss this method with your team and decide if undoing both denominators is a reasonable strategy. How does using this method help you solve the equation? What else do you need to do to find x?

$$\frac{10}{7} = \frac{x}{1505}$$

$$\frac{7 \cdot 1505}{1}\left(\frac{10}{7}\right) = \left(\frac{x}{1505}\right)\frac{7 \cdot 1505}{1}$$

$$(1505)(10) = (x)(7)$$

1-54.　Use each of the strategies from problem 1-53 to solve
the problems below.

a.　When he was little, Miguel could not sleep without
his Captain Terrific action figure. It looked so life-
like because it was a perfect scale model. The
actor who plays Captain Terrific on television is
216 cm tall. Miguel's doll is 10 cm tall. If the
doll's neck is 0.93 cm long, how long is the actor's
neck? Use the Undoing Division Method to solve
this proportion: $\frac{216}{10} = \frac{x}{0.93}$.

b.　The Northwood School Math Club is having a
tamale sale. The school has 1600 students, but
the club members are not sure how many
tamales to make. One day during lunch, the club
asked random students if they would buy a
tamale. They found that 15 out of 80 students
surveyed said they would definitely buy a
tamale. How many tamales should the Math
Club expect to sell? Use the Fraction Busters
Method to solve the proportion $\frac{15}{80} = \frac{x}{1600}$.

c.　On the school copy machine, Mr. Douglas reduced a triangle so that it
would fit better in student portfolios. The shortest side of the original
triangle was 22 cm; other measurements are shown in the diagram. How
long was the longest side of the original triangle? Solve the proportion
$\frac{22}{8} = \frac{x}{12}$ using the Giant One Method.

x

22

12

8

1-55.   Elsie is starting a recycling club at her
         school and hopes to use the money earned
         from recycling cans to buy recycling bins
         for the school.

         Elsie first needs to figure out how much
         the cans that can be collected at her school
         weigh, so she starts by weighing the cans
         in her recycling bin at home. She finds
         that 50 cans weigh 0.8 kg. The next day,
         Elsie counts cans at school and finds that
         her fellow students throw away 1240 cans
         each day.

         Solve the proportion below using a method of your choice to find how much all
         of the school's cans weigh.

$$\frac{50}{0.8} = \frac{1240}{x}$$

1-56.   ANOTHER STRATEGY

         Cross-Multiplication Method:

         Juana's method is shown at right.

$$\frac{10}{4} \diagup\!\!\!\!\diagdown \frac{x}{7}$$
$$(7)(10) = (x)(4)$$

         Explain to Juana why her method is really just a shortcut based on the Fraction
         Busters Method.

METHODS AND MEANINGS

MATH NOTES

Solving Proportions

If a relationship is known to be proportional, ratios from the situation are equal. An equation stating that two ratios are equal is called a **proportion**. Some examples of proportions are:

$$\frac{6 \text{ mi}}{2 \text{ hr}} = \frac{9 \text{ mi}}{3 \text{ hr}} \qquad \frac{5}{7} = \frac{50}{70}$$

Setting up a proportion is one strategy for solving for an unknown part of one ratio. For example, if the ratios $\frac{9}{2}$ and $\frac{x}{16}$ are equal, setting up the proportion $\frac{x}{16} = \frac{9}{2}$ allows you to solve for x.

Giant One: One way to solve this proportion is by using a Giant One to find the equivalent ratio. In this case, since 16 is 2 times 8, you create the Giant One shown at right.

$$\frac{x}{16} = \frac{9}{2} \cdot \boxed{\frac{8}{8}}$$

$$\frac{x}{16} = \frac{9 \cdot 8}{2 \cdot 8}$$

$$\frac{x}{16} = \frac{72}{16}$$

which shows that $x = 72$.

Undoing Division: Another way to solve the proportion is to think of the ratio $\frac{x}{16}$ as, " x divided by 16." To solve for x, use the inverse operation of division, which is multiplication. Multiplying both sides of the proportional equation by 16 "undoes" the division.

$$\frac{x}{16} = \frac{9}{2}$$

$$\left(\frac{16}{1}\right)\frac{x}{16} = \frac{9}{2}\left(\frac{16}{1}\right)$$

$$x = \frac{144}{2}$$

$$x = 72$$

Cross-Multiplication: This method of solving the proportion is a shortcut for using a Fraction Buster (multiplying each side of the equation by the denominators).

Fraction Buster	Cross-Multiplication
$\frac{x}{16} = \frac{9}{2}$	$\frac{x}{16} = \frac{9}{2}$
$2 \cdot 16 \cdot \frac{x}{16} = \frac{9}{2} \cdot 2 \cdot 16$	$\frac{x}{16} \diagdown\!\!\!\!\diagup \frac{9}{2}$
$2 \cdot x = 9 \cdot 16$	$2 \cdot x = 9 \cdot 16$
$2x = 144$	$2x = 144$
$x = 72$	$x = 72$

1-57.   Solve each of the following proportions.

a. $\frac{x}{24} = \frac{30}{36}$ b. $\frac{5}{7} = \frac{x}{3}$

c.   If Joan read 75 pages in 4 hours how long will it take her to read
250 pages?

1-58.   Mr. Wright was making a table to figure out how
much it costs to send a certain number of regular
letters through the mail. Use proportional
reasoning to complete his table at right.

Number of Letters	Cost of Stamps
10	$4.50
2	$0.90
	$6.75
7	
1	
500	
	$18.90

1-59.   Kelly asked some of her classmates how many
hours of sleep they get on school nights. Here
are the results:

   $6, 8, 7\frac{1}{2}, 9, 8, 8, 8, 9, 9, 10, 6, 8\frac{1}{2}, 9, 7, 8$

Copy the set of axes at right and create a
histogram for the data. (Refer to the glossary
for assistance, if needed.)

1-60.   Define a variable and then write and solve an equation for the problem below.
Remember that you can use the 5-D Process (described in the Lesson 1.1.3
Math Notes box) to help you get started. State your solution in a sentence.

Todd is 10 years older than Jamal. The sum of their ages is 64. How old are
Todd and Jamal?

1-61. Throughout this book, key problems have been selected as "checkpoints." Each checkpoint problem is marked with an icon like the one at left. These checkpoint problems are provided so that you can check to be sure you are building skills at the expected level. When you have trouble with checkpoint problems, refer to the review materials and practice problems that are available in the "Checkpoint Materials" section at the back of your book.

This problem is a checkpoint for operations with signed fractions and decimals. It will be referred to as Checkpoint 1.

Simplify the following expressions.

a. $-\frac{1}{3}+-\frac{3}{8}$

b. $2.6-(-1.5)$

c. $\left(-4\frac{1}{5}\right)\left(-\frac{1}{3}\right)$

d. $\left(\frac{2}{3}\right)\div\left(-\frac{1}{2}\right)$

e. $-1\frac{3}{4}+5\frac{1}{3}$

f. $(-2.8)\div(-1.25)$

Check your answers by referring to the Checkpoint 1 materials located at the back of your book.

Ideally, at this point you are comfortable working with these types of problems and can solve them correctly. If you feel that you need more confidence when solving these types of problems, then review the Checkpoint 1 materials and try the practice problems provided. From this point on, you will be expected to do problems like these correctly and with confidence.

Chapter 1 Closure   What have I learned?

Reflection and Synthesis

The activities below offer you a chance to reflect
about what you have learned during this chapter.
As you work, look for concepts that you feel very
comfortable with, ideas that you would like to
learn more about, and topics you need more help
with.

①   SUMMARIZING MY UNDERSTANDING

This section gives you the opportunity to show what you know about
proportional relationships.

Is it Proportional?

Obtain a Chapter 1 Closure Graphic Organizer Resource Page from your
teacher.

Your Task, Part 1: Work
with your team to determine
if the relationship between
the side length of a square
and its area is or is not
proportional. Explain your
reasoning in multiple ways,
being sure to include a table
and a graph.

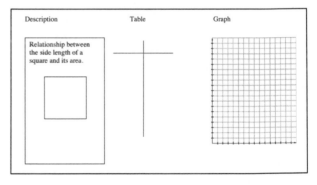

Your Task, Part 2: Work with your team to brainstorm relationships between
quantities other than those you have seen in this chapter. Which ones might be
proportional? Choose one relationship and demonstrate, using multiple reasons,
whether it is or is not proportional. Again, be sure to include a table and a
graph in your explanation.

② WHAT HAVE I LEARNED?

Doing the problems in this section will help you to evaluate which types of problems you feel comfortable with and which ones you need more help with.

Solve each problem as completely as you can. The table at the end of this closure section provides answers to these problems. It also tells you where you can find additional help and where to find practice problems like them.

CL 1-62. Write the coordinates of each point (*A* through *F*) circled on the graph at right in (x, y) form.

CL 1-63. Draw and label *x*- and *y*-axes on graph paper. Find and label the following points:

$G(3, 2)$ $H(1, 4)$ $I(-2, -1)$

$J(4, -2)$ $K(-5, 1)$

CL 1-64. Define a variable and then write and solve an equation for the problem below. Use the 5-D Process, if needed. Show your work in an organized way.

Ralph and Alphonse are shooting marbles. Ralph has five more marbles than Alphonse, and they have a total of 73 marbles. How many marbles does each of them have?

CL 1-65. On graph paper, draw at least six different-sized rectangles that have an area of 64 square units. Then find the perimeter of each rectangle.

CL 1-66. Copy and complete each of the Diamond Problems below.
The pattern used in the Diamond Problems is shown at right.

a.

b.

c.

d.

e.

f.

CL 1-67. Copy the pattern below onto graph paper. Draw the 1st and 5th figures on your paper.

    Figure 2   Figure 3   Figure 4

a. How many tiles are in each figure?

b. Describe how the pattern is changing.

c. How many tiles would the 6th figure have? The 10th figure?

CL 1-68. Zeke lives 30 miles from his aunt, Zelda, and is riding his bike home from her house. Interpret the graph to tell a story about what could have happened on his ride home.

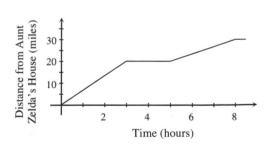

CL 1-69. For each of the problems above, do the following:

- Draw a bar or number line that represents 0 to 10.

- Color or shade in a portion of the bar that represents your level of understanding and comfort with completing that problem on your own.

If any of your bars are less than a 5, choose *one* of those problems and complete one of the following tasks:

- Write two questions that you would like to ask about that problem.
- Brainstorm two things that you DO know about that type of problem.

If all of your bars are a 5 or above, choose *one* of those problems and do one of these tasks:

- Write two questions you might ask or hints you might give to a student who was stuck on the problem.
- Make a new problem that is similar and more challenging than that problem and solve it.

③   WHAT TOOLS CAN I USE?

You have several tools and references available to help support your learning –
your teacher, your study team, your math book, and your Toolkit, to name only
a few. At the end of each chapter you will have an opportunity to review your
Toolkit for completeness as well as to revise or update it to better reflect your
current understanding of big ideas.

The main elements of your Toolkit should be your Learning Logs, Math Notes,
and the vocabulary used in this chapter. Math words that are new to this
chapter appear in bold in the text. Refer to the lists provided below and follow
your teacher's instructions to revise your Toolkit, which will help make it a
useful reference for you as you complete this chapter and prepare to begin the
next one.

Learning Log Entries
- Lesson 1.2.1 – Proportional Relationships

Math Notes
- Lesson 1.1.1 – Fractions, Decimals, and Percents
- Lesson 1.1.2 – Axes, Quadrants, and Graphing
  on an xy-Coordinate Graph
- Lesson 1.1.3 – Solving Problems with the
  5-D Process
- Lesson 1.2.1 – Proportional Relationships
- Lesson 1.2.2 – Solving Proportions

Mathematical Vocabulary

The following is a list of vocabulary found in this chapter. Make sure that
you are familiar with the terms below and know what they mean. For the
words you do not know, refer to the glossary or index. You might also add
these words to your Toolkit so that you can reference them in the future.

5-D Process	area	box plot
coordinates	dependent (variable)	histogram
independent (variable)	integer	input
mean	median	ordered pair
origin	output	perimeter
proportion	proportional relationship	quadrant
stem-and-leaf plot	unit rate	variable
x-axis	y-axis	

Answers and Support for Closure Problems
What Have I Learned?

Note: MN = Math Note, LL = Learning Log

Problem	Solution			Need Help?	More Practice
CL 1-62.	a. $(-5, 3)$	b. $(3, 4)$	c. $(2, -1)$	Lesson 1.1.3	Problems 1-16 and 1-13
	d. $(3, -5)$	e. $(-3, -4)$	f. $(-2, 1)$	MN: 1.1.2	

CL 1-63.		Lesson 1.1.3	Problems 1-16 and 1-13
		MN: 1.1.2	

CL 1-64.	Let a represent the number of marbles Alphonse has, $a + (a + 5) = 73$, $a = 34$ Ralph has 39 marbles, and Alphonse has 34 marbles.	MN: 1.1.3	Problems 1-20 and 1-60

CL 1-65.	Multiple answers are possible. Rectangles with integer sides have dimensions 1 by 64, 2 by 32, 4 by 16, and 8 by 8, with perimeters of 130, 68, 40, and 32 respectively. However, to get more than four rectangles with different dimensions, you need to also use non-integer lengths, such as $\frac{1}{2}$ by 128 (with $P = 257$) or $\frac{1}{3}$ by 192 (with $P = 384\frac{2}{3}$).	Lesson 1.1.1	Problems 1-6 and 1-35

CL 1-66.	a. b. c. d. e. f.	Problem 1-4	Problems 1-15 and 1-33

Problem	Solution	Need Help?	More Practice
CL 1-67.
Figure 1   Figure 5

a. 5, 8, 11, 14, 17

b. Each figure has three more tiles than the one before it.

c. The 6th figure would have 20 tiles. The 10th figure would have 32 tiles. | Lesson 1.1.2 | Problems 1-9, 1-10, and 1-12 |
| CL 1-68. | There are many possible stories for this graph. Make sure your story explains the changes in speed and the stops and starts in the graph. Zeke travels 20 miles during the first 3 hours and then rests for 2 hours. Then he travels 10 miles in the next 3 hours and reaches his house after 8 hours. | Lesson 1.1.1 | Problems 1-1 and 1-50 |

CHAPTER 2   Simplifying with Variables

This chapter begins with a focus on the use of
variables, such as x and y. First, you will use tools
called "algebra tiles" to explore how and where to use
variables. You will write expressions and then learn
how to write them in the most efficient way.

Later in the chapter, you will learn how to compare
two expressions to determine which one is greater.
This will lead to a process of recording your steps so
that anyone can understand your work. Finally, you
will look at what happens when you cannot tell which
expression is greater and consider the question, "What
if they are equal?"

Since the topics in this chapter lay the foundation for
simplifying expressions and solving equations, they
will be revisited and built upon throughout the course.

In this chapter, you will learn:

➢ What a variable is.

➢ How to write and simplify algebraic expressions.

➢ How to compare two complicated algebraic expressions.

➢ How to solve for a variable if you know that two expressions are equal.

Guiding Questions

Think about these questions
throughout this chapter:

What is a variable?

What can I do with a variable?

How can I solve for a variable?

How many different ways can I
write an expression?

Chapter Outline

Section 2.1 This section, the only section of the chapter,
introduces algebra tiles. Using algebra tiles will
help develop the symbolic manipulation skills of
combining like terms and solving linear equations.
A special focus will be placed on the meaning of
"minus" and how to make "zero."

2.1.1 What is a variable?

Exploring Variables and Expressions

In Algebra and in future mathematics courses, you will work with unknown quantities that can be represented using variables. Today manipulatives called "algebra tiles" will be introduced to help you and your teammates answer some important questions, such as *"What is a variable?"* and *"How can we use it?"*

2-1   Your teacher will distribute a set of algebra tiles for your team to use during this course. As you explore the tiles, address the following questions with your team. Be prepared to share your responses with the class.

- How many different shapes are there? What are all of the different shapes?

- How are the shapes different? How are they the same?

- How are the shapes related? Which fit together and which do not?

2-2.   Draw a picture of each type of tile on your paper.

   a.   The algebra tiles will be referred to by their areas. Since the smallest square has a length of 1 unit, its area is 1 square unit. Thus, the name for this tile is "one" or a "unit tile." Label your drawing of this tile with its side lengths and area.

   b.   Can you use the unit tile to find the other lengths? Why or why not?

   c.   If you cannot use the unit tile to measure all of the other side lengths of the other tiles, how can you label them so that you can find their area? Discuss this with your team and be prepared to share your ideas with the class.

   d.   Label your drawings and then name the other tiles using their areas. Be sure to use what you know about the area of a rectangle and the area of a square.

2-3.   JUMBLED PILES

   Your teacher will show you a jumbled pile of algebra tiles and will challenge you to write a name for the collection. What is the best description for the collection of tiles? Is your description the best possible?

2-4.   Build each collection of tiles represented below. Then name the collection
         using a simpler algebraic expression, if possible. If it is not possible to simplify
         the expression, explain why not.

   a. $3x + 5 + x^2 + y + 3x^2 + 2$ b. $2x^2 + 1 + xy + x^2 + 2xy + 5$

   c. $2 + x^2 + 3x + y^2 + 4y + xy$ d. $3y + 2 + 2xy + 4x + y^2 + 4y + 1$

2-5.   LEARNING LOG

         In your Learning Log, explain what a variable is in
         your own words. Describe each type of tile with a
         diagram that includes each dimension and an area label.
         Explain when tiles can and cannot be combined. Be
         sure to include examples to support your statements.
         Title this entry "Algebra Tiles and Variables" and include today's date.

METHODS AND MEANINGS

Non-Commensurate

Two measurements are called **non-commensurate** if no
combination of one measurement can equal a combination of the other.
For example, your algebra tiles are called non-commensurate because no
combination of unit squares will ever be exactly equal to a combination
of x-tiles (although at times they may appear close in comparison). In
the same way, in the example below, no combination of x-tiles will ever
be exactly equal to a combination of y-tiles.

No matter what number of each size tile,
these two piles will never exactly match.

2-6.   Suppose you put one of your x-tiles and two unit tiles with another pile of three x-tiles and five unit tiles. What is in this new pile? Write it as a sum.

2-7.   Suppose one person in your team has two x^2-tiles, three x-tiles, and one unit tile on his desk and another person has one x^2-tile, five x-tiles, and eight unit tiles on her desk. You decide to put all of the tiles together on one desk. What is the name for this new group of tiles?

2-8.   Copy the following figures onto your paper. Then find the area and perimeter of each shape. Assume that all corners are right angles. Show all work.

a.

b.

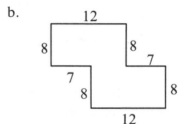

2-9.   One meaning of the word **evaluate** is to find the value of an expression for a specified value of the variable(s). To evaluate, replace a variable with a number and calculate the result. For example, when you are asked to evaluate the expression $4x - 2$ when $x = -7$, you would put –7 in place of the variable and calculate: $4 \cdot (-7) - 2 = -30$.

Evaluate the expressions below for the given values of x and y.

a. $\frac{6}{x} + 9$ if $x = 3$

b. $8x - 3 + y$ if $x = 2$ and $y = 1$

c. $2xy$ if $x = 5$ and $y = -3$

d. $2x^2 - y$ if $x = 3$ and $y = 8$

2-10.   For the following problem, define a variable and write an equation (use the 5-D Process if needed). Then solve the equation to solve the problem. Write your solution as a sentence.

A cable 84 meters long is cut into two pieces so that one piece is 18 meters longer than the other. Find the length of each piece of cable.

2.1.2   What is the perimeter?

· ·

Simplifying Expressions by Combining Like Terms

While Lesson 2.1.1 focused on the area of algebra tiles, today's lesson will focus on the perimeter. What is perimeter? How can you find it? By the end of this lesson, you will be able to find the perimeter of complex shapes formed by collections of tiles.

Your class will also focus on several ways to find perimeter, recognizing that there are different ways to "see" or recognize perimeter. Sometimes, with complex shapes, a convenient shortcut can help you find the perimeter more quickly. Be sure to share any insight into finding perimeter with your teammates and with the whole class.

While working today, ask yourself and your teammates these focus questions:

How did you see it?

How can you write it?

Is your expression as simplified as possible?

2-11.   Your teacher will provide a set of algebra tiles for your team to use today. Separate one of each shape and review its name (area). Then find the *perimeter* of each tile. Decide with your team how to write a simplified expression that represents the perimeter of each tile. Be prepared to share the perimeters you find with the class.

2-12.   Each part of an expression that is separated by addition or subtraction signs is called a **term**. If two terms contain the same variable(s), including the same exponents, if any, they are called **like terms**.

Match the terms in the left column with the like terms that match them in the right column.

A. $3x$ 1. $6y^2$

B. $-4y^2$ 2. $7xy$

C. $6a^4$ 3. 13

D. $10s$ 4. $-7c$

E. -8 5. $9a^4$

F. $6xy$ 6. s

G. c 7. $5x$

Core Connections, Course 3

2-13.   For each of the shapes formed by algebra tiles below:

- Use tiles to build the shape.

- Sketch and label the shape on your paper. Then write an expression that represents the perimeter.

- Simplify your perimeter expression as much as possible. This process of writing the expression more simply by collecting together the parts of the expression that are the same is called **combining like terms**.

a.
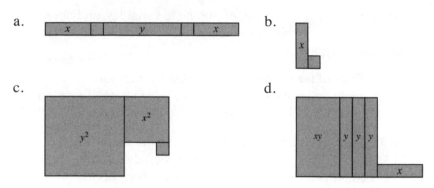

b.

c.

d.

2-14.   Calculate the perimeter of the shapes in problem 2-13 if the length of each x-tile is 3 units and the length of each y-tile is 8 units. Show all work.

2-15.   EXTENSION

The perimeter of the shape at right is 32 units. Find possible values for x and y. Is there more than one possible solution for each variable? If so, find another solution. If not, explain how you know there is only one solution.

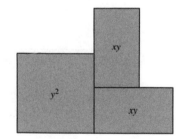

2-16.   LEARNING LOG

In your Learning Log, create your own shape using three different-shaped tiles. Draw the shape and show how to write a simplified expression for its perimeter. Label this entry "Finding Perimeter and Combining Like Terms" and include today's date.

MᴇᴛHODS AND Mᴇᴀɴɪɴɢs

Mathematics Vocabulary

Variable: A letter or symbol that represents one or more numbers.

Expression: A combination of numbers, variables, and operation symbols. For example, $2x + 3(5 - 2x) + 8$. Also, $5 - 2x$ is a smaller expression within the larger expression.

Term: Parts of the expression separated by addition and subtraction. For example, in the expression $2x + 3(5 - 2x) + 8$, the three terms are $2x$, $3(5 - 2x)$, and 8. The expression $5 - 2x$ has two terms, 5 and $-2x$.

Coefficient: The numerical part of a term. In the expression $2x + 3(5 - 2x) + 8$, for example, 2 is the coefficient of $2x$. In the expression $7x - 15x^2$, both 7 and 15 are coefficients.

Constant term: A number that is not multiplied by a variable. In the expression $2x + 3(5 - 2x) + 8$, the number 8 is a constant term. The number 3 is not a constant term, because it is multiplied by a variable inside the parentheses.

Factor: Part of a multiplication expression. In the expression $3(5 - 2x)$, 3 and $5 - 2x$ are factors.

2-17.   Simplify each algebraic expression below, if possible. If it is not possible to simplify the expression, explain why not.

a. $3y + 2y + y^2 + 5 + y$

b. $3y^2 + 2xy + 1 + 3x + y + 2x^2$

c. $3xy + 5x + 2 + 3y + x + 4$

d. $4m + 2mn + m^2 + m + 3m^2$

2-18. If the tiles have the dimensions shown at right, what is the name of the tile collection below? (That is, what is the total area of all of the pieces?) Write the expression algebraically, using x, x^2, y, y^2, and xy.

2-19. Remember that one meaning of the word "evaluate" is to replace a variable with a number and to calculate the result. For example, evaluating the expression x^2 when $x = -2$ results in the solution $(-2)^2 = 4$.

Evaluate the expressions below for the given values.

a. $-4d + 3$ if $d = -1$

b. $k - m$ if $k = 4$ and $m = -10$

c. $\frac{t}{w}$ if $t = 6$ and $w = -3$

d. $x^2 + y^2$ if $x = 7$ and $y = 5$

2-20. Solve the following problems.

a. A typical small bag of colored candies has about 135 candies in it, 27 of which are blue. At this rate, how many blue candies would you expect in a pile of 1000 colored candies?

b. Ten calculators cost $149.50. How much would 100 cost? 1000? 500?

2-21. Examine the graph at right.

a. Name the coordinates of points A, B, C, and D in (x, y) form.

b. Draw a set of axes like the ones shown at right on graph paper. Then plot points $E(5, 2)$, $F(-3, -1)$, $G(0, -4)$, and $H(2, -3)$.

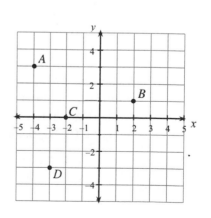

2.1.3 What does "minus" mean?

Writing Algebraic Expressions

In this section, you will look at algebraic expressions and see how they can be interpreted using an Expression Mat. To achieve this goal, you first need to understand the different meanings of the "minus" symbol, which is found in expressions such as $5-2$, $-x$, and $-(-3)$.

2-22.   LEARNING LOG

What does " $-$ " mean? Find as many ways as you can to describe this symbol and discuss how these descriptions differ from one another. Share your ideas with the class and record the different uses in your Learning Log. Title this entry "Meanings of Minus" and include today's date.

2-23.   USING AN EXPRESSION MAT

Your introduction to algebra tiles in Lessons 2.1.1 and 2.1.2 involved only positive values. Today you will look at how you can use algebra tiles to represent "minus." Below are several tiles with their associated values. Note that the shaded tiles are positive and the un-shaded tiles are negative. The diagram at right will appear throughout the text as a reminder.

 $= 5$ $= -3$ $= 3x$ $= -2y$

"Minus" can also be represented with a new tool called an **Expression Mat**, shown at right. An Expression Mat is an organizing tool that will be used to represent expressions. Notice that there is a positive region at the top and a negative (or "opposite") region at the bottom.

Problem continues on next page. →

Core Connections, Course 3

2-23.   *Problem continued from previous page.*

Using the Expression Mat, the value –3 can be shown in several ways, two of which are shown at right.

Value: –3   Value: –3

Note that in these examples, the diagram on the left side uses negative tiles in the "+" region, while the diagram on the right side uses positive tiles in the "–" region.

a.   Build two different representations for $-2x$ using an Expression Mat.

b.   Similarly, build $3x - (-4)$. How many different ways can you build $3x - (-4)$?

2-24.   As you solved problem 2-23, did you see all of the different ways to represent "minus" that you listed in problem 2-22? Discuss how you could use an Expression Mat to represent the different meanings discussed in class.

2-25.   BUILDING EXPRESSIONS

Use the Expression Mat to create each of the following expressions with algebra tiles. Find at least two different representations for each expression. Sketch each representation on your paper. Be prepared to share your different representations with the class.

a. $-3x + 4$ b. $-(y - 2)$ c. $-y - 3$ d. $5x - (3 - 2x)$

2-26.   In problem 2-25, you represented algebraic expressions with algebra tiles. In this problem, you will need to reverse your thinking to write an expression from a diagram of algebra tiles.

Working with a partner, write algebraic expressions for each representation below. Start by building each problem using your algebra tiles.

a.

b.

c.

d.

2-27.   Patti, Emilie, and Carla are debating the answer to part (d) of problem 2-26. Patti wrote $2 - 1 + 2x - 3$. Carla thinks that the answer is $2x + 2 - 4$. Emilie is convinced that the answer is $2x - 2$. Discuss with your team how each person might have arrived at her answer. Who do you think is correct? When you decide, write an explanation on your paper and justify your answer.

2-28.   LEARNING LOG

Reflect about what you have learned from today's lesson as you answer the following question in your Learning Log. Title this entry "Representing Expressions on an Expression Mat" and include today's date.

Using an Expression Mat, find two different ways to represent $x - 1 - (2x - 3)$. Sketch the different representations and write a few sentences to describe the differences in the ways you built each representation.

2-29.   Copy and write the following expressions by combining like terms. Using or drawing sketches of algebra tiles may be helpful.

a. $2x + 3x + 3 + 4x^2 + 10 + x$ b. $4x + 4y^2 + y^2 + 9 + 10 + x + 3x$

c. $2x^2 + 30 + 3x^2 + 4x^2 + 14 + x$ d. $20 + 5xy + 4y^2 + 10 + y^2 + xy$

2-30.   Find a simplified algebraic expression for each Expression Mat below.

a.   b.   c.

2-31.   Write an equation and solve it to find the answer to the question below. Use the 5-D Process to help you write the equation, if needed. Remember to define your variable and to write your answer in a complete sentence.

Susan is buying three different colors of tiles for her kitchen floor. She is buying 25 more red tiles than beige tiles, and three times as many navy-blue tiles as beige tiles. If Susan buys 435 tiles altogether, how many tiles of each color does she buy?

2-32.   Without using a calculator, compute the value of each expression below.

a. $-14 + (-31)$ b. $-(-8) - (-2)$

c. $\frac{-16}{-8}$ d. $-11 \cdot 24$

e. $\frac{1}{2} - \frac{3}{4}$ f. $46 \div (-23)$

Chapter 2: Simplifying with Variables

2-33.   To bake 100 of his favorite cookies, Mr. Wallis needs 350 grams of sugar.

Cookies	Sugar (g)
100	350
10	
20	
2	
1	
5	
	700
	1400

a.   How many grams of sugar would he need to bake 10 cookies? What about 20 cookies? Show all work.

b.   What is the unit rate? That is, how many grams of sugar are needed for 1 cookie?

c.   To help him know how much sugar to use when baking cookies, Mr. Wallis started to make a table, as shown above. Copy and complete his table on your paper.

2.1.4 What makes zero?

•••

Using Zero to Simplify Algebraic Expressions

Today you will continue your work with rewriting algebraic expressions. As you work with your team, ask yourself and your teammates these focus questions:

How did you see it?

How can you write it?

Is your expression as simplified as possible?

2-34.   LIKELY STORY!

Imagine the following situations:

- Julie baby-sits for her neighbor's baby and stuffs the $15 she earned into her purse. When she gets home, the $15 is nowhere to be found. It must have fallen out of her purse.

- The Burton Pumas football team completes a pass and gains 12 yards. But on the very next play, the quarterback holds onto the ball too long and gets sacked, losing 12 yards.

- Rolando is at the beach. He digs a hole in the sand and places the sand he removes in a pile next to his hole. Someone comes along and pushes the pile back into the hole.

What do each of these situations have in common? Can you represent each of them using symbols? How?

2-35.   How can you represent zero with tiles on an Expression Mat? With your team, try to find at least two different ways to do this (and more if you can). Be ready to share your ideas with the class.

2-36. Gretchen used seven algebra tiles to build the expression shown below.

a. Build this collection of tiles on your own Expression Mat and write its value.

b. Represent this same value three different ways, each time using a *different number* of tiles. Be ready to share your representations with the class.

2-37. Build each expression below so that your representation does not match those of your teammates. Once your team is convinced that together you have found four different, valid representations, sketch your representation on your paper and be ready to share your answer with the class.

a. $-3x+5+y$ b. $-(-2y+1)$ c. $2x-(x-4)$

2-38. Write the algebraic expression shown on each Expression Mat below. Build the model and then simplify the expression by removing as many tiles as you can *without changing the value* of the expression. Finally, write the simplified algebraic expression.

a.   b.

2-39. Simplify each of the following expressions by building it on your Expression Mat and removing zeros. Your teacher will give you instructions about how to represent your work on your paper.

a. $3x-(2x+4)$ b. $7-(4y-3)+2y-4$

2-40. LEARNING LOG

In your Learning Log, describe the different ways you can represent zero using your Expression Mat. Include an example and be sure to draw the tiles. Title this entry "Using Zeros to Simplify" and include today's date.

METHODS AND **M**EANINGS

MATH NOTES

Evaluating Expressions and the Order of Operations

To **evaluate** an algebraic expression for particular values of the variables, replace the variables in the expression with their known numerical values and simplify. Replacing variables with their known values is called **substitution**. An example is provided below.

Evaluate $4x - 3y + 7$ for $x = 2$ and $y = 1$.

Replace x and y with their known values of 2 and 1, respectively, and simplify.

$$4(2) - 3(1) + 7$$
$$= 8 - 3 + 7$$
$$= 12$$

When evaluating a complex expression, you must remember to use the **Order of Operations** that mathematicians have agreed upon. As illustrated in the example below, the order of operations is:

Original expression:

$$(10 - 3 \cdot 2) \cdot 2^2 - \frac{13 - 3^2}{2} + 6$$

Circle expressions that are grouped within parentheses or by a fraction bar:

$$\overline{(10 - 3 \cdot 2)} \cdot 2^2 - \frac{\overline{(13 - 3^2)}}{2} + 6$$

Simplify *within* circled terms using the order of operations:

$$\overline{(10 - 3 \cdot 2)} \cdot 2^2 - \frac{\overline{(13 - 3 \cdot 3)}}{2} + 6$$

- Evaluate exponents.

$$\overline{(10 - 6)} \cdot 2^2 - \frac{\overline{(13 - 9)}}{2} + 6$$

- Multiply and divide from left to right.

$$(4) \cdot 2^2 - \frac{4}{2} + 6$$

$$\overline{(4 \cdot 2^2)} - \overline{\left(\frac{4}{2}\right)} + \overline{(6)}$$

- Combine terms by adding and subtracting from left to right.

$$\overline{(4 \cdot 2 \cdot 2)} - \overline{\left(\frac{4}{2}\right)} + \overline{(6)}$$

Circle the remaining terms:

Simplify *within* circled terms using the Order of Operations as described above.

$$16 - 2 + 6$$
$$20$$

2-41. Can zero be represented by any number of tiles? Using only the unit tiles (in other words, only the 1 and –1 tiles), determine whether you can represent zero on an Expression Mat with the number of tiles below. If you can, draw an Expression Mat demonstrating that it is possible. If it is not possible, explain why not.

a.   2 tiles   b.   6 tiles   c.   3 tiles

2-42. Write and simplify the algebraic expression shown in each Expression Mat below.

a.   b.   c.

2-43. Read the Math Notes box in this lesson. Then evaluate each expression below.

   a. $2 + 3x$ for $x = 4$

   b. $4 - 5c$ for $c = -\frac{1}{2}$

   c. $3d^2 - 1$ for $d = -5$

   d. $-4(r - 2)$ for $r = -1$

   e. $3(t - 12)^2 - 1$ for $t = 14$

2-44. Copy and complete each of the Diamond Problems below. The pattern used in the Diamond Problems is shown at right.

a.   b.   c.   d.

2-45.   Find the perimeter of the entire rectangle shown at right (that is, the length of the outside boundary of the figure). Notice that the areas of two of the parts have been labeled inside the rectangle. Also find the total area. Remember to show all work leading to your solution.

2.1.5 How can I simplify the expression?

Using Algebra Tiles to Simplify Algebraic Expressions

Which is greater: 58 or 62? That question might seem easy, because the numbers are ready to be compared. However, if you are asked which is greater, $2x + 8 - x - 3$ or $6 + x + 1$, the answer is not so obvious! In this lesson, you and your teammates will investigate how to compare two algebraic expressions and decide whether one is greater.

2-46.   For each expression below:

   • Use an Expression Mat to build the expression.

   • Find a different way to represent the same expression using tiles.

   a. $7x - 3$ b. $-(-2x + 6) + 3x$

2-47.   COMPARING EXPRESSIONS

Two expressions can be represented at the same time using an **Expression Comparison Mat**. The Expression Comparison Mat puts two Expression Mats side-by-side so you can compare them and see which one is greater. For example, in the picture at right, the expression on the left represents -3, while the expression on the right represents -2. Since $-2 > -3$, the expression on the right is greater.

Build the Expression Comparison Mat shown at right. Write an expression representing each side of the Expression Mat.

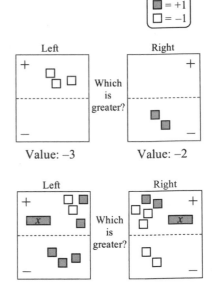

a.   Can you simplify each of the expressions so that fewer tiles are used? Develop a method to simplify both sides of the Expression Comparison Mats. Why does it work? Be prepared to justify your method to the class.

b.   Which side of the Expression Comparison Mat do you think is greater (has the largest value)? Agree on an answer as a team. Make sure each person in your team is ready to justify your conclusion to the class.

2-48.   As Karl simplified some algebraic expressions, he
         recorded his work on the diagrams below.

- Explain in writing what he did to each
  Expression Comparison Mat on the left to get
  the Expression Comparison Mat on the right.

- If necessary, simplify further to determine which
  Expression Mat is greater. How can you tell if
  your final answer is correct?

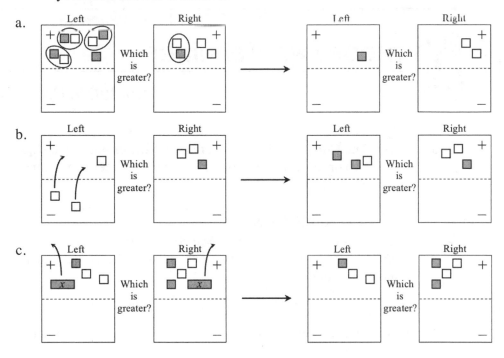

2-49.   Use Karl's "legal" simplification moves to determine which side of each
         Expression Comparison Mat below is greater. Record each of your "legal"
         moves on the Lesson 2.1.5A Resource Page by drawing on it the way Karl did
         in problem 2-49. After each expression is simplified, state which side is greater
         (has the largest value). Be prepared to share your process and reasoning with
         the class.

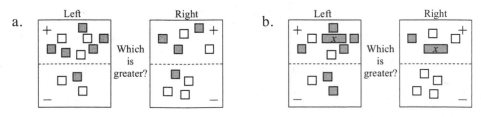

2-50.   **LEARNING LOG**

In your Learning Log, explain each of the types of
"legal" moves that you can use to simplify and compare
expressions. For each type of "legal" move, sketch an
example. Title this entry "Legal Moves for Simplifying
and Comparing Expressions" and include today's date.

METHODS AND MEANINGS

Commutative Properties

The **Commutative Property of Addition** states that when *adding*
two or more numbers or terms together, order is not important.
That is:

$$a + b = b + a \qquad \text{For example, } 2 + 7 = 7 + 2$$

The **Commutative Property of Multiplication** states that when
multiplying two or more numbers or terms together, order is not
important. That is:

$$a \cdot b = b \cdot a \qquad \text{For example, } 3 \cdot 5 = 5 \cdot 3$$

However, *subtraction* and *division* are <u>not</u> commutative, as shown
below.

$$7 - 2 \neq 2 - 7 \text{ since } 5 \neq -5$$

$$50 \div 10 \neq 10 \div 50 \text{ since } 5 \neq 0.2$$

Review & Preview

2-51.   Simplify the following expressions by combining like terms, if possible.

a. $x + x - 3 + 4x^2 + 2x - x$

b. $8x^2 + 3x - 13x^2 + 10x^2 - 25x - x$

c. $4x + 3y$

d. $20 + 3xy - 3 + 4y^2 + 10 - 2y^2$

2-52.   When writing an expression for part (a) of problem 2-42, Ricardo wrote $2x-3-(x+1)$, while Francine wrote $-3+2x-(x+1)$. Francine states that their expressions are equivalent. Is Francine's conclusion true or false? Use algebraic properties to justify your conclusion.

2-53.   The two lines at right represent the growing profits of Companies A and B.

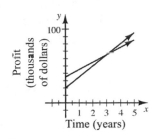

a.   Sketch this graph on your paper. If Company A started out with more profit than Company B, determine which line represents A and which represents B. Label the lines appropriately.

b.   In how many years will both companies have the same profit?

c.   Approximately what will that profit be?

d.   Which company's profits are growing more quickly? How can you tell?

2-54.   Find the value of y, given value of x.

a. $y=2+4.3x$ when $x=-6$ b. $y=(x-3)^2$ when $x=9$

c. $y=x-2$ when $x=3.5$ d. $y=5x-4$ when $x=-2$

2-55.   When baking cupcakes for his class of 21 students, Sammy needed two eggs. Now he wants to bake cupcakes for the upcoming science fair. If he expects 336 people to attend the science fair, how many eggs will he need?

2.1.6 Which is greater?

· ·

Using Algebra Tiles to Compare Expressions

Can you always tell whether one algebraic expression is greater than another? In this lesson, you will compare the values of two expressions, practicing the different simplification strategies you have learned so far.

2-56.   WHICH IS GREATER?

Write an algebraic expression for each side of the Expression Comparison Mats given below. Use the "legal" simplification moves you worked with in Lesson 2.1.5 to determine which expression on the Expression Comparison Mat is greater.

a.

b.

c.

d.

e.

f.

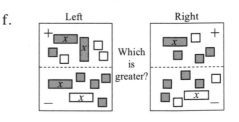

2-57. Build the Expression Comparison Mat shown below with algebra tiles.

a. Simplify the expressions using the "legal" moves that you developed in Lesson 2.1.5.

b. Can you tell which expression is greater? Explain in a few sentences on your paper. Be prepared to share your conclusion with the class.

METHODS AND MEANINGS

Simplifying an Expression ("Legal Moves")

Three common ways to simplify or alter expressions on an Expression Mat are illustrated below.

- Removing an equal number of opposite tiles that are in the same region. For example, the positive and negative tiles in the same region at right combine to make zero.

- Flipping a tile to move it out of one region into the opposite region (i.e., finding its opposite). For example, the tiles in the "−" region at right can be flipped into the "+" region.

- Removing an equal number of identical tiles from both the "−" and the "+" regions. This strategy can be seen as a combination of the two methods above, since you could first flip the tiles from one region to another and then remove the opposite pairs.

2-58.   WHICH IS GREATER?

For each Expression Comparison Mat below, simplify and
determine which side is greater.

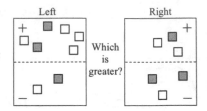

2-59.   Cairo wants to create a graph that
represents the heights and bases of all
rectangles that have an area of 36 square
units. He started by drawing the
rectangles A, B, C, and D at right.
Examine the dimensions (length and
width) of each rectangle.

a.   Copy the graph at right onto graph paper.
Then match the letter of each rectangle
above with a point on the graph. Which
point is not matched?

b.   What are the base, height, and area for the
unmatched point?

c.   Why should the unmatched point not be on Cairo's graph?

d.   Find the dimensions of three more rectangles that have areas of 36 square
units. At least one of your examples should have dimensions that are not
integers. Place a new point on the graph for each new rectangle you find.

e.   Connect all of the points representing an area of 36 square units. Describe
the resulting graph.

Core Connections, Course 3

2-60.   Use substitution to find y.

   a. $y = 3 + 8.5x$, when $x = -4$ b. $y = x - 15$, when $x = 2.65$

   c. $y = (x - 5)(x + 2)$, when $x = 3$ d. $y + 6.2x = -13$, when $x = -4$

2-61.   One of Teddy's jobs at home is to pump gas for his family's sedan and truck. When he fills up the sedan with 12 gallons of gas, he notices that it costs him $50.28.

   a.   How much does one gallon of gas cost? This is also called the unit rate. Explain how you found your answer.

   b.   How much will it cost him to fill up the truck if it needs 25 gallons of gas? Show your work.

   c.   When Teddy filled up the tank on his moped, it cost $5.03. How much gas did his moped need? Explain how you know.

2-62.   The graph below shows distances traveled by Car A and Car B. Car A is represented by the line containing point A, and Car B is represented by the line containing point B. Use the graph to answer the following questions.

   a.   Which car is traveling faster? How can you tell?

   b.   Find the coordinates of point A and point B.

   c.   How fast did Car A travel (in miles per hour)? How fast did Car B travel?

   d.   Does the distance Car A has traveled vary directly with the time? Why or why not?

2.1.7 How can I write it?

Simplifying and Recording Work

Today you will continue to compare expressions as you strengthen your simplification strategies. At the same time, you will work with your class to find ways to record your work so that another student can follow your strategies.

2-63. Use algebra tiles to build the expressions below on an Expression Comparison Mat. Use "legal" simplification moves to determine which expression is greater, if possible. If it is not possible to tell which expression is greater, explain why.

a. Which is greater: $3x - (2 - x) + 1$ or $-5 + 4x + 4$?

b. Which is greater: $2x^2 - 2x + 6 - (-3x)$ or $-(3 - 2x^2) + 5 + 2x$?

c. Which is greater: $-1 + 6y - 2 + 4x - 2y$ or $x + 5y - (-2 + y) + 3x - 6$?

2-64. RECORDING YOUR WORK

Although using algebra tiles can make some things easier because you can "see" and "touch" the math, it can be difficult to remember what you did to solve a problem unless you take good notes.

Use the simplification strategies you have learned to determine which expression on the Expression Comparison Mat at right is greater. Record each step as instructed by your teacher. Also record the simplified expression that remains after each move. This will be a written record of how you solved this problem. Discuss with your team what the best way is to record your moves.

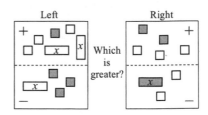

2-65.   While Athena was comparing the expressions shown at right, she was called out of the classroom. When her teammates needed help, they looked at her paper and saw the work shown below. Unfortunately, she had forgotten to explain her simplification steps.

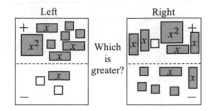

Can you help them figure out what Athena did to get each new set of expressions?

Left Expression	Right Expression	Explanation
$3x+4-x-(-2)+x^2$	$-1+x^2+4x-(4+2x)$	Original expressions
$3x+4-x-(-2)$	$-1+4x-(4+2x)$	
$3x+4-x+2$	$-1+4x-4-2x$	
$2x+6$	$2x-5$	
6	-5	
Because $6>-5$, the left side is greater.		

2-66.   For each pair of expressions below, determine which is greater, carefully recording your steps as you go. If you cannot tell which expression is greater, state, "Not enough information." Make sure that you record your result after each type of simplification. For example, if you flip all of the tiles from the "–" region to the "+" region, record the resulting expression and indicate what you did using either words or symbols. Be ready to share your work with the class.

a.

b.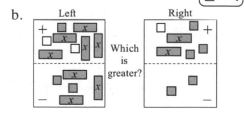

c.   Which is greater: $5-(2y-4)-2$ or $-y-(1+y)+4$?

d.   Which is greater: $3xy+9-4x-7+x$ or $-2x+3xy-(x-2)$?

MathODS AND MEANINGS

Associative and Identity Properties

The **Associative Property of Addition** states that when *adding* three or more numbers or terms together, grouping is not important. That is:

$$(a+b)+c = a+(b+c)$$ For example, $(5+2)+6 = 5+(2+6)$

The **Associative Property of Multiplication** states that when *multiplying* three or more numbers or terms together, grouping is not important. That is:

$$(a \cdot b) \cdot c = a \cdot (b \cdot c)$$ For example, $(5 \cdot 2) \cdot 6 = 5 \cdot (2 \cdot 6)$

However, *subtraction* and *division* are <u>not</u> associative, as shown below.

$$(5-2)-3 \neq 5-(2-3) \text{ since } 0 \neq 6$$

$$(20 \div 4) \div 2 \neq 20 \div (4 \div 2) \text{ since } 2.5 \neq 10$$

The **Identity Property of Addition** states that adding zero to any expression gives the same expression. That is:

$$a+0 = a$$ For example, $6+0 = 6$

The **Identity Property of Multiplication** states that multiplying any expression by one gives the same expression. That is:

$$1 \cdot a = a$$ For example, $1 \cdot 6 = 6$

2-67.   Sylvia simplified the expressions on the Expression Comparison Mat shown at right. Some of her work is shown. Are all of her moves "legal"? Explain.

$\blacksquare = +1$
$\square = -1$

2-68.   Read the Math Notes boxes in this lesson and for Lesson 2.1.5. Then examine the work below that shows one way to simplify the expression $3x+8+(x+10)$. Decide which property was used for each step.

Expression	What property was used?
$3x+8+(x+10)$	Original expression
$(3x+8+x)+10$	a.
$(3x+x+8)+10$	b.
$(4x+8)+10$	Added like terms
$4x+(8+10)$	c.
$4x+18$	Added like terms

2-69.   Examine the tile pattern at right.

Figure 1   Figure 2   Figure 3

a.   On graph paper, draw Figures 4 and 5.

b.   What would Figure 10 look like? How many tiles would it have? What about Figure 100?

c.   Cami has a different tile pattern. She decided to represent the number of tiles of her pattern in a table, as shown below. Can you use the table to predict how many tiles would be in Figure 5 of her tile pattern? How many tiles would Figure 8 have? Explain how you know.

Figure Number	1	2	3	4
Number of Tiles	5	9	13	17

2-70.   Examine the shape made with algebra tiles at right.

a.   Write an expression that represents the perimeter of the shape. Then evaluate your expression for $x=6$ and $y=10$ units.

b.   Write an expression that represents the area of the shape. What is the area if $x=6$ and $y=10$ units?

2-71.   **CALCULATOR CHECK**

Use your scientific calculator to compute the value of each expression in the left-hand column below. Match each result to an answer in the right-hand column.

a. $-3+16-(-5)$

b. $(3-5)(6+2)$

c. $17(-23)+2$

d. $5-(3-17)(-2+25)$

e. $(-4)(-2.25)(-10)$

f. $-1.5-2.25-(-4.5)$

g. $\frac{4-5}{-2}$

1. -16

2. 327

3. 0.5

4. 18

5. -90

6. 0.75

7. -389

2.1.8   What if both sides are equal?

· ·

Using Algebra Tiles to Solve for x

Can you always tell whether one algebraic expression is greater than another? In this section, you will continue to practice the different simplification strategies you have learned so far to compare two expressions and see which one is greater. However, sometimes you do not have enough information about the expressions. When both sides of an equation are equal, you can learn even more about x. As you work today, focus on these questions:

How can you simplify?

How can you get x alone?

Is there more than one way to simplify?

Is there always a solution?

2-72.   **WHICH IS GREATER?**

Build each expression represented below with the tiles provided by your teacher. Use "legal" simplification moves to determine which expression is greater, if possible. If it is not possible to determine which expression is greater, explain why it is impossible. Be sure to record your work on your paper.

a.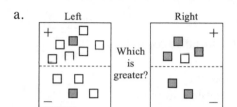

b.   Which is greater:

$x + 1 - (1 - 2x)$ or

$3 + x - 1 - (x - 4)$?

2-73.   **WHAT IF BOTH SIDES ARE EQUAL?**

If the number 5 is compared to the number 7, then it is clear that 7 is greater. However, what if you compare x with 7? In this case, x could be smaller, larger, *or equal to* 7.

Examine the Expression Comparison Mat below.

a.   If the left expression is smaller than the right expression, what does that tell you about the value of x?

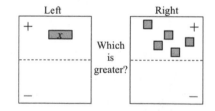

b.   If the left expression is greater than the right expression, what does that tell you about the value of x?

c.   What if the left expression is equal to the right expression? What does x have to be for the two expressions to be equal?

2-74.   SOLVING FOR X

In later courses, you will learn more about situations like parts (a) and (b) in the preceding problem, called "inequalities." For now, to learn more about x , assume that the left expression and the right expression are equal. The two expressions will be brought together on one mat to create an **Equation Mat**, as shown in the figure below. The double line down the center of an Equation Mat represents the word "equals." It is a wall that separates the left side of an equation from the right side.

a.   Obtain the "Equation Mat" resource page from your teacher. Build the equation represented by the Equation Mat at right using algebra tiles. Simplify as much as possible and then solve for x . Be sure to record your work.

b.   Build the equation $2x - 5 = -1 + 5x + 2$ using your tiles by placing $2x - 5$ on the left side and $-1 + 5x + 2$ on the right side. Then use your simplification skills to simplify this equation as much as possible so that x is alone on one side of the equation. Use the fact that both sides are equal to solve for x . Record your work.

2-75.   Now apply the solving skill from problem 2-74 by building, simplifying, and solving each equation below for x . Record your work.

a. $3x - 7 = 2$ b. $1 + 2x - x = x - 5 + x$

c. $3 - 2x = 2x - 5$ d. $3 + 2x - (x + 1) = 3x - 6$

e. $-(x + 3 - x) = 2x - 7$ f. $-4 + 2x + 2 = x + 1 + x$

Ⓜ ETHODS AND MEANINGS

Inverse Properties

MATH NOTES

The **Additive Inverse Property** states that for every number a there is a number $-a$ such that $a + (-a) = 0$. A common name used for the additive inverse is the **opposite**. That is, $-a$ is the opposite of a . For example, $3 + (-3) = 0$ and $-5 + 5 = 0$.

The **Multiplicative Inverse Property** states that for every nonzero number a there is a number $\frac{1}{a}$ such that $a \cdot \frac{1}{a} = 1$. A common name used for the multiplicative inverse is the **reciprocal**. That is, $\frac{1}{a}$ is the reciprocal of a . For example, $6 \cdot \frac{1}{6} = 1$.

2-76.   Translate the Equation Mat at right into an equation. Remember that the double line represents "equals."

2-77.   Decide if each statement below is true or false. Explain how you know and name any properties you use. Refer to the Math Notes boxes in this lesson and in Lessons 2.1.5 and 2.1.7 to help you.

a. $-19 + 7 = -7 + 19$

b. $\frac{4}{5} \cdot 1 = \frac{4}{5}$

c. $\frac{3}{2} \cdot \frac{2}{3} = 1$

d. $5 \cdot 7 - 5 \cdot \frac{1}{5} = 34$

2-78.   Simplify each expression below as much as possible.

a. $3y - y + 5x + 3 - 7x$

b. $-1 - (-5x) - 2x + 2x^2 + 7$

c. $6x + 2 - 1 - 4x - 3 - 2x + 2$

d. $\frac{2}{3}x - 3y + \frac{1}{3}x + 2y$

2-79.   Plot the points $(0, 0)$, $(3, 2)$, and $(6, 4)$ on graph paper. Then draw a line through the points. Name the coordinates of three more points on the same line.

2-80.   Evaluate the expressions below for the given values.

a. $6m + 2n^2$ for $m = 7$ and $n = 3$

b. $\frac{5x}{3} - 2$ for $x = -18$

c. $(6x)^2 - \frac{x}{5}$ for $x = 10$

d. $(k - 3)(k + 2)$ for $k = 1$

2.1.9 What is x?

More Solving Equations

Today you will explore more equations on the Equation Mat and will examine all of the tools you have developed so far to solve for x. While you are working on these problems, be prepared to answer the questions that follow.

How can you simplify?

Can you get the variable alone?

Is there more than one way to simplify?

Is there always a solution?

2-81.   On your paper, write the equation represented in each diagram below. For each equation, simplify as much as possible and then solve for x or y. Be sure to record your work on your paper.

a.

b.

2-82.   IS THERE A SOLUTION?

While solving homework last night, Richie came across three homework questions that he thinks have no solution. Build each equation below and determine if it has a solution for x. If it has a solution, find it. If it does not have a solution, explain why not.

a.

b.

c.

Core Connections, Course 3

2-83.   Continue to develop your equation-solving strategies by solving each equation
         below (if possible). Remember to build each equation, simplify as much as
         possible, and solve for x or y. There are often multiple ways to solve
         equations, so remember to justify that each step is "legal." If you cannot solve
         for x, explain why not. Be sure to record your work.

   a. $-x+2=4$ b. $4x-2+x=2x+8+3x$

   c. $4y-9+y=6$ d. $9-(2-3y)=6+2y-(5+y)$

2-84.   LEARNING LOG

         In your Learning Log, explain when you can solve for x in
         an equation and when you cannot. Be sure to give an
         example of each situation. Title this entry "Solutions of an
         Equation" and include today's date.

METHODS AND MEANINGS

MATH NOTES

Using an Equation Mat

An **Equation Mat** can help
you visually represent an
equation with algebra tiles.

The double line represents the
"equal" sign (=).

For each side of the equation, there is
a positive and a negative region.

For example, the equation
$2x-1-(-x+3)=6-2x$ can be
represented by the Equation Mat at
right. (Note that there are other
possible ways to represent this equation
correctly on the Equation Mat.)

$\square = +1$
$\square = -1$

2-85.   Ling wants to save $87 for tickets to a rock concert. If she has $23 now and
         will save $4 per week, how long will it take her to get enough money to buy the
         tickets? Define a variable and then write and solve an equation. (Use the 5-D
         Process to help you, if needed.) Write your solution as a sentence.

2-86.   When you want to convince someone that $8x + (2x - 3)$ is equivalent to
         $(8x + 2x) - 3$, you can support your claim with the Associative Property of
         Addition.

         Determine if the following statements are true or false. If true, justify your
         conclusion by stating the appropriate algebraic property. If false, explain how
         you know.

         a. $(81)(38) = (38)(81)$ b. $27 + 0 = 27$

         c. $3 - 5 = 5 - 3$ d. $19.4 \cdot 1 = 19.4$

2-87.   Copy and complete each of the Diamond Problems below.
         The pattern used in the Diamond Problems is shown at right.

         a.   b.   c.   d.

2-88.   Ferroza can buy a 24-ounce bag of ferret food for $1.19, or
         she can buy a 36-ounce bag for $2.89. Which is the better
         deal? Justify your conclusion.

2-89.   This problem is a checkpoint for evaluating expressions and using the Order of
Operations. It will be referred to as Checkpoint 2.

Evaluate each expression if $x = -2$, $y = -3$, and $z = 5$.

a. $2x + 3y + z$

b. $x - y$

c. $2\left(\frac{x+y}{z}\right)$

d. $3x^2 - 2x + 1$

e. $3y(x + x^2 - y)$

f. $\frac{-z^2(1-2x)}{y-x}$

Check your answers by referring to the Checkpoint 2 materials located at the
back of your book.

Ideally, at this point you are comfortable working with these types of problems
and can solve them correctly. If you feel that you need more confidence when
solving these types of problems, then review the Checkpoint 2 materials and try
the practice problems provided. From this point on, you will be expected to do
problems like these correctly and with confidence.

Chapter 2 Closure   What have I learned?

Reflection and Synthesis

The activities below offer you a chance to reflect about what you have learned during this chapter. As you work, look for concepts that you feel very comfortable with, ideas that you would like to learn more about, and topics you need more help with.

①   SUMMARIZING MY UNDERSTANDING

This section gives you an opportunity to show what you know about the main math ideas in this chapter.

Simplifying and Solving Equations

Obtain the Chapter 2 Closure Resource Page, Simplifying/Solving Graphic Organizer (GO), from your teacher.

Your Task:

- Imagine that you are the teacher for some students who have just finished this chapter. You need to make a test to determine how well they know how to use algebra tiles to represent an equation as well as how to simplify and solve for the variable.

- With your team, first brainstorm all of the things that such students would need to know about using algebra tiles. This is the list of the concepts that you would assess with your test.

- Then, as a team, create one equation that would allow you, as the teacher, to assess the students' understanding of many of the concepts that you listed. Try to make your equation easy enough for the students to do, but challenging enough that you will be able to tell if they understand the list of concepts very well.

- Use the Chapter 2 Closure Graphic Organizer to create an answer key for the problem that you created. Your key should help you assess the work that students turn in. Be sure to include each step as a tile drawing and as a symbolic equation. Also be sure to write an explanation of what the students would do at each step. If your equation takes more than four steps, then continue your work on another piece of paper or on an additional GO page.

- Check your teammates' answer keys for accuracy.

Core Connections, Course 3

②   WHAT HAVE I LEARNED?

This section will help you evaluate which types of problems you have seen with which you feel comfortable and those with which you need more help.

Solve each problem as completely as you can. The table at the end of this closure section has answers to these problems. It also tells you where you can find additional help and practice on problems like these.

CL 2-90.   Examine the Expression Mat at right.

     a.   Copy the Expression Mat onto your paper.

     b.   Write an expression for the tiles as they appear.

     c.   On your drawing, circle all of the zeros that you can find to simplify the expression.

     d.   Write the completely simplified expression.

CL 2-91.   Write expressions for each side of the Expression Comparison Mat. Use "legal" moves to simplify and determine which side is greater.

CL 2-92.   Define a variable and then write an equation for the following problem. Remember that you can use the 5-D Process to help you do this. Then solve your equation and state your answer in a sentence. Show your work in an organized way.

The number of students attending the fall play was 150 more than the number of adults attending. Student tickets cost $3, and adult tickets cost $5. A total of $4730 was collected. How many students attended the play?

CL 2-93. Simplify each expression with or without algebra tiles. Record your steps.

    a. $3+7x-(2+9x)$ b. $6-(3x-4)+7x-11$

    c. $3x^2+10-y^2+4x-8x^2-5y-8+y^2+3$

CL 2-94. Copy the pattern at right onto graph paper. Draw Figures 1 and 5 on your paper.

    a.   How many tiles are in each figure?

    b.   How is the pattern changing?

    c.   How many tiles would Figure 6 have?

Figure 2   Figure 3   Figure 4

CL 2-95. Evaluate $6x-(3y+7)-xy$ when $x=5$ and $y=3$.

CL 2-96. Molly bought 4.25 pounds of fish for $10.20.

    a.   What is the unit rate (cost per pound)?

    b.   What should six pounds of fish cost at the same rate?

    c.   Write an equation relating cost (c) with pounds (p).

CL 2-97. For each of the problems above, do the following:

- Draw a bar or number line that represents 0 to 10.

- Color or shade in a portion of the bar that represents your level of understanding and comfort with completing that problem on your own.

If any of your bars are less than a 5, choose *one* of those problems and complete one of the following tasks:

- Write two questions that you would like to ask about that problem.
- Brainstorm two things that you DO know about that type of problem.

If all of your bars are a 5 or above, choose *one* of those problems and do one of these tasks:

- Write two questions you might ask or hints you might give to a student who was stuck on the problem.
- Make a new problem that is similar and more challenging than that problem and solve it.

③   WHAT TOOLS CAN I USE?

You have several tools and references available to help support your learning – your teacher, your study team, your math book, and your Toolkit, to name only a few. At the end of each chapter you will have an opportunity to review your Toolkit for completeness as well as to revise or update it to better reflect your current understanding of big ideas.

The main elements of your Toolkit should be your Learning Logs, Math Notes, and the vocabulary used in this chapter. Math words that are new to this chapter appear in bold in the text. Refer to the lists provided below and follow your teacher's instructions to revise your Toolkit, which will help make it a useful reference for you as you complete this chapter and prepare to begin the next one.

Learning Log Entries

- Lesson 2.1.1 – Algebra Tiles and Variables
- Lesson 2.1.2 – Finding Perimeter and Combining Like Terms
- Lesson 2.1.3 – Meanings of Minus
- Lesson 2.1.3 – Representing Expressions on an Expression Mat
- Lesson 2.1.4 – Using Zeros to Simplify
- Lesson 2.1.5 – Legal Moves for Simplifying and Comparing Expressions
- Lesson 2.1.9 – Solutions of an Equation

Math Notes

- Lesson 2.1.1 – Non-Commensurate
- Lesson 2.1.2 – Mathematics Vocabulary
- Lesson 2.1.3 – Combining Like Terms
- Lesson 2.1.4 – Evaluating Expressions and the Order of Operations
- Lesson 2.1.5 – Commutative Properties
- Lesson 2.1.6 – Simplifying an Expression ("Legal Moves")
- Lesson 2.1.7 – Associative and Identity Properties
- Lesson 2.1.8 – Inverse Properties
- Lesson 2.1.9 – Using an Equation Mat

Mathematical Vocabulary

The following is a list of vocabulary found in this chapter. Some of the words you have been seen in the previous chapter or in previous coursework. The words in bold are the words new to this chapter. Make sure that you are familiar with the terms below and know what they mean. For the words you do not know, refer to the glossary or index. You might also add these words to your Toolkit so that you can reference them in the future.

Additive Identity	**Additive Inverse**	**Associative Property**
combining like terms	**Commutative Property**	**Equation Mat**
evaluate	**Expression (Comparison) Mat**	
Multiplicative Identity	**Multiplicative Inverse**	**non-commensurate**
Order of Operations	**term**	variable

Answers and Support for Closure Problems
What Have I Learned?

Note: MN = Math Note, LL = Learning Log

Problem	Solution	Need Help?	More Practice
CL 2-90.	b. $2x - x + 3 - 2 - (x - x + 2 - 1)$ c. One possible answer: d. x	Lesson 2.1.3 and 2.1.4 MN: 2.1.3 and 2.1.6 LL: 2.1.3 and 2.1.4	Problems 2-26, 2-38, and 2-42
CL 2-91.	Left: $-1 + 2x + 3 - (2x - 2) = 4$ Right: $2x + 2 - x - (2x - x - 2 + 1) = 3$ The left expression is greater than the right expression.	Lesson 2.1.5 MN: 2.1.3 and 2.1.6 LL: 2.1.3, 2.1.4, and 2.1.5	Problems 2-47, 2-56, 2-57, 2-58, 2-63, 2-67, and 2-73
CL 2-92.	Let s represent the number of students, $3s + 5(s - 150) = 4730$, $s = 685$, so 685 students attended the play.	MN: 1.1.3	Problems 2-10, 2-31, and 2-85
CL 2-93.	a. $-2x + 1$ b. $4x - 1$ c. $-5x^2 + 4x - 5y + 5$	Lessons 2.1.1, 2.1.2, and 2.1.5 MN: 2.1.3 and 2.1.6 LL: 2.1.2, 2.1.4, and 2.1.5	Problems 2-4, 2-17, 2-29, 2-51, 2-69, and 2-78
CL 2-94.	a. Figure 1 Figure 5 b. Each figure has three more tiles than the one before it. c. Figure 6 would have 17 tiles.	Lesson 1.1.2	Problems 1-9, 1-10, 1-12, and 2-69
CL 2-95.	$6 \cdot 5 - (3 \cdot 3 + 7) - 5 \cdot 3 = -1$	Problem 2-9 MN: 2.1.4	Problems 2-9, 2-19, 2-80, and 2-86

Problem	Solution	Need Help?	More Practice
CL 2-96.	a. $2.40 b. $14.40 c. $c = 2.40p$	Lessons 1.2.1 and 1.2.2 MN: 1.2.1 and 1.2.2 LL: 1.2.1	Problems 1-42, 1-43, 1-44, and 1-57

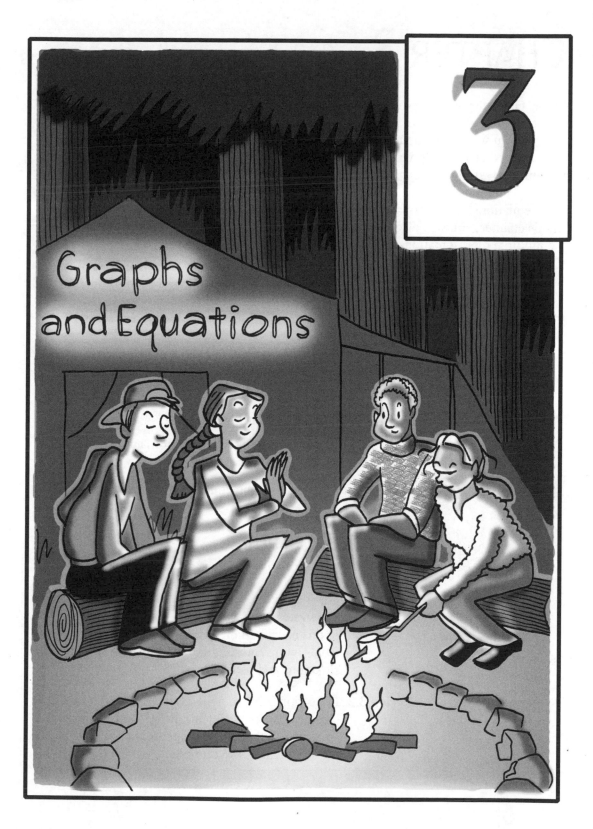

3

Graphs
and Equations

CHAPTER 3　　　　　Graphs and Equations

In this chapter, you will extend your understanding of the use of variables, such as x and y. You will learn about tools like graphing calculators that will help you explore how variables affect tile patterns, tables, and graphs. You will continue to develop your ability to solve equations, which you started in Chapter 2. In this chapter, you will also begin to learn about the multiple representations of data. You will study the connections between graphing and solving equations in Chapter 4.

In this chapter, you will learn:

➢ How to find a rule from a table.

➢ How to represent a situation using a table, a rule, and a graph.

➢ How to graph linear and parabolic rules using an appropriate scale.

➢ What it means for something to be the solution to an equation, and what it means for an equation to have no solution.

➢ How to determine the number of solutions to an equation.

Guiding Questions

Think about these questions throughout this chapter:

What is a variable?

What is the pattern?

How many different ways can I represent it?

How can I solve it?

How can I check my answer?

Chapter Outline

Section 3.1　In this section, you will add to your existing graphing skills. You will learn new graphing skills and strategies that will help you throughout the rest of this course. You will also learn how to create tables, write rules, and draw graphs to represent situations and patterns.

Section 3.2　In Section 3.2, you will extend the work you did in Chapter 2. You will learn how to solve linear equations without using algebra tiles and will learn the significance of solutions.

3.1.1 What is the rule?

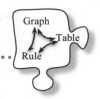

Extending Patterns and Finding Rules

You have been learning how to work with variables and how to find values for variables in equations. In this section, you will learn how to extend patterns and how to generalize your pattern with a rule. As you work with your team, use these questions to focus your ideas:

How is the pattern growing?

What is the rule?

Is there another way to see it?

How can you tell if your rule is correct?

3-1. Some people describe mathematics as "the study of patterns." For each tile pattern below, draw Figure 1 and Figure 5 on graph paper. First try it individually, and then consult with your team. What does Figure 100 look like? Explain how you know.

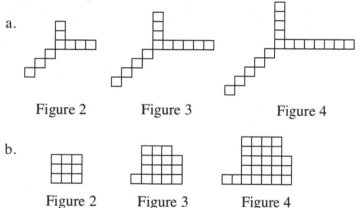

a.

Figure 2   Figure 3   Figure 4

b.

Figure 2   Figure 3   Figure 4

3-2.   FINDING RULES FROM TABLES

How can you describe the rule that governs a pattern or table? Obtain the
Lesson 3.1.1A Resource Page from your teacher and find the tables below. As
a class, find the pattern, fill in the missing parts, and extend each table with at
least two more $x \rightarrow y$ pairs that fit the pattern. Then generalize the pattern's rule
in words.

a.

IN (x)	OUT (y)
	C
L	N
	F
Q	
W	Y

Rule:

b.

IN (x)	OUT (y)
easy	
	light
hot	cold
up	down
left	

Rule:

c.

IN (x)	OUT (y)
△	⬠
⬠	
	⬡
⬡	⬡
⬡	

Rule:

d.

IN (x)	OUT (y)
8	17
−2	
	9
12	25
10	21

Rule:

e.

IN (x)	OUT (y)
100	51
4	
6	4
30	16
	31

Rule:

f.

IN (x)	OUT (y)
4	16
−1	1
	9
12	
−6	

Rule:

3-3. Obtain the Lesson 3.1.1B Resource Page from your teacher. For each $x \to y$ table given, find the pattern and fill in the missing entries. Then write the rule for the pattern in words. Be sure to share your thinking with your teammates.

a.

IN (x)	OUT (y)
	8
0	-2
-4	-10
10	18
-2	
	198
0.5	

Rule:

b.

IN (x)	OUT (y)
3	-9
10	
-1	3
	6
0	
	-36
-5	15

Rule:

c.

IN (x)	OUT (y)
0.5	
	37
2	5
-10	101
-5	
0	1
	50

Rule:

d.

IN (x)	OUT (y)
6	
11	5
	-4
23	17
-7	
	40
-4	-10

Rule:

e.

IN (x)	OUT (y)
2	6
4	20
10	110
-3	
	30
7	56
1	

Rule:

f.

IN (x)	OUT (y)
-8	
10	53
3	18
0	
	8
19	
4	23

Rule:

METHODS AND MEANINGS

Patterns in Nature

MATH NOTES

   Patterns are everywhere, especially in nature. One famous pattern that appears often is called the Fibonacci Sequence, a sequence of numbers that starts $1, 1, 2, 3, 5, 8, 13, 21, \ldots$

The Fibonacci numbers appear in many different situations in nature. For example, the number of petals on a flower is often a Fibonacci number, and the number of seeds on a spiral from the center of a sunflower is, too.

To learn more about Fibonacci numbers, search the Internet or check out a book from your local library. The next time you look at a flower, look for Fibonacci numbers!

3-4. For each $x \to y$ table given, copy the table, find the pattern and fill in the missing entries. Then write the rule for the pattern in words.

a.

IN (x)	OUT (y)
	23
2	8
–2	–4
8	26
0	
	302
1.5	

Rule:

b.

IN (x)	OUT (y)
2	5
9	
–2	–5
	–7.5
0	
	27.5
–4	–10

Rule:

c.

IN (x)	OUT (y)
1	
	4
4	3
–20	–9
–10	
0	1
	–2.5

Rule:

3-5. At the fair, Kate found a strange machine with a sign on it labeled, "Enter a number." When she pushed the number 15, the machine displayed 9. When she entered 23, the machine displayed 17. Perplexed, she tried 100, and the machine displayed 94.

a. What is the machine doing?

b. What would the machine display if she entered 77?

3-6. Ms. Nguyen needs to separate $385 into three parts to pay some debts. The second part must be five times as large as the first part. The third part must be $35 more than the first part. How much money must be in each part? Write and solve an equation.

3-7. On your paper, write the equation represented on the Equation Mat at right. Simplify as much as possible and then solve for x.

Core Connections, Course 3

3-8.   GO GOLDEN GOPHERS!

The graph below describes the distance two
cars have traveled after leaving a football
game at the University of Minnesota.

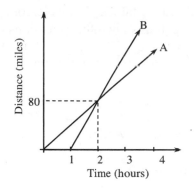

a.   Which car was traveling faster? How
      can you tell?

b.   The lines cross at (2, 80). What does
      this point represent?

c.   Assuming that Car A continued to
      travel at a constant rate, how far did
      Car A travel in the first 4 hours?

3.1.2 How can I make a prediction?

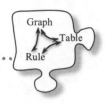

Using Tables, Graphs, and Rules to Make Predictions

In Lesson 3.1.1, you wrote rules for patterns found in $x \rightarrow y$ tables. In this lesson, you will focus on using variables to write algebraic rules for patterns and other situations. You will use a graph to help predict the output for fractional x-values. Then you will use a rule to predict the output when the input is too large and does not appear on the graph.

While working today, focus on these questions:

How can you write the rule without words?

What does x represent?

How can you make a prediction?

3-9.   SILENT BOARD GAME

During Lesson 3.1.1, you created written rules for patterns that had no tiles or numbers. You will now write algebraic rules using a table of jumbled in/out numbers. Focus on finding patterns and writing rules as you play the Silent Board Game. Your teacher will put an incomplete $x \rightarrow y$ table on the board. Study the input and output values and look for a pattern. Then write the rule in words and symbols that finds each y-value from its x-value.

3-10.   JOHN'S GIANT REDWOOD, Part One

John found the data in the table below about his
favorite redwood tree. He wondered if he could use
it to predict the height of the tree at other points of
time. Consider this as you analyze the data and
answer the questions below. Be ready to share and
justify your answers with the class.

Number of Years after Planting	3	4	5
Height of Tree (in feet)	17	21	25

a.   How much did the tree grow each year?

b.   How tall was the tree 2 years after it was
planted? What about 7 years after it was
planted? How do you know?

c.   How tall was the tree the year it was planted?

d.   Estimate the height of the tree 50 years after it was planted. How did you
make your prediction?

3-11.   John decided to find out more about his favorite redwood tree by graphing the
data.

a.   On the Lesson 3.1.2B Resource Page provided by your teacher, plot the
points that represent the height of the tree over time. What does the graph
look like? Does the graph represent a proportional relationship? Justify
your answer.

b.   Does it make sense to connect the points? Explain your thinking.

c.   According to the graph, what was the height of the tree 1.5 years after it
was planted?

d.   Can you use your graph to predict the height of the redwood tree 20 years
after it was planted? Why or why not?

3-12.   John is still not satisfied. He wants to be able to
         predict the height of the tree at any time after it was
         planted.

   a.   Find John's table on your resource page and
         extend it to include the height of the tree in
         the 0th year, 1st year, 2nd year, and 6th year.

   b.   If you have not done so already, use the ideas from the Silent Board Game
         to write an algebraic rule for the data in your table. Be sure to work with
         your team and check that the rule works for all of the data.

   c.   Use your rule to check your prediction in part (c) of problem 3-10 for how
         tall the tree will be in its 50th year. How close was your prediction?

3-13.   Copy and use your pattern skills to complete the table below.

IN (x)	2	10	6	7	−3		−10	100	x
OUT (y)	5	21	13			−15			

   a.   Explain in words what is being done to the input value, x, to produce the
         output value, y.

   b.   Write the process you described in part (a) in algebraic symbols.

3-14.   Write the equation represented in each diagram below on your
         paper. For each part, simplify as much as possible and then solve
         for x. Be sure to record your work on your paper.

   a.

   b.

3-15.   Evaluate the following expressions given the values below.

a. $ab + bc + ac$ for $a = 2$, $b = 5$, and $c = 3$

b. $\frac{20 - x^2}{y - x}$ for $x = -2$ and $y = 6$

3-16.   Use the order of operations to simplify the following expressions.

a. $5 - 2 \cdot 3^2$ b. $(-2)^2$

c. $18 \div 3 \cdot 6$ d. -2^2

e. $(5 - 3)(5 + 3)$ f. $24 \cdot \frac{1}{4} \div (-2)$

g.   Why are your answers for parts (b) and (d) different?

3-17.   Mrs. Swanson gives out only one type of candy for Halloween. The local discount store sells six pounds of butterscotch candies for $7.50. Use proportional reasoning to answer the questions below. Be sure to explain your answer and organize your reasoning.

a.   What is the cost of 18 pounds of butterscotch candies?

b.   What is the cost of 10 pounds of butterscotch candies?

c.   What is the unit rate for butterscotch candies?

3.1.3 What is a graph and how is it useful?

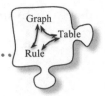

Using the Graphing Calculator and Identifying Solutions

In the last two lessons, you examined several patterns. You learned how to represent the patterns in a table and with a rule. For the next few days, you will learn a powerful new way to represent a pattern and make predictions.

As you work with your team today, use these focus questions to help direct your discussion:

What is the rule?

How can you represent the pattern?

3-18.   On the Lesson 3.1.3 Resource Page provided by your teacher, find the "Big C's" pattern shown at right.

Figure 1   Figure 2   Figure 3

a.   Draw Figure 0 and Figure 4 on the grid provided on the resource page.

b.   On the resource page, represent the number of tiles in each figure with:

   - An $x \rightarrow y$ table.

   - An algebraic rule.

   - A graph.

c.   How many tiles will be in Figure 5? Justify your answer in at least two different ways.

d.   What will Figure 100 look like? How many tiles will it have? How can you be sure?

Core Connections, Course 3

3-19.   Use the graphing technology provided by your teacher to
analyze the pattern further and make predictions.

    a.   Enter the information from your $x \to y$ table for
problem 3-18 into your graphing calculator. Then
plot the points using a window of your choice. What
do you notice?

    b.   Find another $x \to y$ pair that you think belongs in your table. Use your
graphing calculator to plot the point. Does it look correct? How can you
tell?

    c.   Imagine that you made up 20 new $x \to y$ pairs. Where do you think their
points would lie if you added them to the graph?

3-20.   In the same window that contains the data points, graph the algebraic equation
for the pattern from problem 3-18.

    a.   What do you notice? Why did that happen?

    b.   Charles wonders about connecting
the points of the "Big C's" data.
When the points are connected
with an unbroken line or curve,
the graph is called **continuous**.
If the graph of the tile pattern is
continuous, what does that
suggest about the tile pattern?
Explain.

    c.   Jessica prefers to keep the graph of the tile-pattern data as separate points.
This is called a **discrete** graph. Why might a discrete graph be appropriate
for this data?

3-21.   If necessary, re-enter your data from the "Big C's" pattern into your graphing calculator. Re-enter the rule you found in problem 3-18 and graph the data and rule in the same window.

For the following problems, justify your conclusions with the *graph*, the *rule*, and the *figure* (whenever practical). Your teacher may ask your team to present your solution to one of these problems. Be sure to justify your ideas using all three representations.

Note: This stoplight icon will appear periodically throughout the text. Problems with this icon display common errors that can be made. Be sure not to make the same mistakes yourself!

a.   Frangelica thinks that Figure 6 in the "Big C's" pattern has 40 tiles. Decide with your team whether she is correct and justify your answer by using the rule, drawing Figure 6, and adding the point to your graph of the data. Be prepared to show these three different ways to justify your conclusion.

b.   Giovanni thinks that the point $(16, 99)$ belongs in the table for the "Big C's" pattern. Decide with your team whether he is correct, and justify your conclusion by examining the graph and the rule.

c.   Jeremiah is excited because he has found another rule for the "Big C's" pattern! He thinks that $y = x + 8$ also works. Prove or disprove Jeremiah's claim. Be prepared to convince the class that your conclusion is correct.

d.   LaTanya has been thinking hard and has found another rule for the same pattern! She is sure that $y = 3(2x + 1)$ is also correct. Prove or disprove LaTanya's position in as many ways as you can.

3-22.   Look back at the prediction you made in problem 3-18 for Figure 100 in the "Big C's" pattern. Decide now if your prediction was correct, and be ready to defend your position with all of the math tools you have.

METHODS AND MEANINGS

Discrete and Continuous Graphs

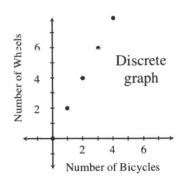

When a graph of data is limited to a set of separate, non-connected points, that relationship is called **discrete**. For example, consider the relationship between the number of bicycles parked at your school and the number of bicycle wheels. If there is one bicycle, it has two wheels. Two bicycles have four wheels, while three bicycles have six wheels. However, there cannot be 1.3 or 2.9 bicycles. Therefore, this data is limited because the number of bicycles must be a whole number, such as 0, 1, 2, 3, and so on.

When graphed, a discrete relationship looks like a collection of unconnected points. See the example of a discrete graph above.

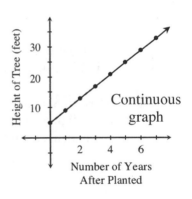

When a set of data is not confined to separate points and instead consists of connected points, the data is called **continuous**. "John's Giant Redwood," problem 3-11, is an example of a continuous situation, because even though the table focuses on integer values of years (1, 2, 3, etc.), the tree still grows between these values of time. Therefore, the tree has a height at any non-negative value of time (such as 1.1 years after it is planted).

When data for a continuous relationship are graphed, the points are connected to show that the relationship also holds true for all points between the table values. See the example of a continuous graph above.

Note: In this course, tile patterns will represent elements of continuous relationships and will be graphed with a continuous line or curve.

3-23.   Find the value of x that makes each equation below true.

   a. $x + 7 = 2$ b. $-5 = \frac{1}{2}x$

   c. $3x = -45$ d. $2 = -x$

   e. $-5 = \frac{x}{2}$ f. $x^2 = 9$ (*all* possible values for x)

3-24.   For the following equations, draw a picture of the tiles on an Equation Mat, simplify, and solve for the variable. Record your work.

   a. $3c - 7 = -c + 1$ b. $-2 + 3x = 2x + 6 + x$

3-25.   On your paper, write the equation represented at right. Simplify as much as possible and then solve for x.

3-26.   Solve this problem by defining a variable and solving an equation. Write your solution in a sentence.

   West High School's population is 250 students fewer than twice the population of East High School. The two schools have a total of 2858 students. How many students attend East High School?

3-27.   Calculate the following values using the Order of Operations. Show your steps. Verify your answers with your calculator.

   a. $(-4)(-2) - 6(2 - 5)$ b. $23 - (17 - 3 \cdot 4)^2 + 6$

   c. $14(2 + 3 - 2 \cdot 2) \div (4^2 - 3^2)$ d. $12.7 - 18.5 + 15 + 6.3 - 1 + 28.5$

3-28. Copy the table below onto your paper and use your pattern skills to complete it.

IN (x)	2	10	0	7	–3		–10	100	x
OUT (y)	–6	–30	0			15			

a. Explain in words what is done to the input value, x, to produce the output value, y.

b. Write the process you described in part (a) in algebraic symbols.

3-29. For the following equations, draw a picture of the tiles on an Equation Mat, use "legal" moves to simplify, and solve for the variable. Record your work.

a. $-3x+7=-x-1$ b. $1-2p+5=4p+6$

3-30. Write the equation represented on the Equation Mat below.

a. Simplify as much as possible and solve for x.

b. Evaluate both the left side and the right side using your solution from part (a). Remember that if your solution is correct, both sides should have the same value.

3-31. Tickets to 50 home baseball games would cost $1137.50. How much would it cost to get tickets for all 81 home games? How many games could you go to for $728? What is the cost of one game?

3-32. Combine like terms in each part below.

a. Liha has three x^2-tiles, two x-tiles, and eight unit tiles, while Makulata has five x^2-tiles and two unit tiles. At the end of class, they put their pieces together to give to Ms. Singh. Write an algebraic expression for each student's tiles and find the sum of their pieces.

b. Simplify the expression $4x+6x^2-11x+2+x^2-19$.

c. Write the length of the line below as a sum. Then combine like terms.

3.1.4 How should I graph?

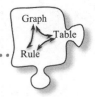

Completing Tables and Drawing Graphs

In Lesson 3.1.3, you used a graphing tool to represent all of the $x \rightarrow y$ pairs that follow a particular rule. Today you will learn how to make your own graphs for rules and how to recognize patterns in graphs.

3-33. CLASS GRAPH

Your teacher will give your team some x-values. For each x-value, calculate the corresponding y-value that fits the rule $y = -5x + 12$. Then mark the point you have calculated on the class graph.

3-34. Use the rule $y = 2x + 1$ to complete parts (a) through (c) below.

   a. Make a table like the one below and use the rule provided above to complete it.

IN (x)	−4	−3	−2	−1	0	1	2	3	4
OUT (y)									

   b. Examine the numbers in the table. What are the greatest x- and y-values in the table? What are the smallest x- and y-values? Use this information to set up x- and y-axes that are scaled appropriately.

   c. Plot and connect the points on a graph. Be sure to label your axes and write numbers to indicate scale.

3-35. Calculate the y-values for the rule $y = -3x + 1$ and complete the table below.

IN (x)	−4	−3	−2	−1	0	1	2	3	4
OUT (y)									

   a. Examine the x- and y-values in the table. Is it possible to use the same set of axes as problem 3-34? If so, graph and connect these points on the axes from problem 3-34. If not, plot and connect the points on a new set of axes.

   b. What does your graph look like? Describe the result.

   c. How is this graph similar to the graph in problem 3-34? How is it different?

3-36.   Calculate the y-values for the rule $y = x^2$ and complete the table below.

IN (x)	−4	−3	−2	−1	$-\frac{1}{2}$	0	$\frac{1}{2}$	1	2	3	4
OUT (y)											

a.   Examine the x- and y-values in the table. Use this information to set up a new set of x- and y-axes that are scaled appropriately. Plot and connect the points on your graph, and then label your graph with its rule.

b.   This graph is an example of a **parabola**. Read about parabolas in the Math Notes box below. Where is the **vertex** of the parabola you graphed in part (a)?

METHODS AND MEANINGS

Parabolas

One kind of graph you will study in this class is called a **parabola**. Two examples of parabolas are graphed at right. Note that parabolas are smooth "U" shapes, not pointy "V" shapes.

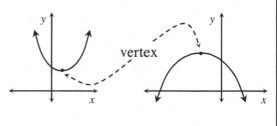

vertex

The point where a parabola turns (the highest or lowest point) is called the **vertex**.

3-37.   Complete a table like the one provided in problem 3-34 for the rule $y = x + 2$. Plot and connect the points on graph paper. Be sure to label the axes and include the scale.

3-38. For the following equations, draw a picture of the tiles on an Equation Mat like the one shown at right. Then use "legal" moves to simplify and solve for the variable. Record your work.

$\blacksquare = +1$
$\square = -1$

a. $-2 + x = -x + 2$

b. $2 + 3x = x + 7$

3-39. Evaluate each equation below.

a. For $y = 5 + 8x$ when $x = 4$, what does y equal?

b. For $a = 3 - 5c$ when $c = -0.5$, what does a equal?

c. For $n = 2d^2 - 5$ when $d = -2$, what does n equal?

d. For $v = -3(r - 3)$ when $r = -1$, what does v equal?

3-40. Peggy Sue decided to enter her famous "Five-Alarm Chili" at her local chili-cooking contest. Normally, she needs five tomatoes to make enough chili for her family of seven.

a. How many tomatoes should she expect to use to make her famous recipe for 100 people?

b. When she gets to the contest, she realizes that she only packed 58 tomatoes. How many people can she expect to feed?

3-41. At the annual dog show, Chantel noticed that there were three more Scotties than Schnauzers. She also realized that the number of Wirehaired Terriers was five less than twice the number of Schnauzers. If there were 78 dogs in all (counting Schnauzers, Scotties, and Wirehaired Terriers), how many Schnauzers were there? Write and solve an equation.

3.1.5 How can I graph it?

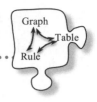

Graphs, Tables, and Rules

In Lesson 3.1.4, you practiced setting up the correct axes to graph data from a table. Today you will graph a rule by first making a table, and then by plotting the points from your table on a graph. You will also continue to find patterns in tables and graphs.

3-42. SILENT BOARD GAME

Your teacher will put an incomplete $x \rightarrow y$ table on the board. Try to find the pattern (rule) that gets each y-value from its x-value. Find and write the rule for the pattern you find.

3-43. GOOD TIPPER

Mr. Wallis needs your help. He is planning to take his new girlfriend out to dinner. He will, of course, leave a tip for the wait staff at the end of the meal. He decides to create a "tip table" that will help him quickly determine how much tip to leave.

a. Create a table like the one shown below. What are reasonable values of x? Mr. Wallis needs a tip table that will help him quickly determine a tip for a bill that may occur after a nice dinner for two. Discuss this with your team and then choose eight values for x.

Dinner Bill (in dollars)								
Amount of Tip (in dollars)								

b. Mr. Wallis is planning to leave a 15% tip. That means that for a bill of $10, he would leave a $1.50 tip. Determine the tip for all of the values in your table from part (a). This is Mr. Wallis's tip table.

c. Use the tip table to estimate the tip quickly if the bill is $36. What if the bill is $52.48?

Problem continues on next page. →

3-43.   *Problem continued from previous page.*

    d.   Mr. Wallis is worried that he may not be able to estimate very quickly if he uses his table for unusual amounts, such as $52.48. He would like a graph to help him determine a 15% tip for *all possible* dollar amounts between $10 and $100. With your team, determine how to set up axes. Then graph the points from the tip table. Use the questions below to help guide your discussion.

- Should the tip be graphed on the *x*-axis or the *y*-axis? Read the Math Notes box for this lesson about **dependent variables** and **independent variables** to help you decide.

- Which quadrants are useful for this graph? Why?

- What are the greatest and smallest values of *x* and *y* that must fit on the graph? How can you scale your axes to create the most effective graph for Mr. Wallis?

    e.   Use your tip graph from part (d) to test your estimations in part (c). Which representation (table or graph) helped to find the most accurate tip? Which was easiest to use? Explain.

3-44.   ONE OF THESE POINTS IS NOT LIKE THE OTHERS, Part One

    a.   Plot and connect the points in the table below.

IN (*x*)	−2	4	1	6	−5	0
OUT (*y*)	−6	−2	−3	2	−9	−4

    b.   Identify the point that does not appear to fit the pattern.

    c.   Correct the point found in part (b) above so it fits the pattern.

3-45.   Copy and complete the table below for the rule $y = \frac{1}{2}x + 6$.

IN (*x*)	−4	−3	−2	−1	0	1	2	3	4
OUT (*y*)									

    a.   Graph and connect the points from your table on graph paper. Remember to label the graph with its rule.

    b.   Does the point (10, 12) lie on this graph? How can you tell?

Methods and Meanings

Independent and Dependent Variables

When one quantity (such as the height of a redwood tree) depends on another (such as the number of years after the tree was planted), it is called a **dependent variable**. That means its value is determined by the value of another variable. The dependent variable is usually graphed on the *y*-axis.

If a quantity, such as time, does not depend on another variable, it is referred to as the **independent variable**, which is graphed on the *x*-axis.

For example, in problem 3-46, you compared the amount of a dinner bill with the amount of a tip. In this case, the tip depends on the amount of the dinner bill. Therefore, the tip is the dependent variable, while the dinner bill is the independent variable.

3-46. Create an $x \rightarrow y$ table using at least eight points from the graph at right. Write the rule for the pattern in the table.

3-47. For each rule below, make a table of *x*- and *y*-values. Then graph and connect the points from your table on graph paper using an appropriate scale. Label each graph with its equation.

a. $y = -2x + 7$

b. $y = 11x$

3-48.   **WHICH IS GREATER?**

Write the algebraic expressions shown below. Use "legal" simplification moves to determine which expression in the Expression Comparison Mat is greater.

a.

b.

3-49.   Simplify each expression.

a. $\frac{2}{3}(0.8)$

b. $\frac{4}{3} \cdot \frac{3}{7}$

c. $-\frac{5}{6} \cdot \frac{4}{7}$

d. $-\frac{4}{5} \cdot (-1\frac{1}{3})$

3-50.   For the following equations, simplify and solve for the variable. Record your work.

a. $2x - 7 = -2x + 1$

b. $-2x - 5 = -4x + 2$

3.1.6 What makes a complete graph?

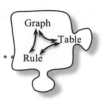

Complete Graphs

Over the past several days, you have learned to make graphs from tables, then graphs from rules. Today you will continue to study graphs by deciding what needs to go into a graph to make it complete.

3-51.   SILENT BOARD GAME

Your teacher will put an incomplete $x \rightarrow y$ table on the board. Try to find the pattern (rule) that gets each y-value from its x-value. Find and write the rule for the pattern you find.

3-52.   Examine the following graphs and answer the question associated with each one. What do you notice?

a.   What are the coordinates of point A?

b.   Where will the line be when $x = 5$?

c.   What is t when $k = 1$?

3-53.   Make your own complete graph for each of the following rules.

a. $y = -x + 1$ b. $y = 0.5x + 2$ c. $y = x^2 - 4$

3-54.   Examine the graphs from problem 3-53.

   a.   How are they different? Be as specific as you can.

   b.   Label the (x, y) coordinates on each of your graphs for the point where each graph crosses the y-axis. These points are called **y-intercepts**.

   c.   Label the (x, y) coordinates on each of your graphs for the point or points where each graph crosses the x-axis. These points are called **x-intercepts**.

3-55.   LEARNING LOG

   On your own graph paper, graph $y = -3x + 2$. Then, as a class, decide what needs to be included to make a graph complete. Copy the qualities of a complete graph as a Learning Log entry. Title this entry "Qualities of a Complete Graph" and include today's date.

3-56.   Complete a table for the rule $y = x^2 + 2$. Then plot and connect the points on a graph. Be sure to label the axes and include the scale. Use negative and positive values for x, as well as a value of 0.

3-57.   Complete a table for the rule $y = -x + 3$. Then plot and connect the points on a graph. Be sure to label the axes and include the scale. Use negative and positive values for x, as well as a value of 0.

3-58.   On graph paper, draw Figure 0 and Figure 4 for the pattern below. Describe Figure 100 in detail.

Figure 1   Figure 2   Figure 3

3-59.   Write an expression that represents the perimeter
         of the shape built with algebra tiles at right. Then
         find the perimeter if $x = 3$ units and $y = 7$ units.

3-60.   Copy and simplify the following expressions by combining like terms.

   a. $y + 2x - 3 + 4x^2 + 3x - 5y$ b. $2x - 6x^2 + 9 - 1 - x - 3x$

   c. $2y^2 + 30x - 5y^2 + 4x - 4y - y$ d. $-10 + 3xy - 3xy + y^2 + 10 - y^2$

3.1.7 What is wrong with this graph?

Identifying Common Graphing Errors

In this chapter you have used rules to find y-values to go with x-values in tables. Then you graphed the $x \rightarrow y$ pairs you found. Today you will be examining how rules, tables, and graphs can be used to represent new situations. You will also learn how to avoid common graphing errors. As you work, revisit the questions below.

What x-values should go in my table?

How can I correct this error?

How should I scale my graph?

3-61.   Ms. Cai's class is studying the "dented square" shape shown at right. This shape is formed by removing a square with side length 1 from a larger square. Her students decided to let x represent the side length of the large square and y represent the perimeter of the entire shape.

a.   What is the perimeter of the "dented square?" That is, what rule could help you find the perimeter for any value of x?

b.   Make a table for the rule you found. Make sure the x-values you use are appropriate for this situation. What are the possible x-values?

c.   In this situation, x has a lower boundary value. This means that it must be greater than a specific value for the situation to make sense. Using what you know about writing inequalities, write an inequality statement for this limitation.

d.   If you were to graph the inequality in part (c) on a number line, it would have an open circle. Why? How do you think this could be shown on a coordinate graph for this situation? Discuss this with your team and share your ideas with your class.

e.   Do you think the points on your graph should be connected? Justify your answer.

f.   Using what you decided in parts (d) and (e), make a graph from your $x \rightarrow y$ table.

3-62.   GOOFY GRAPHING

x	y
2	8
3	17
5	35
6	44

Now Ms. Cai's class is studying a tile pattern. Her students decided to represent the pattern with the $x \to y$ table at right.

a.   Ms. Cai wants her class to graph the data in this table. Write (x, y) coordinates for each point that needs to be plotted.

b.   When Ms. Cai's students started to graph this data, they made mistakes right from the beginning. The diagrams below show how some of Ms. Cai's students set up their axes. Your teacher will assign your team one of these diagrams.

Your Task: Find all of the mistakes the students made in setting up the graph your teacher assigns you. (There may be more than one mistake in each graph!) Explain why this is an incorrect way to set up a graph, or why this is not the best way to set up the graph for this problem. Be ready to present your team's ideas to the class.

i.

ii.

iii.

iv.

3-63.   Sheila is in Ms. Cai's class. She noticed that the graph of the
         perimeter for the "dented square" in problem 3-61 was a line.
         "I wonder what the graph of its area looks like," she said to
         her teammates.

   a.   Write an equation for the area of the "dented square" if x
         represents the length of the large square and y represents
         the area of the square.

   b.   On graph paper, graph the rule you found for the area in part (a). Why
         does a 1st-quadrant graph make sense for this situation? Are there other
         values of x that cannot work in this situation? Be sure to include an
         indication of this on your graph, as necessary.

   c.   Explain to Sheila what the graph of the area looks like.

   d.   Use the graph to approximate x when the area of the shape is 20 square
         units.

3-64.   LEARNING LOG

         Looking back at the mistakes Ms. Cai's students made,
         write a Learning Log entry that includes a checklist of
         errors you should avoid when setting up a graph. Title this
         entry "Graphing Errors" and label it with today's date.

3-65.   ONE OF THESE POINTS IS NOT LIKE THE OTHERS, Part Two

   a.   Plot and connect the points listed in the table below.

IN (x)	−2	4	1	−4	0	3	−3	2
OUT (y)	0	12	−3	12	−4	5	−2	0

   b.   Identify the point that does not fit the pattern.

   c.   What shape does the graph appear to make?

   d.   Correct the point identified in part (b) so it fits the
         pattern. Write the points in (x, y) notation.

Core Connections, Course 3

3-66. For each rule below, make a table of x- and y-values and then graph the rule on graph paper. Label each graph with its equation.

    a. $y = x^2$ b. $y = -x^2$

    c.   Compare the graphs. What do you notice?

    d.   For the graph of $y = x^2$, estimate the x-values corresponding to $y = 5$.

    e.   For the graph of $y = -x^2$, estimate the x-values corresponding to $y = -10$.

3-67. The amount of money Theresa earns at her job varies directly with the number of hours she works. This means that her earnings are proportional with the time she works. She knows that when she works 2 hours, she earns $12. When she works 3 hours, she earns $18.

    a.   How much do you predict Theresa would earn after working 5 hours?

    b.   Use the unit rate to explain how can you find Theresa's earnings (y) if she works for x hours.

    c.   Create a complete graph of Theresa's earnings over time. Should the graph be continuous or discrete? Explain your decision.

3-68. Paris is trying to solve the equation $3x^2 - (2x - 4) = 3 + 3x^2 + 1$. Her work is partially recorded below. Copy her table and fill in her missing work to solve for x.

Left Expression	Right Expression	Explanation
$3x^2 - (2x - 4)$	$3 + 3x^2 + 1$	Starting expressions.
$3x^2 - 2x + 4$	$3 + 3x^2 + 1$	
		Remove $3x^2$ from both sides.
$-2x$	0	
		Divide both sides by -2.

3-69. Copy and complete each of the Diamond Problems below. The pattern used in the Diamond Problems is shown at right.

a.

b.

c.

d.

3.2.1 How can I check my answer?

Solving Equations and Checking Solutions

In Section 2.2, you learned to solve equations on an Equation Mat. In this section, you will practice your equation-solving skills while adding a new element: You will check your answer to make sure it is correct.

While solving equations in this lesson, keep these focus questions in mind:

What is your goal?

How can you start?

How can you simplify?

Can you get x alone?

3-70.   For this activity, share algebra tiles and an Equation Mat with your partner.

a.   Start by setting up your Equation Mat as shown at right. Write the equation on your paper.

b.   Next, solve the equation on your Equation Mat one step at a time. Every time you make a step, record your work in two ways:

  • Record the step that was taken to get from the old equation to the new equation.

  • Write a new equation that represents the tiles on the Equation Mat.

c.   With your partner, find a way to check if your solution is correct.

Core Connections, Course 3

3-71.   **WHAT IS A SOLUTION?**

In this lesson you have found a solution to an algebraic equation.
But what exactly is a solution? Answer each of these questions
with your study team, but *do not use algebra tiles*. Be prepared to
justify your answers!

a.   Preston solved the equation $3x - 2 = 8$ and got the solution $x = 100$. Is he
correct? How do you know?

b.   Edwin solved the equation $2x + 3 - x = 3x - 5$ and got the solution $x = 4$.
Is he correct? How do you know?

c.   With your partner, discuss what you think a solution to an equation is.
Write down a description of what you and your partner agree on.

3-72.   Work with your partner to solve these equations, being careful to record your
work. After solving each equation, be sure to check your solution, if possible.

a. $3x + 4 = x + 8$ b. $4 - 2y = y + 10$

c. $5x + 4 - 2x = -(x + 8)$ d. $-2 - 3k - 2 = -2k + 8 - k$

3-73.   **IS THERE ANOTHER WAY?**

Compare your solution to part (c) of problem 3-72 with the solution that another
pair of students got. Did both solutions involve the same steps? Were the steps
used in the same order? If not, copy the other pair's solution onto your paper.
If both pairs used the same steps in the same order to solve the equation, come
up with a different way to solve the problem and record it on your paper.

METHODS AND **M**EANINGS

MATH NOTES

Complete Graph

A complete graph has the following components:

- *x*-axis and *y*-axis labeled, clearly showing the scale.

- Equation of the graph near the line or curve.

- Line or curve extended as far as possible on the graph.

- Coordinates of special points stated in (x, y) format.

x	-1	0	1	2	3
y	6	4	2	0	-2

Tables can be formatted horizontally, like the one above, or vertically, as shown below.

x	y
-1	6
0	4
1	2
2	0
3	-2
4	-4

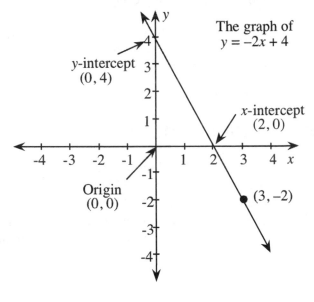

Throughout this course, you will continue to graph lines and other curves. Be sure to label your graphs appropriately.

3-74. For the following equations, solve for x. Be sure to check your answer, if possible. Show all work.

    a. $3x + 7 = -x - 1$ b. $-3x = x - (6 - 2x)$

    c.   Use a diagram of an Equation Mat or some other method to explain why $-(x - 3) = -x + 3$.

3-75. For each equation, a possible solution is given. Check to see if the given solution is correct.

    a.   If $3x + 7 = x - 1$, then does $x = -4$?

    b.   If $-2x - 4 = -4x + 3$, then does $x = 3$?

    c.   If $-3x + 5 + 5x - 1 = 0$, then does $x = 2$?

    d.   If $-(x - 1) = 4x - 5 - 3x$, then does $x = 3$?

3-76. For the rule $y = -2x + 1$, calculate the y-values that complete the table below.

IN (x)	−4	−3	−2	−1	0	1	2	3	4
OUT (y)									

    a.   Graph your rule on a set of axes. Be sure to create a *complete* graph. If necessary, see the Math Notes box for this lesson to review what makes a graph complete.

    b.   Describe your resulting graph. What does your graph look like?

3-77. Simplify each expression below.

    a. $4x + 7 + 3y - (1 + 3y + 2x)$ b. $16x^2 - 4x + 5 - (16x^2 - 8x) + 1$

    c. $(32x - 7y) - (28x - 11y)$ d. $y + 2 + 2y + 2 + 2y - 2x + y$

3-78.   Burgers-o-Rama is the best hamburger place in town. The owner, Ms. Hamm, buys two 5-pound packages of meat for $27.50. Use proportional reasoning to determine the information below. Be sure to explain your answer and organize your reasoning.

     a.   What should Ms. Hamm pay for 25 pounds of meat?

     b.   How many pounds can Ms. Hamm buy for $55.00?

3.2.2 How many solutions are there?

Determining the Number of Solutions

In Lesson 3.2.1, you reviewed your equation-solving skills to remember how to find a solution to an equation. But do all equations have a solution? And how can you tell if an equation does not have a solution?

Today you will continue to practice solving equations and will continue to investigate the meaning of a solution.

3-79.   GUESS MY NUMBER

Today you will play the "Guess My Number" game. Your teacher will think of a number and tell you some information about that number. You will try to figure out what your teacher's number is, using paper and a pencil if needed. When you think you know what the mystery number is, sit silently and do not tell anyone else. This will give others a chance to think about it.

3-80.   Use the process your teacher illustrated to analyze Game #3 of "Guess My Number" algebraically.

   a.   Start by writing an equation that expresses the information in the game.

   b.   Solve your equation, writing down each step as you go. When you reach a conclusion, discuss how it agrees with the answer for Game #3 you found as a class.

   c.   Repeat this process to analyze Game #4 algebraically.

3-81.   How many solutions does each equation below have? To answer this question, solve these equations, recording all of your steps as you go along. Check your solution, if possible.

   a. $4x - 5 = x - 5 + 3x$ b. $-x - 4x - 7 = -2x + 5$

   c. $3 + 5x - 4 - 7x = 2x - 4x + 1$ d. $4x - (-3x + 2) = 7x - 2$

   e. $x + 3 + x + 3 = -(x + 4) + (3x - 2)$ f. $x - 5 - (2 - x) = -3$

3-82.   Create your own "Guess My Number" game like the ones you worked with in class today. Start it with, "I'm thinking of a number that…" Make sure it is a game for which you actually know the answer! Write the equation and solve it.

3-83.   LEARNING LOG

In your Learning Log, explain how to find the number of solutions to an equation. How do you know when an equation has no solution? How do you know when an equation has an infinite number of solutions? Give examples of each kind of equation, as well as an equation with exactly one solution. Title your entry "How Many Solutions?" and label it with today's date.

METHODS AND MEANINGS

Circle Vocabulary, Circumference, and Area

The **radius** of a circle is a line segment from its center to any point on the circle. The term is also used for the length of these segments. More than one radius are called **radii**.

A **chord** of a circle is a line segment joining any two points on a circle.

A **diameter** of a circle is a chord that goes through its center. The term is also used for the length of these chords. The length of a diameter is twice the length of a radius.

The **circumference** (C) of a circle is its perimeter, or the "distance around" the circle.

The number π (read "pi") is the ratio of the circumference of a circle to its diameter. That is, $\pi = \frac{\text{circumference}}{\text{diameter}}$. This definition is also used as a way of computing the circumference of a circle if you know the diameter, as in the formula $C = \pi d$ where C is the circumference and d is the diameter. Since the diameter is twice the radius ($d = 2r$), the formula for the circumference of a circle using its radius is $C = \pi(2r)$ or $C = 2\pi \cdot r$.

$$C = \pi \cdot d$$

The first few digits of π are 3.141592.

To find the **area** (A) of a circle when given its radius (r), square the radius and multiply by π. This formula can be written as $A = r^2 \cdot \pi$. Another way the area formula is often written is $A = \pi \cdot r^2$.

3-84.   On graph paper, draw Figure 0 and Figure 4 for the pattern below.

   a.   Represent the number of tiles
         in each figure with:

           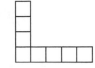

         • An $x \rightarrow y$ table.

         • An algebraic rule.   Figure 1   Figure 2   Figure 3

         • A graph.

   b.   Without drawing Figure 5, predict where its point would lie on the graph.
         Justify your prediction.

3-85.   Examine the graph at right.

   a.   Use the graph to complete the table:

IN (x)					
OUT (y)					

   b.   Use the graph to find the rule:

         $y =$ _____

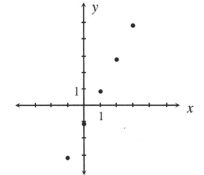

3-86.   Find the area and circumference of a circle with a diameter of 15 cm. If you
         need help remembering how to do this, read the Math Notes box in this lesson.

3-87.   Simplify each of the following equations and solve for the variable. Show all
         work and check your solution, if possible.

   a. $3x - 7 + 9 - 2x = x + 2$ b. $-2m + 8 + m + 1 = 0$

   c. $2 = x + 6 - 2x$ d. $0.5p = p + 5$

3-88. Mr. Wallis has done it again! He has started to create more tables to help him figure out things like how many gallons of gas it takes to travel a certain number of miles or how many minutes it takes to walk a certain number of blocks. Use proportional reasoning to complete his tables below.

a.

# of Books	Days
2	10
10	50
	60
3	
1	
$\frac{1}{5}$	
	365

b.

Minutes	Blocks
10	25
5	12.5
1	
20	
30	
	0
	35

c.

Miles	Gallons
280	14
140	7
	21
20	
100	
1000	
	17.5

3.2.3 How can I use my equation-solving skills?

Solving Equations to Solve Problems

In the last two lessons, you have practiced solving equations. In this lesson, you will apply your equation-solving skills to the patterns you found at the beginning of this chapter. As you solve these problems, keep the following questions in mind:

How can you simplify?

Is there more than one way to solve?

Can you get x alone?

How can you check your solution?

3-89. In Lesson 3.1.3, you investigated the "Big C's" pattern of tiles, shown at right. The rule you found for this pattern was $y = 6x + 3$, where x represented the figure number and y represented the number of tiles in the figure.

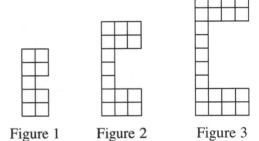

Figure 1   Figure 2   Figure 3

Penelope wants to know how many tiles will be in Figure 50. How can you determine this? Write out in words what you would need to do with your rule to answer her question. Then answer Penelope's question: How many tiles will be in Figure 50?

3-90. Lew wants to reverse the process. He says he has a "Big C's" figure made up of 45 tiles and wants to know which figure number this pattern is.

a. In the rule $y = 6x + 3$, which variable must equal 45 to solve Lew's problem?

b. Write an equation you could use to solve Lew's problem. Then solve your equation, recording all of your steps. Which "Big C's" figure is made up of 45 tiles?

c. How can you check your answer to be sure it is correct? Check your solution.

3-91.   Norm says he has a "Big C's" pattern made up of 84 tiles. He wants to know
        which figure number this pattern is. Write and solve an equation as you did in
        problem 3-90. Does your solution make sense? Why or why not?

3-92.   For the following equations, solve for x. Record your work and check your
        solution.

   a. $\frac{1}{2}x - 2 = x - 4$ b. $8 - 0.25x = 0.5x + 2$

   c. $x + 2 - 0.5x = 1 + 0.5x + 1$ d. $7x - 0.15 = 2x + 0.6$

3-93.   Can an equation be solved using a graph? Consider this as you answer the
        questions below.

   a.   Solve the equation $5 = 1.6x + 1$. Check your solution.

   b.   Complete a table for the rule $y = 1.6x + 1$. Then, on graph paper, graph the
        line.

   c.   Use the graph from part (b) to find x when $y = 5$. Did you get the same
        result as in part (a)?

Core Connections, Course 3

METHODS AND MEANINGS

Solving a Linear Equation

When solving an equation like the one shown below, several important strategies are involved.

- **Simplify.** Combine like terms and "make zeros" on each side of the equation whenever possible.

$$3x - 2 + 4 = x - 6$$
$$3x + 2 = x - 6 \qquad \text{combine like terms}$$
$$\underline{-x \qquad = -x} \qquad \text{subtract } x \text{ on both sides}$$
$$2x + 2 = -6$$

- **Keep equations balanced.** The equal sign in an equation indicates that the expressions on the left and right are balanced. Anything done to the equation must keep that balance.

$$\underline{-2 = -2}$$
$$\frac{2x}{2} = \frac{-8}{2} \qquad \text{subtract 2 on both sides}$$
$$x = -4 \qquad \text{divide both sides by 2}$$

- **Get x alone.** Isolate the variable on one side of the equation and the constants on the other.

- **Undo operations.** Use the fact that addition is the opposite of subtraction and that multiplication is the opposite of division to solve for x. For example, in the equation $2x = -8$, since the 2 and x are multiplied, dividing both sides by 2 will get x alone.

Review & Preview

3-94.   For the following equations, solve for x. Check your solution, if possible. Record your work.

a. $3x - 7 = 3x + 1$

b. $-2x - 5 = -4x + 2$

c. $2 + 3x = x + 2 + 2x$

d. $-(x - 2) = x + 2$

3-95.   Evaluate the expressions below for the given values.

   a. $30 - 2x$ for $x = -6$ b. $x^2 + 2x$ for $x = -3$

   c. $-\frac{1}{2}x + 9$ for $x = -6$ d. $\sqrt{k}$ for $k = 9$

3-96.   The length of a rectangle is three centimeters more than twice the width. The perimeter is 78 centimeters. Define a variable and write and solve an equation to find out how long and how wide the rectangle is.

3-97.   For the rule $y = 4 - x^2$, calculate the y-values that complete the table below. The first value is given for you.

IN (x)	−3	−2	−1	0	1	2	3
OUT (y)	−5						

   a.   Create an x-axis and a y-axis and label your units. Plot and connect the points on your graph, and then label your graph with its rule.

   b.   What does your graph look like?

3-98.   Simplify each expression.

   a. $\frac{5}{4} \div \frac{7}{16}$ b. $-\frac{10}{13} \cdot \frac{5}{11}$

   c. $\frac{9}{11} \div (-\frac{20}{21})$ d. $-\frac{8}{3} \div (-\frac{5}{18})$

3.2.4 How can I use my equation-solving skills?

More Solving Equations to Solve Problems

In this section, you have solved many equations. Sometimes these equations were given to you. Other times they came from specific situations. You have begun to solve equations without using algebra tiles. In this lesson, you will continue to focus on how to show your work.

3-99.   JOHN'S GIANT REDWOOD, Part Two

In Lesson 3.1.2, you looked at how a tree increases in height as it gets older. Review the data below and, if possible, find your work from problem 3-10.

Number of Years after Planting	3	4	5
Height of Tree (in feet)	17	21	25

a.   Assuming the tree continues to grow at a constant rate, find a rule for the height of the tree using x and y.

b.   In your rule, what real-world quantity does x stand for? What real-world quantity does y stand for?

c.   John wants to know how tall the tree will be when it is 20 years after planting. Use your rule to answer his question.

d.   The tallest tree in the world, in Montgomery Woods State Reserve in California, is 367 feet high. John wants to know how long it would take for his tree to get that tall if it keeps growing at the same rate. Write and solve an equation you could use to answer John's question. Be sure to check your solution.

e.   Did you use algebra tiles to solve the equation in part (d)? Would it be easy to use algebra tiles to do so? Why or why not?

3-100.   For the following equations, solve for the given variable. Record your work and check the solution, if possible.

a. $75c - 300 = 25c + 200$

b. $26y - 4 - 11y = 15y + 6$

c. $-\frac{1}{2}x = 6$

d. $0.8 - 2t = 1 - 3t$

3-101.   MR. WALLIS IS BACK!

After much consideration, Mr. Wallis decided to use the tip table below to help him estimate what a 15% tip would be for various costs of dinner.

Cost of Dinner	$10	$20	$30	$35	$40	$45	$50	$100
Amount of Tip	$1.50	$3	$4.50	$5.25	$6	$6.75	$7.50	$15

a.   Find a rule for his table. That is, find a rule that calculates the amount of tip (y) based on the cost of the dinner (x). How did you find your rule?

b.   After dinner, Mr. Wallis was so distracted that he forgot to write down the cost of the meal in his checkbook. All he remembers is that he left a $9 tip. What was the original cost of the meal before he paid the tip? Use your equation from part (a) to answer this question. Show all work.

c.   What was the total cost of the meal including the tip?

METHODS AND MEANINGS

Solutions to an Equation with One Variable

MATH NOTES

A **solution** to an equation gives a value of the variable that makes the equation true. For example, when 5 is substituted for x in the equation at right, both sides of the equation are equal. So $x = 5$ is a solution to this equation.

$$4x - 2 = 3x + 3$$
$$4(5) - 2 = 3(5) + 3$$
$$18 = 18$$

An equation can have more than one solution, or it may have no solution. Consider the examples at right.

Notice that no matter what the value of x is, the left side of the first equation will never equal the right side. Therefore, you say that $x + 2 = x + 6$ has **no solution**.

Equation with no solution:
$$x + 2 = x + 6$$

However, in the equation $x - 3 = x - 3$, no matter what value x has, the equation will always be true. All numbers can make $x - 3 = x - 3$ true. Therefore, you say the solution for the equation $x - 3 = x - 3$ is **all numbers**.

Equation with infinite solutions:
$$x - 3 = x - 3$$

3-102.   Copy and complete each of the Diamond Problems below. The pattern used in the Diamond Problems is shown at right.

a.   b.   c.   d.

3-103.   Joe is downloading songs from the Internet. He can download them at a rate of 8 songs every 10 minutes. Jasmine, who is also downloading songs, can download at a rate of 12 songs every 15 minutes. Who is downloading songs faster? What is the unit rate (songs per minute) for each person?

3-104.   For each of the following equations, simplify and solve for the variable. Show all work and check your solution, if possible.

a. $-2 + x = -x + 2$

b. $-(x - 1) = -4x - 2$

c. $2 + 3x = 3x + 2$

d. $-(-x + 6) = -3x$

3-105.   Use your pattern-finding skills to copy and complete the table below.

IN (x)	1	2	3		5	6	8	12	24	x
OUT (y)	24	12		6	4.8	4		2		

a.   Explain the pattern you found in your table. How are x and y related?

b.   Write the rule you described in part (a) with algebraic symbols.

c.   Use the points in your table to graph this rule on graph paper. Describe the resulting shape.

3-106.   Translate each algebraic expression into words.

a. $5x - 3$ b. $2(x + y)$ c. $3 - (x + 5)$

3.2.5 How can I solve complicated equations?

Distributive Property Equations

Not all equations are as simple as the equations you have solved so far. However, many equations that look complicated just need to be broken into simpler, familiar parts. In this lesson, you will use algebra tiles to work with situations that combine addition and multiplication. Then you will solve equations that contain complicated parts.

3-107.   So far in this course, you have solved single-variable equations like $3x + 7 = -x - 3$. Consider this change to that equation: $3(x + 7) = -x - 3$. What is different about the equations? How will the changes made to the original equation change the steps needed to solve the equation?

3-108.   Use algebra tiles to build, draw, and simplify each expression.

   a. $3(x + 4)$

   b. $4(2x - 1)$

   c. $2(x + 5) + 3$

   d. $3(x - 2) + 5$

3-109.   In a previous class, you used the **Distributive Property** to rewrite problems with parentheses similar to the ones above. Use the Distributive Property to complete and simplify each expression below. Read the Math Notes box at the end of this lesson if you need help getting started.

   a. $2(x + 5) = 2 \cdot x + 2 \cdot 5 = 2x + \underline{\quad}$

   b. $3(2x + 1) = 3 \cdot 2x + 3 \cdot \underline{\quad} = \underline{\qquad}$

   c. $-2(x + 3) = -2 \cdot \underline{\quad} + -2 \cdot \underline{\quad} = \underline{\qquad}$

   d. $-3(2x - 5) = \underline{\qquad} = \underline{\qquad}$

3-110.   Now use what you learned in the previous three problems to solve for x in the equation $3(x + 7) = -x - 3$. Show your steps and check your answer. You may want to use algebra tiles and an Equation Mat to help you visualize the equation.

3-111.   Solve each of the following equations for x. Show your steps and check your answers.

   a. $3x - 2(5x + 3) = 14 - 2x$

   b. $3(x + 1) - 8 = 14 - 2(3x - 4)$

3-112. Earlier in this course, you learned that $-(x-3)$ was the same as $-x+3$, because $(x-3)$ in the "$-$" region could be "flipped" to $-x+3$ in the "$+$" region, as shown below.

Use what you have learned in this lesson to explain *algebraically* why "flipping" works. That is, why does $-(x-3)=-x+3$?

METHODS AND MEANINGS

The Distributive Property

The **Distributive Property** states that for any three terms a, b, and c:

$$a(b+c) = ab+ac$$

That is, when a multiplies a group of terms, such as $(b + c)$, it multiplies *each* term of the group. For example, when multiplying $2(x+4)$, the 2 multiplies both the x and the 4. This can be represented with algebra tiles, as shown below.

$$2(x+4) = 2 \cdot x + 2 \cdot 4 = 2x+8$$

The 2 multiplies each term.

3-113. Solve each equation.

    a. $3(5x+2)=8x+20$ b. $-2(x-3)+4x=-(-x+1)$

3-114. Simplify the following expressions.

    a. $x+3x-3+2x^2+8x-5$ b. $3y+14y^2-6y^2-9y+1-y-3y$

    c. $2y^2+30xy-2y^2+4y-4x$ d. $x-0.2x$

3-115. Louis recorded how many times he could jump rope without stopping. Here is his data:

        50 15 102 64 29 55 100 97 48 81 61

Find the median, upper quartile, and lower quartile of his data.

3-116. Find the area and perimeter of the shape below. Show your work.

3-117.   This problem is a checkpoint for unit rates and proportions. It will be referred to as Checkpoint 3.

In parts (a) through (c), use the given information to find the unit rate. In parts (d) through (f), write and solve a proportion based on the given information.

$ (y-axis)

Bottles Refilled (x-axis)

a.   If $2\frac{1}{4}$ pounds of bananas cost $1.89, what is the cost per pound?

b.   What is the weight per cm?

weight (g)	9	12	18	30
length (cm)	15	20	30	50

c.   Use the graph at right to find the refill cost per bottle.

d.   If 200 vitamins cost $4.75, what should 500 vitamins cost?

e.   If a basketball player made 72 out of 85 free-throw attempts, how many could she expect to make in 200 attempts?

f.   A cookie recipe uses $\frac{1}{2}$ teaspoon of vanilla with $\frac{3}{4}$ cup of flour. How much vanilla should be used with five cups of flour?

Check your answers by referring to the Checkpoint 3 materials located at the back of your book.

Ideally, at this point you are comfortable working with these types of problems and can solve them correctly. If you feel that you need more confidence when solving these types of problems, then review the Checkpoint 3 materials and try the practice problems provided. From this point on, you will be expected to do problems like these correctly and with confidence.

Chapter 3 Closure   What have I learned?

Reflection and Synthesis

The activities below offer you a chance to reflect about
what you have learned during this chapter. As you
work, look for concepts that you feel very comfortable
with, ideas that you would like to learn more about,
and topics you need more help with.

①   SUMMARIZING MY UNDERSTANDING

This section gives you an opportunity to show what you know about certain
math topics or ideas.

Multiple Representations

In this chapter, you learned about how data can be shown in one of four
representations. These include a situation or tile pattern, a graphical display, a
table of values, and a symbolic rule. Show what you know about these
representations by doing the following activity with your team. While you have
not fully investigated all of these representations so far, this exercise will
prepare you to make important connections in Chapter 4.

1. Pick a pattern or problem from the chapter that
    you think can best demonstrate your
    understanding of these four representations.

2. Obtain a Chapter 3 Closure Resource Page:
    Multiple Representations GO (Graphic
    Organizer) from your teacher, a reduced copy
    of which is shown at right.

3. In the middle of the page, copy the problem
    that you have selected. Then represent it using
    each of the four different representations
    shown on the page.

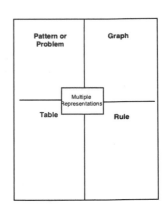

4. Use color or other means to show any connections that you see between
    each of the representations.

②

WHAT HAVE I LEARNED?

Doing the problems in this section will help you to evaluate which types of problems you feel comfortable with and which ones you need more help with.

Solve each problem as completely as you can. The table at the end of this closure section provides answers to these problems. It also tells you where you can find additional help and where to find practice problems like them.

CL 3-118. For the $x \rightarrow y$ table below, fill in the missing values and find the rule.

IN (x)	–10	0	5	1	25	–6	8	–1	6	10
OUT (y)		5		3	–45	17				–15

CL 3-119. One year ago, Josie moved into a new house and noticed a beautiful vine growing on the back fence. She recorded the data in the table below.

Weeks Since Josie Moved In	4	5	6
Height of Vine (in inches)	16	19	22

Assume that the vine continues to grow at a constant rate as you answer the questions below.

a. How tall was the vine 7 weeks after Josie moved in?

b. How tall was the vine 3 weeks after Josie moved in?

c. How tall was the vine when Josie moved in? How do you know?

d. Predict how tall the vine was 19 weeks after Josie moved into her house. Justify your answer.

e. Predict when the vine reached the top of the garage (94 inches tall). How did you find your answer?

CL 3-120. Clifford is making a really big white cake for his sister's birthday. The recipe calls for 1.5 times as much flour as sugar. It also calls for $\frac{1}{2}$ as much butter as sugar. All the butter, flour, and sugar together total 7.5 cups. How much butter, sugar and flour does Clifford need? Write and solve an equation. Remember to define your variable and to state your answer in a sentence.

CL 3-121. Simplify the expression $3x^2 - 5x - 4 + xy - (2xy + 2x^2)$. Then evaluate the result if $x = -1$ and $y = 6$.

CL 3-122. Follow the order of operations to simplify each expression below.

a. $6^2 - (5 - 4) + 2(8 - 2^2) \div 8$

b. $\frac{2(9-6)^2}{18}$

CL 3-123. Raphael had 5 hits in 7 at-bats. If he continues this pattern, how many hits will he have in 210 at-bats?

CL 3-124. Solve $6 - x - 3 = 4x - 12$ for x, recording your steps as you work.

CL 3-125. Make an $x \rightarrow y$ table from the points on the graph at right. Then write a rule for the table.

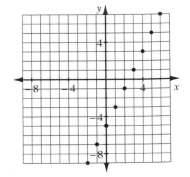

CL 3-126. Jessica was solving an equation. After she finished simplifying, her result was $0 = 2$. This result confused her. Explain to Jessica what her result means. Explain your reasoning thoroughly.

CL 3-127.   For each of the problems above, do the following:

- Draw a bar or number line that represents 0 to 10.

- Color or shade in a portion of the bar that represents your level of understanding and comfort with completing that problem on your own.

If any of your bars are less than a 5, choose *one* of those problems and complete one of the following tasks:

- Write two questions that you would like to ask about that problem.
- Brainstorm two things that you DO know about that type of problem.

If all of your bars are a 5 or above, choose *one* of those problems and do one of these tasks:

- Write two questions you might ask or hints you might give to a student who was stuck on the problem.
- Make a new problem that is similar and more challenging than that problem and solve it.

③   WHAT TOOLS CAN I USE?

You have several tools and references available to help support your learning – your teacher, your study team, your math book, and your Toolkit, to name only a few. At the end of each chapter you will have an opportunity to review your Toolkit for completeness as well as to revise or update it to better reflect your current understanding of big ideas.

The main elements of your Toolkit should be your Learning Logs, Math Notes, and the vocabulary used in this chapter. Math words that are new to this chapter appear in bold in the text. Refer to the lists provided below and follow your teacher's instructions to revise your Toolkit, which will help make it a useful reference for you as you complete this chapter and prepare to begin the next one.

Learning Log Entries

Lesson 3.1.6 – Qualities of a Complete Graph
Lesson 3.1.7 – Graphing Errors
Lesson 3.2.2 – How Many Solutions?

Math Notes

Lesson 3.1.1 – Patterns in Nature
Lesson 3.1.3 – Discrete and Continuous Relationships
Lesson 3.1.4 – Parabolas
Lesson 3.1.5 – Independent and Dependent Variables
Lesson 3.2.1 – Complete Graph
Lesson 3.2.2 – Circle Vocabulary, Circumference, and Area
Lesson 3.2.3 – Solving a Linear Equation
Lesson 3.2.4 – Solutions to an Equation with One Variable
Lesson 3.2.5 – The Distributive Property

Mathematical Vocabulary

The following is a list of vocabulary found in this chapter. Some of the words have been seen in previous chapters. The words in bold are the words new to this chapter. Make sure that you are familiar with the terms below and know what they mean. For the words you do not know, refer to the glossary or index. You might also add these words to your Toolkit so that you can reference them in the future.

combining like terms	**continuous graph**	dependent variable
discrete	**Distributive Property**	evaluate
independent variable	Order of Operations	**parabola**
solution	term	variable
vertex	***x*-intercepts**	***y*-intercepts**

Core Connections, Course 3

Answers and Support for Closure Problems
What Have I Learned?

Note: MN = Math Note, LL = Learning Log

Problem	Solution	Need Help?	More Practice
CL 3-118.	In order, the missing y-values are 25, $-5, 11, 7$, and -7. The rule is $y = -2x + 5$.	Lesson 3.1.1	Problems 3-2, 3-3, 3-13, 3-28, and 3-113
CL 3-119.	a. 25 inches b. 13 inches c. 4 inches d. 61 inches e. 30 weeks after Josie moved in	Lesson 3.1.2	Problems 3-11 and 3-99
CL 3-120.	Let x represent the amount of sugar, $x + 1.5x + 0.5x = 7.5$, $x = 2.5$, 2.5 cups of sugar, 3.75 cups of flour and 1.25 cups of butter.	MN: 1.1.3	Problems 3-6, 3-26, and 3-96
CL 3-121.	$x^2 - xy - 5x - 4$ $= (-1)^2 - (-1)(6) - 5(-1) - 4$ $= 8$	MN: 2.1.3, 2.1.5, and 2.1.6	Problems 3-15, 3-32, 3-39, 3-77, and 3-94
CL 3-122.	a. 36 b. 1	MN: 2.1.3	Problems 3-16 and 3-27
CL 3-123.	150 hits	Lessons 1.2.1 and 1.2.2 MN: 1.2.1 and 1.2.2 LL: 1.2.1	Problems 3-17, 3-40, 3-67, and 3-78
CL 3-124.	$x = 3$	Lessons 2.1.8 and 2.1.9 MN: 2.1.8 and 2.1.9 LL: 2.1.9	Problems 3-23, 3-24, 3-29, 3-38, 3-50, 3-74, 3-92, and 3-104

CL 3-125.

x	–2	–1	0	1	2	3	4	5	6
y	–9	–7	–5	–3	–1	1	3	5	7

$y = 2x - 5$

Lesson 3.1.4

Problems 3-46 and 3-85

CL 3-126.   There is no solution for x in this equation.

Lesson 3.2.1

MN: 3.2.4

Problems 3-72, 3-81, and 3-94

CHAPTER 4 Multiple Representations

This chapter builds on the work you did in the previous two chapters. Chapter 4 contains only one section, as it focuses solely on the connections between the four representations of data: patterns, tables, graphs, and equations (also referred to as "rules").

In this chapter, you will learn:

➤ How to change any representation of data (such as a pattern, table, graph or rule) to any of the other representations.

➤ How to use the connections between patterns, tables, graphs, and rules to solve problems.

Guiding Questions

Think about these questions throughout this chapter:

What is the connection?

Is there a pattern?

How does the pattern grow?

In how many different ways can it be represented?

How does the pattern show up in the table, graph, and rule?

Chapter Outline

Section 4.1 You will shift between different representations of linear patterns, using the web diagram shown at left. By finding connections between each representation, you and your team will find ways to change from one representation to each of the other three representations.

4.1.1 What is the connection?

. . . .

Finding Connections Between Representations

In Chapter 3, you studied different ways to represent patterns. You organized information into tables, graphed information about patterns, and learned how to find the rules that govern specific patterns.

Starting today and continuing throughout this chapter, you will find connections between different representations of the same pattern. You will also explore each representation in further depth. This work will develop efficient ways to go from one representation to another. By the end of this chapter, you will have a deeper understanding of many of the most powerful tools of algebra.

4-1. TILE PATTERN TEAM CHALLENGE

Your teacher will assign your team a tile pattern (one of the patterns labeled (a) through (e) on the next page). Your team's task is to create a poster showing every way you can represent your pattern and highlighting all of the connections between the representations that you can find. *Finding and showing the connections are the most important parts of this activity.* Clearly presenting the connections between representations on your poster will help you convince your classmates that your description of the pattern makes sense.

Pattern Analysis:

- Extend the pattern by drawing Figures 0, 4, and 5. Then describe Figure 100. Give as much information as you can about Figure 100. What will it look like? How will the tiles be arranged? How many tiles will it have?

- Find the number of tiles in each figure. Record your data in a table and on a graph.

- Generalize the pattern by writing a rule that will give the number of tiles in any figure in the pattern. Show how you got your answer.

- Demonstrate how the pattern grows. Use color, arrows, labels, and other math tools to help you show and explain. Show growth in each representation.

- What connections do you see between the different representations (figures, $x \rightarrow y$ table, and graph)? How can you show these connections?

Problem continues on next page. →

4-1.   *Problem continued from previous page.*

Presenting the Connections:

As a team, organize your work into a large poster that clearly shows each representation of your pattern, as well as a description of Figure 100. When your team presents your poster to the class, you will need to support each statement with a reason from your observations. Each team member must explain something mathematical as part of your presentation.

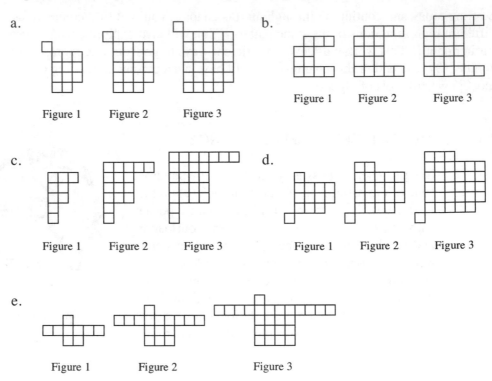

a.   Figure 1   Figure 2   Figure 3

b.   Figure 1   Figure 2   Figure 3

c.   Figure 1   Figure 2   Figure 3

d.   Figure 1   Figure 2   Figure 3

e.   Figure 1   Figure 2   Figure 3

Core Connections, Course 3

4-2. For each tile pattern in problem 4-1, draw Figures 0, 4, and 5 on graph paper. If it helps, copy Figures 1, 2, and 3 onto your paper.

4-3. On graph paper, draw Figure 0 and Figure 4 for the pattern at right.

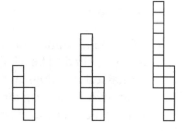

a. Represent the number of tiles in each figure in an $x \rightarrow y$ table. Let x be the figure number and y be the total number of tiles.

b. Use the table to graph the pattern.

Figure 1   Figure 2   Figure 3

c. Without drawing Figure 5, predict where its point would lie on the graph. Justify your prediction.

4-4 Evaluate the expressions below for the given values.

a. $3(2x+1)$ for $x = -8$

b. $\frac{x-6}{4} - 1$ for $x = -14$

c. $-2m^2 + 10$ for $m = -6$

d. $k \cdot k \div k \cdot k \div k$ for $k = 9$

4-5. Copy and simplify the following expressions by combining like terms.

a. $x + 3x - 3 + 2x^2 + 8 - 5x$

b. $2x + 4y^2 - 6y^2 - 9 + 1 - x + 3x$

c. $2x^2 + 30y - 3y^2 + 4xy - 14 - x$

d. $20 + 3xy - 3xy + y^2 + 10 - y^2$

4-6. Use the Distributive Property to rewrite each expression.

a. $3(2x-7)$

b. $-2(x-7) + 5x$

c. $5x + 10$

d. $8x + 12y$

4-7. Make an $x \rightarrow y$ table for the rule $y = x^2 - 2x$.

    a. Plot and connect the points on a complete graph.

    b. Does your graph look like a full parabola? If not, add more points to your table and graph to complete the picture.

4-8. THE GAME SHOW

Susan had an incredible streak of good fortune as a guest on an exciting game show called "The Math Is Right." She amassed winnings of $12,500, a sports car, two round-trip airline tickets, and five pieces of furniture.

In an amazing finish, Susan then landed on a "Double Your Prize" square and answered the corresponding math question correctly. She instantly became the show's biggest winner ever, earning twice the amounts of all her previous prizes.

A week later, $25,000, a sports car, four round-trip airline tickets, and five pieces of furniture arrived at her house. Susan felt cheated. What was wrong?

4-9. Write the equation represented by the diagram at right.

    a. Simplify as much as possible and then solve for x.

    b. Check your solution.

4-10. Copy and simplify the following expressions by combining like terms.

    a. $y + 3x - 3 + 2x^2 + 8x - 5y$ b. $2x + 4x^2 - 6x^2 - 9 + 1 - x - 3x$

    c. $14 + 3y^2 + 30y - 3y^2 - 14y - 14 - 16y$ d. $-10x + 13y - 6x + 5y^2 + 10y - 5y^2$

4-11. Use your pattern-finding techniques to fill in the missing entries for the table below. Then find a rule for the pattern.

IN (x)	4	8	3	−2	−6	0	5	7
OUT (y)	17	65	10	5		1	26	

4.1.2   How does it grow?

· ·

Seeing Growth in Different Representations

In Lesson 4.1.1, you looked at four different ways of representing patterns and began to find connections between them.

Throughout this chapter, you will explore connections between and find efficient ways to move from one type of representation to another. Today, you will look for specific connections between geometric patterns and equations.
As you work, keep these questions in mind:

How can you see growth in the rule?

How do you know your rule is correct?

What does the representation tell you?

What are the connections between the representations?

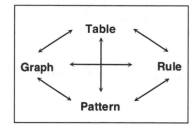

At the end of this lesson, put your work from today in a safe place. You will need to use it during Lesson 4.1.3.

4-12.   **Tile Pattern #1:**

Examine the tile pattern shown at right and on the Lesson 4.1.2 Resource Page that your teacher gives you.

Figure 1   Figure 2   Figure 3

a.   What do you notice? After everyone has had a moment to examine the figures independently, discuss what you see with your team.

b.   Sketch the next figure in the sequence (Figure 4) on your resource page. Sketch Figure 0, which is the figure that comes before Figure 1.

c.   How is the tile pattern growing? Where are the tiles being added with each new figure? On your resource page, use a marker or colored pencil to color in the new tiles in each figure.

d.   What would Figure 100 look like? Describe it in words. How many tiles would be in the 100th figure? Find as many ways as you can to justify your conclusion. Be prepared to report back to the class with your team's findings and methods.

4-13.   For each of the patterns below, answer questions (a) through (d) from problem
4-12. Use color to shade in the new tiles on each pattern on your resource page.
Choose one color for the new tiles in part (a) and a different color for the new
tiles in part (b).

a.   **Tile Pattern #2:**

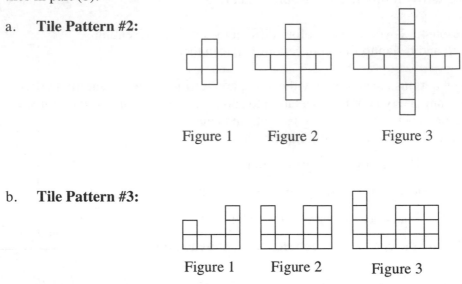

Figure 1   Figure 2   Figure 3

b.   **Tile Pattern #3:**

Figure 1   Figure 2   Figure 3

4-14.   PUTTING IT TOGETHER

Look back at the three different tile patterns in problems 4-12 and 4-13 to
answer the following questions.

a.   When you compare these three patterns, what is the same and what is
different? Explain in a few sentences.

b.   Find an equation (rule) for the number of tiles in each pattern. Label each
tile pattern on your resource page with its rule.

c.   What connections do you see between your equations and the tile pattern?
Show and explain these connections.

d.   Imagine that the team next to you created a new tile pattern that grows in
the same way as the ones you have just worked with, but they refused to
show it to you. What other information would you need to be able to
predict the number of tiles in Figure 100? Explain your reasoning.

4-15.   Consider **Tile Pattern #4**, shown below.

a.   Draw Figures 0 and 4 on the resource page.

Figure 1   Figure 2   Figure 3

b.   Find an equation (rule) for the number of tiles in this pattern. On your resource page, label Tile Pattern #4 with its rule. Then use a new color to show where the numbers in your rule appear in the tile pattern.

c.   What is the same about this pattern and Tile Pattern #3? What is different? What do those similarities and differences look like in the tile pattern? In the equation?

d.   How is the number of tiles by which the pattern increases each time you move from one figure to the next figure in the sequence represented in each equation?

Remember to put your work from today in a safe place, because you will need to use it during the next lesson.

4-16.   LEARNING LOG

For today's Learning Log entry, draw a web of the different representations, starting with the diagram below. Draw lines and/or arrows to show which representations you have studied so far in this course. Explain the connections you learned today. Be sure to include anything you figured out about how the numbers in equations (rules) relate to tile patterns. Title this entry "Representations of Patterns Web" and label it with today's date.

4-17.   Simplify each of the following equations and solve for x. Show all work and check your solution.

a. $7 - 3x = -x + 1$ b. $-2 + 3x = -(x + 6)$

4-18.   Leala can write a 500-word essay in an hour. If she writes an essay in 10 minutes, approximately how many words do you think the essay contains?

4-19.   Copy and complete the table below.

IN (x)	2	10	6	7	–3		–10	1000	x
OUT (y)	9	25	17			15			

a.   Explain in words what is done to the input value (x) to produce the output value (y).

b.   Write the rule you described in part (a) with algebraic symbols.

4-20.   When Susan's brother went to college, she and her two sisters evenly divided his belongings. Among his possessions were 3 posters, 216 books, and 24 CDs. How were these items divided?

4-21.   Kelso's mom wants to put a floating blanket over the family's circular wading pool to keep the heat in and the leaves out. The pool has a diameter of 10 feet.

a.   How many square feet of blanket will Kelso's mother need?

b.   If the pool supply store charges $0.10 per square foot for the blanket, how much will the material for the blanket cost?

4.1.3 How does it grow?

Connecting Linear Rules and Graphs

You have been looking at geometric patterns and ways in which those patterns can be represented with $x \rightarrow y$ tables, graphs, and equations. In Lesson 4.1.2, you worked with four different tile patterns and looked for connections between the geometric shapes and the numbers in the equations. Today you will go back to those four equations and look for connections to other representations.

By the end of this lesson, you should be able to answer these target questions:

How is growth shown in a graph?

How is growth shown in a rule?

How can you determine the number of tiles in Figure 0 from a graph?

How can you determine which tile pattern grows faster from a graph?

4-22.   Examine your Lesson 4.1.2 Resource Page ("Pattern Analysis") and obtain a Lesson 4.1.3 Resource Page from your teacher.

   a.   Make sure you have a rule for each tile pattern.

   b.   Complete the table for each rule.

   c.   Create a graph for each pattern. Put all patterns on the same set of axes. Use different colors for each pattern, matching the color you used to show the tile pattern's growth on the 4.1.2 Resource Page.

   d.   Explain how the growth appears in the pattern, in the table, in the graph, and in the rule.

   e.   What connections do you see between these representations? Describe any connections you see.

4-23.   The graph at right gives information about
three new tile patterns. Remember that in this
course, tile patterns will be considered to be
elements of continuous relationships and thus
will be graphed with a continuous line or
curve.

Answer the following questions as a team.

a.   What information does the circled
point (○) on the graph tell you about
tile pattern A?

b.   Find the growth of each tile pattern. For
example, how much does tile pattern A
increase from one figure to the next? Explain how you know.

c.   Look at the lines for tile patterns A and B. What is the same about the two
lines? What conclusion can you make about these tile patterns? What is
different about the lines? What does this tell you about the tile patterns?
Use what you see on the graph to justify your answers.

d.   Look at lines A and C on the graph. What do these two lines have in
common? In what ways are the lines different? What does this tell you
about the tile patterns? Explain completely.

4-24.   LEARNING LOG

In your Learning Log, answer the target questions for this
lesson, reprinted below.

How is growth shown in a graph?

How is growth shown in a rule?

How can you determine the number of tiles in Figure 0 from a graph?

How can you determine which tile pattern grows faster from a graph?

Be sure to include at least one example. Title this entry "Connecting Linear
Rules and Graphs" and label it with today's date.

4-25.   Two of the connections in your Representations of Patterns Web are
         pattern → table and pattern → rule. Practice these connections as you answer
         the questions below.

         a.   On graph paper, draw Figure 0 and
              Figure 4 for the pattern at right.

         Figure 1   Figure 2   Figure 3

         b.   Represent the number of tiles in
              each figure with a table.

         c.   Represent the number of tiles in each figure with an algebraic rule.

4-26.   Use the formula for the area of a circle to solve for the radius of the circle if the
         area is 78.5 cm^2.

4-27.   For each of the equations below, solve for x. Show all work and check your
         solution.

         a. $-2 + 2x = -x + 2 + x$ b. $2 - 3x = x + 2$

4-28.   Another one of the connections in your
         Representations of Patterns Web is graph → table.
         In Chapters 1 through 3, you developed tools to find
         a table from a graph. Consider this connection as
         you complete the table below. The table is based on
         the graph at right.

         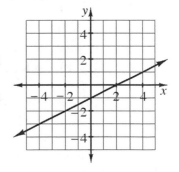

IN (x)	−3	−2	−1	0	1	2	3
OUT (y)							

4-29.   Joe drove 100 miles from San Francisco to Gilroy and used 4 gallons of gas.
         How much gas should he expect to use for a 3000-mile trip to New York City?
         What is the unit rate (miles per gallon)? Be sure to justify your reasoning.

4.1.4 What is the rule? How can I use it?

$y = mx + b$

In Lessons 4.1.2 and 4.1.3, you investigated connections between tile patterns, $x \rightarrow y$ tables, graphs, and rules (equations). Today you will use your observations about growth and Figure 0 to write rules for linear patterns and to create new tile patterns for given rules.

4-30.   With your team, list some of the equations you have been working with in the past two lessons. What do all of these rules have in common?

4-31.   UNDERSTANDING $y = mx + b$

Rules for linear patterns can all be written in the form $y = mx + b$.
In $y = mx + b$, x and y represent variables, while m and b represent **parameters**. Parameters are numbers that stay the same in the equation after they are chosen. Discuss these questions with your team:

a.   What does m tell you about the pattern?

b.   What does b tell you about the pattern?

4-32.   GRAPH $\rightarrow$ RULE

Allysha claims she can find the equation of a line by its graph without using a table. How is that possible? Discuss this idea with your team and then try to find the equation of the line at right without first making a table. Be ready to share with the class how you found the rule.

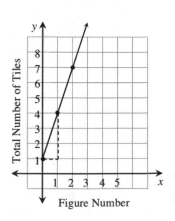

162

4-33.   TABLE → RULE

Allysha wonders if she can use the idea of m and b to find the equation of a line from its table.

a.   For example, if she knows the information about a linear pattern given in the table below, how can she find the equation of the line? Work with your team to complete the table and find the rule.

IN (x)	0	1	2	3	4	5	6
OUT (y)	−2						

+5   +5   +5   +5   +5   +5

b.   Use this same idea to find the rule of the linear tile patterns represented by the tables below.

i.

IN (x)	−1	0	1	2	3	4	5
OUT (y)	3	5	7	9	11	13	15

ii.

IN (x)	0	1	2	3	4	5	6
OUT (y)	7	4	1	−2	−5	−8	−11

c.   Write a summary statement explaining how you used your knowledge about m and b to quickly write a rule.

4-34.   RULE → PATTERN

In each problem below, invent your own pattern that meets the stated conditions.

a.   Draw Figures 0, 1, 2, and 3 for a tile pattern that has $y = 4x + 3$ as a rule.

b.   A tile pattern decreases by 2 tiles. Figure 2 of the pattern has 8 tiles. Draw Figures 0, 1, 2, and 3 and write the rule (equation) for the pattern.

4-35.   Invent two different tile patterns that grow by adding 4 every time but have different $x \rightarrow y$ tables. Draw Figures 0, 1, 2, and 3 and find rules for each of your patterns. What is different about your rules? What is the same?

4-36.   LEARNING LOG

The linear equations you have been working with can be written in this general form: $y = mx + b$

In your Learning Log, summarize what you know about m and b so far. What does the m tell you about a pattern? What does the b tell you about a pattern? Where can you see m and b in each representation? Sketch examples if it helps. Title this entry "$y = mx + b$" and label it with today's date.

4-37.   Examine the $x \rightarrow y$ table at right.

a.   Invent a tile pattern that fits this data.

b.   How is the pattern growing? Show where the pattern of growth appears in the $x \rightarrow y$ table and the tile pattern.

c.   Write a rule for this pattern.

Figure Number	Number of Tiles
0	5
1	9
2	13
3	17

4-38.

Figure Number

Look at the graph at left. What statements can you make about the tile pattern the graph represents? How many tiles are in Figure 0? Figure 1? What is the pattern of growth? What is the rule for the pattern?

4-39.   For each equation below, solve for x. Check your solution, if possible, and show all work.

a. $3x - 6 + 1 = -2x - 5 + 5x$

b. $-2x - 5 = 2 - 4x - (x - 1)$

4-40.   I am thinking of a number. When I double my number and then subtract the result from five, I get negative one. What is my number? Write and solve an equation.

4-41.   On your paper, copy the table below and use your pattern skills to complete it.

IN (x)	2	10				-3			x
OUT (y)	4	28	13	-17	10		2.5	148	$3x - 2$

a.   Explain in words what is done to the input value, x, to produce the output value, y.

b.   Explain the process you used to find the missing input values.

4.1.5 What are the connections?

Checking the Connections

In the last several lessons, you have been finding
connections and relationships between different
representations of patterns. You have worked backward
and forward. You have also used information about
Figure 0 (or the starting point) and the pattern of growth
to write rules. In today's activity, you will use pieces of
information from various parts of the web to generate a
complete pattern.

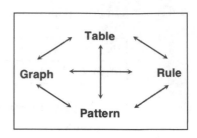

4-42.   CHECKING THE CONNECTIONS: TEAM CHALLENGE

Today you are going to apply what you know about the starting point
(Figure 0), the pattern of growth, and the connections between representations
to answer some challenging questions. The information in each question, parts
(a) through (d), describes a different pattern. The graph of each pattern is a line.
From this information, generate the rule, $x \rightarrow y$ table, graph, and tile pattern
(Figures 0 through 3) that follow the pattern. You may answer these questions
in any order, but make sure you answer each one completely before starting
another problem.

Work together as a team. The more you
listen to how other people see the
connections and the more you share your
own ideas, the more you will know at the
end of the lesson. Stick together and be
sure to talk through every idea.

Each person will turn in his or her own
paper at the end of this activity, showing
four complete representations for each
pattern. Your work does not need to be
identical to your teammates' work, but
you should have talked and agreed that all
explanations are correct.

Problem continues on next page. →

4-42.   *Problem continued from previous page.*

a.

Figure 3

b.

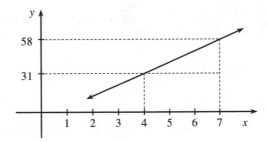

c.

Figure Number	Number of Tiles
0	
1	
2	
3	12

Figure 8

d. $y = -3x + 7$

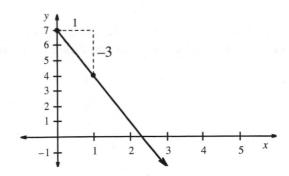

4-43.   REPRESENTATIONS OF PATTERNS WEB

Update your Representations of Pattern
Web from problem 4-16 with any new
connections that you can make between
representations following today's work.
Pay attention to the direction of any arrows
that you draw.

4-44.   Complete a table for the rule $y = 3x - 2$.

a.   Draw a complete graph for this rule.

b.   Is $(-50, -152)$ a point on the graph? Explain how you know.

x	y
3	25
5	39
6	46
1	11

4-45.   Write down everything you know about the tile pattern represented
by the $x \rightarrow y$ table at right. Be as specific as possible.

4-46.   Find the area and circumference of a circle that has a diameter of 17 mm. Write
your answers in terms of π and as a decimal approximation.

4-47.   Copy and complete each of the Diamond Problems below.
The pattern used in the Diamond Problems is shown at right.

a.

b.

c.

d.

4-48.   Simplify each of the expressions below. You may use an Equation Mat and
tiles.

a. $-(5x + 1)$

b. $6x - (-5x + 1)$

c. $-(1 - 5x)$

d. $-5x + (x - 1)$

4-49.   Invent a tile pattern that grows by 4 each time. Draw Figures 0, 1, 2, and 3. Use color or shading to show the growth.

4-50.   Complete a table for the rule $y = 3 - x$.

    a.   Draw a complete graph for this rule.

    b.   Is $(32, -29)$ a point on this graph? Explain why or why not.

4-51.   For each equation below, solve for the given variable. Check your solutions, if possible, and show all work.

    a. $3p - 7 + 9 - 2p = p + 2$, solve for p b. $-2x + 5 + (-x) - 5 = 0$, solve for x

    c. $12 = r + 6 - 2r$, solve for r d. $-(y^2 - 2) = y^2 - 5 - 2y^2$, solve for y

4-52.   Solve each equation below for x. Then check your solutions.

    a. $\frac{x}{8} = \frac{3}{4}$ b. $\frac{2}{5} = \frac{x}{40}$ c. $\frac{1}{8} = \frac{x}{12}$ d. $\frac{x}{10} = \frac{12}{15}$

4-53.   Sketch a graph to match each story below using axes labeled as shown at right.

    a.   Luis rides his skateboard at the same speed all the way home. It takes him ten minutes to get there.

    b.   Corinna jogs along at the same speed until she reaches a hill, and then she slows down until she finally stops to rest.

    c.   Sergei is talking with his friends at the donut shop when he realizes that it is almost time for math class. He runs toward school, but he slows to a walk when he hears the bell ring and realizes that he is already late. He sits down in class four minutes after he left the donut shop.

4.1.6 How can I use growth?

Graphing a Line Without an $x \rightarrow y$ Table

You have now used your knowledge of growth patterns and Figure 0 to create tile patterns and $x \rightarrow y$ tables directly from rules. You have also looked at graphs to determine the equation or rule for the pattern. Today you will reverse that process and use an equation to create a graph without the intermediate step of creating an $x \rightarrow y$ table.

4-54.   For each of the graphs below:

- Write a rule.

- Describe how the pattern changes and how many tiles are in Figure 0.

a.

b.

c.

d.

e.

f.
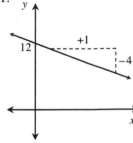

4-55.   Now reverse the process. Graph the following rules without first making a table. Parts (a) and (b) can go on the same set of axes, as can parts (c) and (d). Label each line with its equation, y-intercept (where it crosses the y-axis), and a growth triangle.

a. $y = 4x + 3$ b. $y = 3x$

c. $y = -3x + 8$ d. $y = x - 1$

4-56.   Sketch a graph that fits each description below and then label each line with its equation. You can put all of the graphs on one set of axes if you label the lines clearly. Use what you know about the growth pattern and Figure 0 to help you.

a.   A pattern that has three tiles in Figure 0 and adds four tiles in each new figure.

b.   A pattern that shrinks by three tiles between figures and starts with five tiles in Figure 0.

c.   A pattern that has two tiles in all figures.

4-57.   Now reverse your process to describe the pattern represented by the rule $y = -2x + 13$. Be as detailed as you can.

4-58.   CONSOLIDATING YOUR LEARNING

a.   Find the Representations of Patterns Web that you updated at the end of Lesson 4.1.5. On it, add arrows for any new connections between representations that you can now make.

b.   LEARNING LOG

In your Learning Log, write a step-by-step process for graphing directly from a rule. A student who has not taken this course should be able to read your process and understand how to create a graph. It may help you to think about these questions as you write:

What information do you get from your rule?

How does that information show up on the graph?

Where does your graph start?

How do you figure out the next point?

What should you label to make it a complete graph?

Title this entry "Graphing Without an $x \rightarrow y$ Table," and label it with today's date.

4-59. Use what you know about *m* and *b* to graph each rule below without making a table. Draw a growth triangle for each line.

a. $y = 2x - 3$

b. $y = -2x + 5$

c. $y = 3x$

d. $y = \frac{1}{2}x + 1$

4-60. Examine the graph below, which displays three tile patterns.

a. What do you know about Figure 0 for each of the three patterns?

b. Which pattern changes most quickly? How quickly does it change? Show how you know.

c. Which figure number has the same number of tiles in patterns B and C? Explain how you know.

d. Write a rule for pattern B.

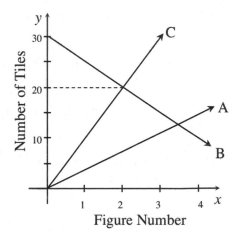

4-61. Translate these algebraic statements into words: $y = 2x + 5$ and $y = 6x + 5$.

a. What do you know about Figure 0 for each pattern?

b. Which pattern grows most quickly? How do you know?

4-62. Find the area and perimeter of each shape. Show your work.

a.

b.

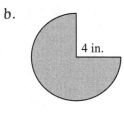

4-63.   Ms. B is making snickerdoodle cookies. Her recipe uses one-and-a-half teaspoons of cinnamon to make two-dozen cookies. If she needs to make thirteen-dozen cookies to give one cookie to each of her students, how much cinnamon will she need? There are three teaspoons in one tablespoon. How many tablespoons and teaspoons will Ms. B need?

4.1.7 What are the connections?

Completing the Web

After all of the work you have done with equations in $y = mx + b$ form, you know a lot about starting with one representation of a pattern and moving to different representations. Today you will work with your team to make sure you are confident moving around the Representations of Patterns Web.

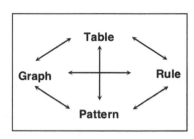

Answer problems 4-64 and 4-65 on graph paper. Discuss each problem with your team to get as much as you can out of these problems.

4-64.   GRAPH → PATTERN and TABLE → PATTERN

On graph paper, draw tile patterns (Figures 0, 1, and 2) that could represent the data shown below. Be creative, but make sure that the growth of each pattern makes sense to your teammates.

a.

b.

x	y
0	14
1	11
2	8
3	5
4	2

4-65.   REVISITING "GROWING, GROWING, GROWING"

Problem 1-10 from Chapter 1 asked you to determine which figure in the pattern shown below would have 79 tiles. Now that you know more about tile patterns, $x \rightarrow y$ tables, graphs, and rules, you can show the answer to this question in multiple ways.

Figure 2   Figure 3   Figure 4

Your Task: Solve this problem by completing the following tasks. Use a graphing calculator or other graphing technology to help you find a graph and a table. Be sure to record your work and justify your thinking.

- Copy the three figures above onto a piece of graph paper. On your graph paper, extend the pattern to include Figures 1 and 5.

- Find a table, a graph, and a rule, for this pattern.

- Which figure will have 79 tiles? Use as many representations as you can to justify your answer.

4-66.   EXTENSION

Invent an equation to fit these clues: The x-intercept is 2, and the pattern grows by 4. Show and explain your reasoning.

METHODS AND **M**EANINGS

Representations of Patterns Web

Consider the **tile patterns** below. The number of tiles in each figure can also be represented in an $x \rightarrow y$ **table**, on a **graph**, or with a **rule** (equation).

Remember that in this course, tile patterns will be considered to be elements of continuous relationships and thus will be graphed with a continuous line or curve.

Figure 0   Figure 1   Figure 2

Tile Pattern

Graph

$$y = 2x + 3$$

Rule (Equation)

Figure Number (x)	0	1	2
Number of Tiles (y)	3	5	7

$x \rightarrow y$ **Table**

4-67.   Use what you know about m and b to graph each equation below without making a table. Show a growth triangle on each graph and label the x- and y-intercepts.

a. $y = 3 - 2x$ b. $y = 2x$

c. $y = 3$ d. $y = -\frac{1}{2}x + 3$

4-68. On your paper, copy and complete each $x \rightarrow y$ table below. Using what you know about m and b, write an equation that represents the data in the table.

a.

x	y
0	5
1	7
2	9
3	11
4	13
30	
200	
	505
x	

b.

x	y
0	4
1	2
2	0
3	-2
4	-4
30	
150	
300	
x	

c.

x	y
-2	7
-1	4
0	1
1	-2
2	-5
3	
100	
	70
x	

4-69. For a tile pattern with the rule $y = 6x + 4$ (where x represents the figure number and y represents the number of tiles), which figure number has 40 tiles in it? How do you know?

4-70. Josie and Jules are building a model car. They find that the real car is 54 inches tall and 180 inches long. They decide to make their model 3 inches tall, but now they are having a disagreement. Josie thinks that their model should be 10 inches long and Jules thinks it should be 129 inches long. Help them settle their argument by deciding if either of them is correct. Explain how you know exactly how long their model should be.

4-71. This problem is a checkpoint for area and perimeter of circles and complex figures. It will be referred to as Checkpoint 4.

Find the area and perimeter or circumference of each figure.

a. Circle with radius 3 cm.

b. Circle with diameter 10 feet.

c. Only the shaded region (each sector has equal area).

d.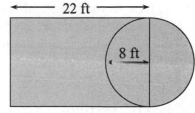

Check your answers by referring to the Checkpoint 4 materials located at the back of your book.

Ideally, at this point you are comfortable working with these types of problems and can solve them correctly. If you feel that you need more confidence when solving these types of problems, then review the Checkpoint 4 materials and try the practice problems provided. From this point on, you will be expected to do problems like these correctly and with confidence.

Chapter 4 Closure   What have I learned?

Reflection and Synthesis

The activities below offer you a chance to reflect about
what you have learned during this chapter. As you work,
look for concepts that you feel very comfortable with,
ideas that you would like to learn more about, and topics
you need more help with.

①   SUMMARIZING MY UNDERSTANDING

This section gives you an opportunity to show your understanding of how to
move between the different representations of a pattern (situation, table, graph,
and rule), which is the main idea of this chapter.

Team Representations Poster

In this chapter, you have learned how to move
directly from one representation to another.
Now you have an opportunity to demonstrate
what you know about these concepts. Today
you and your team will create a poster that
illustrates the skills and knowledge that you
have developed in this area.

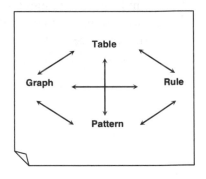

Make Connections: Follow your teacher's
instructions to work with your team to find or
create problems that demonstrate all of the connections between the different
representations shown in the Representations of Patterns Web.

Along with the solutions to each of your problems, you will need to explain
the process involved. To give an example for every connection on the web,
you will need one of each of the following:

graph → table	graph → pattern	graph → rule
table → graph	table → pattern	table → rule
pattern → graph	pattern → table	pattern → rule
rule → graph	rule → table	rule → pattern

Team Poster: Follow the model above to label and construct the sections of
your poster from the pieces that your team has created. Decide together on a
creative title for your poster.

WHAT HAVE I LEARNED?

Doing the problems in this section will help you to evaluate which types of problems you feel comfortable with and which ones you need more help with.

Solve each problem as completely as you can. The table at the end of this closure section provides answers to these problems. It also tells you where you can find additional help and where to find practice problems like them.

CL 4-72. Examine the pattern below, and then complete parts (a) through (f) that follow.

Figure 1   Figure 2   Figure 3

a.   On graph paper, sketch Figure 0 and Figure 4.

b.   Make a table showing Figure 0 through Figure 4.

c.   Write a rule to represent the pattern.

d.   On graph paper, create a graph of the number of tiles in each figure.

e.   What is the growth for the pattern?

f.   Predict how many tiles Figure 100 will have.

CL 4-73. Are the two expressions below equal? Show how you know.

$$4x^2 + 2x - 5 - 3x \quad \text{and} \quad 6x^2 - x + 3 - 2x^2 - 8$$

CL 4-74. Examine the graph at right.

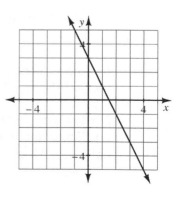

a.   Give two ways you can tell that the rule $y = 2x - 3$ does not match the graph.

b.   Make a graph that matches the rule $y = 2x - 3$.

c.   Find a rule that represents the graph at right.

CL 4-75. Consider the rule $y = 5x + 7$.

    a.   How many tiles are in Figure 0?

    b.   Which figure has 37 tiles?

    c.   In the equation $y = mx + b$, what do the letters m and b represent?

CL 4-76. Molly read 75 pages of the latest thriller mystery novel in 45 minutes. What is her unit rate? At the same rate, how long will it take her to read the entire 425-page novel?

CL 4-77. Solve this equation to find x: $2 - (3x - 4) = 2x - 9$.

CL 4-78. Simplify the following expressions, if possible.

    a. $x + 4x - 3 + 3x^2 - 2x$ b. $2x + 4y^2 - 6y^2 - 9 - x + 3x$

    c. $3x^2 + 10y - 2y^2 + 4x - 14$ d. $20 + 3xy - 4xy + y^2 + 10 - y^2$

    e.   Evaluate the expressions in parts (a) and (b) above when $x = 5$ and $y = -2$.

CL 4-79. Copy and complete the table for the linear pattern below.

IN (x)	−4	−3	−2	−1	0	1	2	3	4
OUT (y)					−2	3	8		

    a.   What is the y-intercept? What is the pattern of growth?

    b.   Find the rule for this line.

    c.   If the output number (y) is −52, what was the input number (x)?

CL 4-80. For the problem below, define a variable, write an equation, and solve it. Use the 5-D Process, if needed, to help you set up your equation.

For the school play, the advance tickets cost $3, while tickets at the door cost $5. Thirty more tickets were sold at door than in advance, and $2630 was collected. How many of each kind of ticket were sold? Write your answer in a sentence.

CL 4-81. For each of the problems above, do the following:

- Draw a bar or number line that represents 0 to 10.

- Color or shade in a portion of the bar that represents your level of understanding and comfort with completing that problem on your own.

If any of your bars are less than a 5, choose *one* of those problems and complete one of the following tasks:

- Write two questions that you would like to ask about that problem.
- Brainstorm two things that you DO know about that type of problem.

If all of your bars are a 5 or above, choose *one* of those problems and do one of these tasks:

- Write two questions you might ask or hints you might give to a student who was stuck on the problem.
- Make a new problem that is similar and more challenging than that problem and solve it.

You have several tools and references available to help support your learning – your teacher, your study team, your math book, and your Toolkit, to name only a few. At the end of each chapter you will have an opportunity to review your Toolkit for completeness as well as to revise or update it to better reflect your current understanding of big ideas.

The main elements of your Toolkit should be your Learning Logs, Math Notes, and the vocabulary used in this chapter. Math words that are new to this chapter appear in bold in the text. Refer to the lists provided below and follow your teacher's instructions to revise your Toolkit, which will help make it a useful reference for you as you complete this chapter and prepare to begin the next one.

Learning Log Entries

- Lesson 4.1.2 – Representations of Patterns Web
- Lesson 4.1.3 – Connecting Linear Rules and Graphs
- Lesson 4.1.4 – $y = mx + b$
- Lesson 4.1.6 – Graphing Without an $x \rightarrow y$ Table

Math Notes

- Lesson 4.1.7 – Representations of Patterns

Mathematical Vocabulary

The following is a list of vocabulary found in this chapter. Some of the words you have been seen in previous chapters. The words in bold are the words new to this chapter. Make sure that you are familiar with the terms below and know what they mean. For the words you do not know, refer to the glossary or index. You might also add these words to your Toolkit so that you can reference them in the future.

graph	**growth triangle**	parabola
parameter	rule	solution
tile pattern	variable	$x \rightarrow y$ table
y-intercept		

Answers and Support for Closure Problems
What Have I Learned?

Note: MN = Math Note; LL = Learning Log

Problem	Solution	Need Help?	More Practice
CL 4-72.		Sections 3.1 and 4.1 MN: 4.1.7 LL: 4.1.2	Problems 4-12, 4-13, 4-15, 4-25, 4-37, 4-38, 4-42, 4-54, 4-64, and 4-65

a.

Figure 0

Figure 4

b.

Figure Number	0	1	2	3	4
Number of Tiles	5	11	17	23	29

c. $y = 6x + 5$

d.

Number of Tiles

Figure Number

e. Each figure has 6 more tiles than the previous figure.

f. Figure 100 will have 605 tiles.

Problem	Solution	Need Help?	More Practice
CL 4-73.	Yes; $4x^2 - x - 5 = 4x^2 - x - 5$	MN: 2.1.3, 2.1.5, 2.1.6, and 2.1.7	Problems 3-32, 3-77, and 4-10
CL 4-74.	a. The line goes down as x increases. The y-intercept is at +3. b. See graph at right. c. $y = -2x + 3$	Lessons 4.1.3, 4.1.4, and 4.1.6 MN: 4.1.7 LL: 4.1.3 and 4.1.4	Problems 4-23, 4-32, 4-38, 4-54, 4-55, 4-56, 4-59, and 4-60

Problem	Solution	Need Help?	More Practice
CL 4-75.	a. There are 7 tiles in Figure 0. b. Figure 6 has 37 tiles. c. m represents the growth, and b represents the number of tiles in Figure 0.	Lessons 4.1.2 and 4.1.4 MN: 4.1.7 LL: 4.1.2, 4.1.3, and 4.1.4	Problems 4-14, 4-15, 4-34, 4-36, 4-57, 4-59, 4-61, and 4-67
CL 4-76.	Unit rate = 1.67 pages per minute, 255 minutes	Lessons 1.2.1 and 1.2.2 MN: 1.2.1 and 1.2.2 LL: 1.2.1	Problems 4-18, 4-29, 4-63, and 4-70
CL 4-77.	$x = 3$	Lessons 2.1.8 and 2.1.9 MN: 2.1.3, 2.1.8, and 2.1.9 LL: 2.1.9	Problems 2-75 and 2-83
CL 4-78.	a. $3x^2 + 3x - 3$ b. $-2y^2 + 4x - 9$ c. It cannot be simplified any further. d. $-xy + 30$ e. (a) 87; (b) 3	Lesson 2.1.3 MN: 2.1.3, 2.1.5, and 2.1.6	Problems 4-4, 4-10, and 4-48
CL 4-79.	<table><tr><td>IN (x)</td><td>−4</td><td>−3</td><td>−2</td><td>−1</td></tr><tr><td>OUT (y)</td><td>−22</td><td>−17</td><td>−12</td><td>−7</td></tr></table>*table continued:* <table><tr><td>0</td><td>1</td><td>2</td><td>3</td><td>4</td></tr><tr><td>−2</td><td>3</td><td>8</td><td>13</td><td>18</td></tr></table>a. The starting value is −2. The growth pattern is adding 5. b. $y = 5x - 2$ c. −10	Lesson 4.1.4 MN: 4.1.7	Problems 4-11, 4-33, 4-37, 4-41, and 4-68
CL 4-80.	$5(x + 30) + 3x = 2630$, 310 tickets were sold in advance, and 340 tickets were sold at the door.	MN: 1.1.3 and 3.2.4	Problems 3-7, 3-28, and 3-103

Systems of
Equations

5

CHAPTER 5   Systems of Equations

In the last chapter, you worked with the connections between different representations of patterns. In this chapter, most of your work will focus on rules (equations). Specifically, you will focus on how to solve them.

In Section 5.1, you will solve equations with multiple variables for one of the variables, creating an equivalent equation. You will also learn an efficient way to solve equations with fractions or decimals.

In Section 5.2, you will explore situations that can be represented by a line and study what it means when two lines intersect (cross each other). By the end of this chapter, you will know how to use graphs, tables, patterns, and rules to solve almost any problem involving lines.

In this chapter, you will learn:

➤ How to solve multi-variable equations for one of the variables.

➤ How to solve equations with fractional coefficients.

➤ How to find the point where two lines intersect.

➤ How to use the connections between graphs, tables, rules, and patterns to solve problems.

Guiding Questions

Think about these questions throughout this chapter:

How can I solve it?

Is there another way?

In how many different ways can it be represented?

How does the pattern show up in the rule, table, and graph?

How does the pattern grow?

Chapter Outline

$y = mx + b$

Section 5.1 In Section 5.1, you will continue the solving focus that you began in Chapter 3. You will study how to solve multi-variable equations for one of the variables. You will also learn how to solve equations that contain fractions.

Section 5.2 This section will start by examining word problems in which two amounts are compared. You will use your knowledge of graphs and rules to write equations for word problems. Then, using the Equation Mat, you will solve a pair of linear equations to determine where two lines cross.

Core Connections, Course 3

5.1.1 How can I change it to $y=mx+b$ form?

Working with Multi-Variable Equations

So far in this course, you have used your Equation Mat and/or symbols to find solutions for all types of linear equations with one variable. Today you will learn how to apply these skills to solving linear equations with two variables. As you work today, keep these questions in mind:

What is a solution to an equation? What does it look like?

What is the growth pattern?

What is the y-intercept?

5-1. You now have a lot of experience working with equations that compare two quantities. For example, while working with the height of a tree, you found the relationship $y = 4x + 5$, which compared x (the number of years after it was planted) with y (its height in feet). Use the equation for this tree to answer the questions below.

a. What was its starting height? How can you tell from the equation?

b. What was its growth rate? That is, how many feet did the tree grow per year? Justify your answer.

5-2. CHANGING FORMS

You can find the growth rate and starting value for $y = 4x + 5$ quickly, because the equation is in $y = mx + b$ form. But what if the equation is in a different form? Explore this situation below.

a. The line $-6x + 2y = 10$ is written in **standard form**. Can you tell what the growth of the line is? Its y-intercept? Predict these values.

b. The equation $-6x + 2y = 10$ is shown on the Equation Mat at right. Set up this equation on your Equation Mat using tiles. Using only "legal" moves, rearrange the tiles to get y by itself on the left side of the mat. Record each of your moves algebraically.

c. Now use your result from part (b) to find the growth pattern and y-intercept of the line $-6x + 2y = 10$. Did your result match your prediction in part (a)?

5-3.   Your teacher will assign you one of the linear equations listed below. For your equation:

- Use algebra tiles to set up the equation on your Equation Mat.

- Using only "legal" moves, rearrange your tiles to create an equation that starts with "$y = \ldots$" Be sure to record all of your moves algebraically and be prepared to share your steps with the class.

- What is the pattern of growth for your line? What is the y-intercept? How can you tell?

a. $2x + y = 3x - 7$ b. $x + 2y = 3x + 4$

c. $3y + 2 = 2y - 5x$ d. $2(y - 3) = 2x - 6$

e. $5 - 3(x + 1) = 2y - 3x + 2$ f. $x - (y + 2) = 2(2x + 1)$

5-4.   Solve each of the following equations for the indicated variable. Use your Equation Mat if it is helpful. Write down each of your steps algebraically.

a.   Solve for y: $2(y - 3) = 4$

b.   Solve for x: $2x + 5y = 10$

c.   Solve for y: $6x + 3y = 4y + 11$

d.   Solve for x: $3(2x + 4) = 2 + 6x + 10$

e.   Solve for x: $y = -3x + 6$

f.   Solve for p: $m = 8 - 2(p - m)$

g.   Solve for q: $4(q - 8) = 7q + 5$

h.   Solve for y: $x^2 + 4y = 2(3x - 6 - x) + x^2$

METHODS AND MEANINGS

Linear Equations

MATH NOTES

A **linear equation** is an equation that forms a line when it is graphed. This type of equation may be written in several different forms. Although these forms look different, they are equivalent; that is, they all graph the same line.

Standard form: An equation in $ax + by = c$ form, such as $-6x + 3y = 18$.

$y = mx + b$ **form:** An equation in $y = mx + b$ form, such as $y = 2x + 6$.

You can quickly find the **growth** and **y-intercept** of a line in $y = mx + b$ form. For the equation $y = 2x - 6$, the growth is 2, while the y-intercept is $(0, -6)$.

$$y = 2x - 6$$

growth   y-intercept

5-5.   A tile pattern has 5 tiles in Figure 0 and adds 7 tiles in each new figure. Write the equation of the line that represents the growth of this pattern.

5-6.   Solve each equation below for the indicated variable, if possible. Show all steps.

a.   Solve for x: $2x + 22 = 12$ b.   Solve for y: $2x - y = 3$

c.   Solve for x: $2x + 15 = 2x - 15$ d.   Solve for y: $6x + 2y = 10$

5-7.   Solve each of the following equations for x. Then check each solution.

a. $\frac{x}{16} = \frac{7}{10}$ b. $\frac{6}{15} = \frac{3}{x}$ c. $\frac{2x}{5} = \frac{12}{8}$ d. $-8 = \frac{2}{x}$

5-8.   Graph the lines $y = -4x + 3$ and $y = x - 7$ on the same set of axes. Then find their point of intersection.

5-9.   Draw Figures 1, 2, and 3 for a tile pattern that could be described by $y = -3x + 10$.

5.1.2 How can I eliminate fractions in equations?

Solving Equations with Fractions

Earlier in this course, you worked with proportions such as $\frac{3}{5} = \frac{x}{8}$. One way to begin solving a proportion is to eliminate the fractions and create an equivalent equation. When you eliminate the fractions, it is easier to solve.

Fraction elimination is not just for proportions, however. It also applies to other equations with fractions. In this lesson, you will learn how to eliminate fractions in equations. Then you will be able to use what you learned about solving equations to complete the problems.

5-10.   Hannah wants to solve $0.04x + 1 = 2.2$. *"I think that I need to use my calculator because of the decimals,"* she told Michael. Suddenly Hannah blurted out, *"No, wait! What was the way we learned to rewrite a proportion equation without fractions? Maybe we can use that idea here to get rid of the decimals."*

a.   What is Hannah talking about? Explain what she means. Then rewrite the equation so that it has no decimals.

b.   Now solve the new equation (the one with no decimals). Check your solution.

5-11.   Rewriting $0.04x + 1 = 2.2$ in the previous problem gave you a new, equivalent equation that was easier to solve. If needed, review the Math Notes box in this lesson for more information about equivalent equations.

How can each equation below be rewritten so that it is easier to solve? With your team, find an equivalent equation for each equation below. If the original equation has large numbers, make sure the equivalent equation has smaller numbers. If the original equation has fractions or decimals, eliminate the fractions or decimals in the equivalent equation. Solve each new equation and check your answer.

a. $2.1x + 0.6 = 17.4$ b. $100x + 250 = -400$

c. $\frac{2x}{3} = 30$ d. $\frac{x}{5} + 1 = -6$

5-12.   Examine the equation $\frac{x}{3}+\frac{x}{5}=16$, and then answer the questions below.

a.   Multiply each term by 3. What happened? Do any fractions remain?

b.   If you had multiplied each term in the original equation by 5 instead of 3, would you have eliminated all of the fractions?

c.   Find a number that you can use to multiply by all of the terms that will get rid of all of the fractions. How is this number related to the numbers in the equation?

d.   Solve your new equation from part (c) and check your equation.

5-13.   Use the strategy you developed in problem 5-12 to solve each of the following equations.

a. $\frac{a}{7}+\frac{a}{3}=10$ b. $\frac{3y}{5}+\frac{3}{2}=\frac{7y}{10}$

c. $\frac{(2x-3)}{6}=\frac{2x}{3}+\frac{1}{2}$ d. $\frac{b+3}{3}-\frac{b}{4}=\frac{b-2}{5}$

5-14.   Sam can paint an apartment living room in 3 hours, and Pam can paint the same room in 2 hours. The solution to the equation $\frac{x}{3}+\frac{x}{2}=1$ describes how long it will take them to paint the living room if they work together. Before solving this problem, make a guess about the answer. Then solve the equation. How did your guess compare? Most people are surprised with the correct solution!

5-15.   Review your solution to part (b) of problem 5-13. You probably multiplied each fraction by the lowest (least) common denominator (LCD), which, in this case, is 10. But what would you do if you could not determine the LCD? You will explore this idea in parts (a) through (e) below.

a.   Multiply the three denominators: $5 \cdot 2 \cdot 10$.

b.   Multiply both sides of the equation $\frac{3y}{5}+\frac{3}{2}=\frac{7y}{10}$ by the product you got in part (a). This gives you an equivalent equation. Have your partner multiply both sides of the equation by 10 and find a different equivalent equation.

c.   Now, solve your equation for y and check your answer. While you solve your equation, your partner will be solving his or her equation.

d.   Compare your result with your partner's.

e.   Why do both your method and your partner's method work? That is, why do both using the product of the denominators and using the LCD of 10 both successfully eliminate fractions from equations?

Core Connections, Course 3

5-16. Copy the following table on your paper. Fill in each of the lines labeled (a) through (e) to explain how the equation to its left was obtained from the equation above it.

Solving Steps	Explanation
$\frac{4x}{3} + \frac{3x}{2} = \frac{17}{6}$	Original equation
$6\left(\frac{4x}{3} + \frac{3x}{2}\right) = 6\left(\frac{17}{6}\right)$	a.
$6\left(\frac{4x}{3}\right) + 6\left(\frac{3x}{2}\right) = 6\left(\frac{17}{6}\right)$	b.
$8x + 9x = 17$	c.
$17x = 17$	d.
$x = 1$	e.

5-17. LEARNING LOG

In your Learning Log, describe how to create an equivalent equation from an equation that has fractions or decimals. Explain how to decide what number to use to multiply. Also explain any other important things to remember when using this process. Title this entry "Solving Equations with Fractions" and label it with today's date.

ETHODS AND MEANINGS

MATH NOTES

Equivalent Equations

Two equations are **equivalent** if they have all the same solutions. There are many ways to change one equation into a different, equivalent equation. Common ways include: *adding* the same number to both sides, *subtracting* the same number from both sides, *multiplying* both sides by the same number, *dividing* both sides by the same (non-zero) number, and *rewriting* one or both sides of the equation.

For example, the equations below are all equivalent to $2x + 1 = 3$:

$$20x + 10 = 30 \qquad\qquad 2(x + 0.5) = 3$$

$$\frac{2x}{3} + \frac{1}{3} = 1 \qquad\qquad 0.002x + 0.001 = 0.003$$

5-18.   Solve each equation below.

    a. $\frac{x}{2}+\frac{x}{6}=7$ b. $\frac{x}{9}+\frac{2x}{2}=\frac{1}{3}$

5-19.   Fisher thinks that any two lines must have a point of intersection. Is he correct?
          If so, explain how you know. If not, produce a **counterexample** and explain
          your reasoning. (In this case, a counterexample would be an example of two
          lines that do not have a point of intersection.)

5-20.   In the last election, candidate B received twice as
          many votes as candidate A. Candidate C received
          15,000 fewer votes than candidate A. If a total of
          109,000 votes were cast, how many votes did
          candidate B receive?

5-21.   Jamila wants to play a game called "Guess My Line." She gives you the
          following hint: "Two points on my line are (1, 1) and (2, 4)."

    a.   What is the growth rate of her line? A graph of the line may help.

    b.   What is the y-intercept of her line?

    c.   What is the equation of her line?

5-22.   Solve each of the following equations. Be sure to show your work carefully
          and check your answers.

    a. $2(3x-4)=22$ b. $6(2x-5)=-(x+4)$

    c. $2-(y+2)=3y$ d. $3+4(x+1)=159$

5.2.1 When are they the same?

Introduction to Systems of Equations

In Section 4.1, you graphed lines and curves that represented tile patterns. But what happens when you graph two lines at the same time? What can you learn? Today you will use data, graphs, and rules to examine what happens when two lines or curves intersect.

5-23. The Iditarod Trail Sled Dog Race is famous for its incredible length and its use of dogs. The sled drivers, known as mushers, start their dog sleds at Fairbanks, Alaska and ride through the snow for several days until they reach Nome, Alaska. Along the route, there are stations where the competitors check in, so data is kept on the progress of each team.

Joyla and her team of dogs have made it through the first five checkpoints. Her buddy Evie left Nome (the finish line) on the day the race started in an effort to meet Joyla and offer encouragement. Evie traveled along the route toward the racers on her snowmobile. The progress of each person is shown on the graph that follows.

Your Task: With your team, analyze the data on the graph. Consider the questions below as you work. Be prepared to defend your results.

- Which data represents Evie? Which represents Joyla? How can you tell?

- When did Evie meet Joyla?

- How long was the race? How can you tell?

- Who traveled faster? Explain how you know.

- Approximately how long did it take Joyla to finish the race? How did you find your answer?

5-24. The point where two lines (or curves) cross is called a **point of intersection**. Two or more lines (or curves) are called a **system of equations**. When you work with data, points of intersection can be meaningful, as you saw in the last problem.

a. On graph paper, graph $y = 3x - 4$ and $y = -2x + 6$ on the same set of axes.

b. Find the point of intersection of these two lines and label the point with its coordinates; that is, write it in the form (x, y).

c. What is the significance of this point for the two rules in part (a)?

5-25. The meaning of a point of intersection depends on what the graph is describing. For example, in problem 5-23, the point where Joyla's and Evie's lines cross represents when they met during the race.

Examine each of the graphs below and write a brief story that describes the information on the graph. Include a sentence explaining what the point of intersection represents.

a.

b.

c.

d.

5-26. LEARNING LOG

In your Learning Log, write your own situation like the ones in problem 5-25 and make a graph. Have two lines or curves that intersect. Explain what is happening in the graph (like in problem 5-25) and what the point of intersection represents in your situation. Title this entry "Points of Intersection" and label it with today's date.

Core Connections, Course 3

METHODS AND MEANINGS

Solving Equations with Fractions (also known as Fraction Busters)

Example: Solve $\frac{x}{3} + \frac{x}{5} = 2$ for x.

This equation would be much easier to solve if it had no fractions. Therefore, the first goal is to find an equivalent equation that has no fractions.

$$\frac{x}{3} + \frac{x}{5} = 2$$

To eliminate the denominators, multiply both sides of the equation by the common denominator. In this example, the lowest common denominator is 15, so multiplying both sides of the equation by 15 eliminates the fractions. Another approach is to multiply both sides of the equation by one denominator and then by the other.

The lowest common denominator of $\frac{x}{3}$ and $\frac{x}{5}$ is 15.

$$15 \cdot \left(\frac{x}{3} + \frac{x}{5}\right) = 15 \cdot 2$$

$$15 \cdot \frac{x}{3} + 15 \cdot \frac{x}{5} = 15 \cdot 2$$

Either way, the result is an equivalent equation without fractions:

$$5x + 3x = 30$$
$$8x = 30$$

The number used to eliminate the denominators is called a **Fraction Buster**. Now the equation looks like many you have seen before, and it can be solved in the usual way.

$$x = \frac{30}{8} = \frac{15}{4} = 3.75$$

$$\frac{3.75}{3} + \frac{3.75}{5} = 2$$

Once you have found the solution, remember to check your answer.

$$1.25 + 0.75 = 2$$

5-27.   To ride to school, Elaine takes 7 minutes to ride 18 blocks. What is her unit rate (blocks per minute)? Assuming she rides at a constant speed, how long should it take her to go 50 blocks? Justify your answer.

5-28.   Gale and Leslie are riding in a
         friendly 60-mile bike race that
         started at noon. The graph at right
         represents their progress so far.

         a.   What does the intersection
               of the two lines represent?

         b.   At approximately what time did
               Leslie pass Gale?

         c.   About how far had Leslie traveled
               when she passed Gale?

         d.   What do you think happened to Gale between 1:30 and 3:00?

         e.   If Leslie continues at a steady pace, when will she complete the race?

5-29.   Write an equation (rule) for each of the $x \to y$ tables below. Then, on one set of
         axes, use each rule to graph.

a.

x	y
8	23
2	5
−3	−10
9	26
x	

b.

x	y
6	32
−2	−8
0	2
10	52
x	

5-30.   Translate each part below from symbols into words or from words into symbols.

         a. $-y+8$ b. $2x-48$ c. $(x+3)^2$

         d.   The opposite of six times the square of a number.

         e.   A number multiplied by itself, then added to five.

5-31.   Solve each of the following equations for the indicated variable. Show all of
         your steps.

         a. $y=2x-5$ for x b. $p=-3w+9$ for w

         c. $2m-6=4n+4$ for m d. $3x-y=-2y$ for y

Core Connections, Course 3

5.2.2 When are they the same?

Writing Rules from Word Problems

In Lesson 5.2.1, you discovered that the point of intersection of two lines or curves can have an important meaning. Finding points of intersection is another strategy you can use to solve problems, especially those with two quantities being compared.

Analyze the following situations using the multiple tools you have studied so far.

5-32.   BUYING BICYCLES

Latanya and George are saving up money because they both want to buy new bicycles. Latanya opened a savings account with $50. She just got a job and is determined to save an additional $30 a week. George started a savings account with $75. He is able to save $25 a week.

Your Task: Use at least two different ways to find the time (in weeks) when Latanya and George will have the same amount of money in their savings accounts. Be prepared to share your methods with the class.

5-33.   Did you graph the scenario in problem 5-32? If not, graph a line for Latanya and another line for George on the same set of axes. Confirm your answer to problem 5-32 on the graph. Consider the questions below to help you decide how to set up the graph.

- What should the *x*-axis represent? What should the *y*-axis represent?

- How should the axes be scaled?

- Should the amounts in the savings accounts be graphed on the same set of axes or graphed separately? Why?

5-34.   If you have not done so already, consider how to use rules to confirm the point
         of intersection for Latanya's and George's lines.

   a.   Write a rule for Latanya's savings account.

   b.   Write a rule for George's savings account.

   c.   Use the rules to check your solution to problem 5-32.

5-35.   Gerardo decided to use tables to find the point of intersection of the lines
         $y = 4x - 6$ and $y = -2x + 3$. His tables are shown below.

$y = 4x - 6$

IN (x)	−3	−2	−1	0	1	2	3
OUT (y)	−18	−14	−10	−6	−2	2	6

$y = -2x + 3$

IN (x)	−3	−2	−1	0	1	2	3
OUT (y)	9	7	5	3	1	−1	−3

   a.   Examine his tables. Is there a common point that makes both rules true?
         If not, can you describe where the point of intersection is?

   b.   Now graph the rules on the same set of axes. Where do the lines intersect?

   c.   Use the rules to confirm your answer to part (b).

METHODS AND MEANINGS

MATH NOTES

Systems of Equations Vocabulary

The point where two lines or
curves intersect is called a **point of
intersection**. This point's significance
depends on the context of the problem.

Two or more lines or curves used to find
a point of intersection are called a **system
of equations**. A system of equations can
represent a variety of contexts and can be
used to compare how two or more things are related. For example, the
system of equations graphed above compares the temperature in two
different cities over time.

5-36.   It is the end of the semester, and the clubs at school
         are recording their profits. The Science Club started
         out with $20 and has increased its balance by an
         average of $10 per week. The Math Club has saved
         $5 per week after starting out with $50 at the
         beginning of the semester.

   a.   Create an equation for each club. Let x
         represent the number of weeks and y represent
         the balance of the club's account.

   b.   Graph both lines on one set of axes. When do the clubs have the same
         balance?

   c.   What is the balance at that point?

5-37.   Examine the rectangle formed with algebra tiles at right.

   a.   Find the area of the entire rectangle. That is, what is the
         sum of the areas of the algebra tiles?

   b.   Find the perimeter of the entire rectangle. Show all work.

5-38.   On graph paper, plot the points $(-3, 7)$ and $(2, -3)$ and draw a line through
         them. Then name the x- and y-intercepts of the line.

5-39.   A local restaurant offers a Dim Sum lunch
         special that includes two dumplings, three
         egg rolls, a sweet bun, and a drink. Susan
         and her friends ordered four Dim Sum lunch
         specials.

         How many of each item should they receive?

5-40.   Solve for x.

   a. $\frac{x}{2} + \frac{x}{5} = 1$ b. $\frac{x}{3} + \frac{x-1}{4} = 2 + x$

5.2.3 When are they the same?

Solving Systems Algebraically

So far in Section 5.2, you have solved systems of equations by graphing two lines and finding where they intersect. However, it is not always convenient (nor accurate) to solve by graphing.

Today you will explore a new way to approach solving a system of equations. Questions to ask your teammates today include:

How can you find a rule?

How can you compare two rules?

How can you use what you know about solving?

5-41.   CHUBBY BUNNY

Use tables and a graph to find and check the solution for the problem below.

Barbara has a bunny that weighs 5 pounds and gains 3 pounds per year. Her cat weighs 19 pounds and gains 1 pound per year. When will the bunny and the cat weigh the same amount?

5-42.   SOLVING SYSTEMS OF EQUATIONS ALGEBRAICALLY

In problem 5-41, you could write rules like those shown below to represent the weights of Barbara's cat and bunny. For these rules, x represents the number of years and y represents the weight of the animal.

$$y = \underbrace{5 + 3x}_{\substack{\text{weight of} \\ \text{bunny}}} \quad \text{and} \quad y = \underbrace{19 + x}_{\substack{\text{weight of} \\ \text{cat}}}$$

Since you want to know when the weights of the cat and bunny are the same, you can use an Equation Mat to represent this relationship, as shown at right.

a.   Problem 5-41 asked you to determine when the weight of the cat and the bunny are the same. Therefore, you want to determine when the expressions on the left (for the bunny) and the right (for the cat) are equal. Write an equation that represents this balance.

b.   Solve your equation for x, which represents years. According to your solution, how many years will it take for the bunny and the cat to weigh the same number of pounds? Does this answer match your answer from the graph of problem 5-41?

c.   How much do the cat and bunny weigh at this time?

5-43.   CHANGING POPULATIONS

Post Falls High School in Idaho
has 1160 students and is growing
by 22 students per year.
Richmond High School in Indiana
has 1900 students and is shrinking
by 15 students per year.

a.   Without graphing, write a rule that represents the population at Richmond
      High School and another rule that represents the population at Post Falls
      High School. Let x represent years and y represent population.

b.   Graphing the rules for part (a) is challenging because of the large numbers
      involved. Using a table could take a long time. Therefore, this problem is
      a good one to solve algebraically, the way you solved problem 5-42.

      Use the rules together to write an equation that represents when these high
      schools will have the same population. Then solve your equation to find
      out when the schools' populations will be the same.

c.   What will the population be at that time?

5-44.   PUTTING IT ALL TOGETHER

Find the solution to the problem below by graphing and also by solving an
equation. The solutions using both methods should match, so be sure to review
your work carefully if the results disagree.

Imagine that your school planted two trees when it was first opened. One tree,
a ficus, was 6 feet tall when it was planted and has grown 1.5 feet per year. The
other tree, an oak, was grown from an acorn on the ground and has grown 2 feet
per year. When will the trees be the same height? How tall will the trees be
when they are the same height?

5-45.   Ms. Harlow calls the method you have been using today to solve equations the
         Equal Values Method. Explain why this name makes sense.

5-46.   LEARNING LOG

In your Learning Log, describe how to find the
intersection point or solution of two equations when they
are written in the form $y = \dots$. Create an example and
show how to solve it. Title this entry "Equal Values
Method" and label it with today's date.

MATH NOTES

METHODS AND MEANINGS

The Equal Values Method

The **Equal Values Method** is a non-graphing method to find the point of
intersection or solution to a system of equations.

Start with two equations in $y = mx + b$ form,
such as $y = -2x + 5$ and $y = x - 1$. Take the two
expressions that equal y and set them equal to
each other. Then solve this new equation to
find x. See the example at right.

$$-2x + 5 = x - 1$$
$$-3x = -6$$
$$x = 2$$

Once you know the x-coordinate of the point of
intersection, substitute your solution for x into
either original equation to find y. In this
example, the first equation is used.

$$y = -2x + 5$$
$$y = -2(2) + 5$$
$$y = 1$$

A good way to check your solution is to
substitute your solution for x into *both*
equations to verify that you get equal y-values.

$$y = x - 1$$
$$y = (2) - 1$$
$$y = 1$$

Write the solution as an ordered pair to
represent the point on the graph where the
equations intersect.

$$(2, 1)$$

5-47.   Ariyonne claims that $(3, 6)$ is the point of intersection of the lines $y = 4x - 2$ and $y = \frac{1}{2}x + 5$. Is she correct? How do you know?

5-48.   Graph the lines $y = 2x - 3$ and $y = -x + 3$.

   a.   Where do they intersect? Label the point on the graph.

   b.   Find the point of intersection using the Equal Values Method. That is, start by combining both equations into one equation that you can solve for x.

   c.   Which method is easier for you, graphing or using algebra to solve?

5-49.   Solve for the variable.

   a. $\frac{7y}{8} - \frac{3y}{5} = \frac{11}{2}$ b. $\frac{a+4}{3} - \frac{a}{7} = \frac{a+7}{5}$

5-50.   Graph the lines $y = 2x - 3$ and $y = 2x + 1$.

   a.   Where do they intersect?

   b.   Solve this system using the Equal Values Method.

   c.   Explain how your graph and algebraic solution relate to each other.

5-51.   Janelle came to bat 464 times in 131 games. At this rate, how many times should she expect to have at bat in a full season of 162 games?

5.2.4 What if systems are not in $y = mx + b$ form?

Strategies for Solving Systems

You have been introduced to systems of linear equations that are used to represent various situations. You have used the Equal Values Method to solve systems algebraically. Just as in linear equations you found that sometimes there were no solutions or an infinite number of solutions, today you will discover how this same situation occurs for systems of equations.

5-52.   Sara has agreed to help with her younger sister's science fair experiment. Her sister planted string beans in two pots. She is using a different fertilizer in each pot to see which one will grow the tallest plant. Currently, plant A is 4 inches tall and grows $\frac{2}{3}$ inch per day, while plant B is 9 inches tall and grows $\frac{1}{2}$ inch per day. If the plants continue growing at these rates, in how many days will the two plants be the same height? Which plant will be tallest in six weeks? Write a system of equations and solve.

5-53.   Felipe applied for a job. The application process required him to take a test of his math skills. One problem on the test was a system of equations, but one of the equations not in $y = mx + b$ form. The two equations are shown below.

$$y = \tfrac{2}{5}x - 5$$
$$3x + 2y = 9$$

Work with your team to find a way to solve the equations using the Equal Values Method.

5-54.   Using the Equal Values Method can lead to messy fractions. Sometimes this cannot be avoided. But some systems of equations can be solved by simply examining them. This approach is called **solving by inspection**. Consider the two cases below.

Case I: $3x + 2y = 2$ Case II: $2x - 5y = 3$
$3x + 2y = 8$ $4x - 10y = 6$

a.   Compare the left sides of the two equations in Case I. How are they related?

b.   Use the Equal Values Method for solving a system of equations, write a relationship for the two right sides of the equations in Case I, and explain your result.

c.   Graph the two equations in Case I to confirm your result for part (b) and to see how the graphs of the two equations are related.

d.   Recall that a **coefficient** is a number multiplied by a variable and that a **constant term** is a number alone.

Compare the coefficients of x, the coefficients of y, and the two constant terms in the equations in Case II. How is each pair of integers related?

e.   Half of your team should multiply the coefficients and constant term in the first equation of Case II by 2 and then solve the system using the Equal Values Method. The other half of your team should divide all three values in the second equation of Case II by 2 and then solve using the Equal Values Method. Compare the results from each method. What does your result mean?

f.   Graph the two equations in Case II to confirm your result in part (e).

5-55.   **Additional Challenge:** At the beginning of 1990, oil prices were $20 a barrel. Some oil investors predicted that the price of oil would increase by $2.25 a barrel per year.

In the beginning of 2005, the price of oil was $30 a barrel. With increasing demand for oil around the world, oil investors in 2005 predicted that the price of oil would increase by $5.00 a barrel each year.

a.   Let x represent the number of years since 2005. Write an equation that predicts the price of oil, y, using the information available in 2005.

b.   Investors in 1990 did not have the benefit of the 2005 information. Write an equation that represents the prediction made in 1990, using the same variables as in part (a). Remember that x represents the number of years *since 2005*.

c.   Use the equations you wrote in parts (a) and (b) to determine when the cost of a barrel of oil would be the same for both price predictions.

d.   In the spring of 2011, a barrel of oil was selling for about $112. Which prediction was closer? Was it a pretty good prediction?

5-56.   Felipe's sister thought that he should try some more complicated systems of equations. Use what you learned in part (b) of problem 5-53 to solve these two systems of equations.

a. $x = 3 + 3y$
        $2x + 9y = 11$

b. $x - \frac{y}{2} = -1$
        $x + y = -7$

METHODS AND **M**EANINGS

MATH NOTES

Solutions to a System of Equations

A **solution** to a system of equations gives a value for each variable that makes both equations true. For example, when 4 is substituted for x and 5 is substituted for y in both equations at right, both equations are true. So $x = 4$ and $y = 5$ or $(4, 5)$ is a solution to this system of equations. When the two equations are graphed, $(4, 5)$ is the point of intersection.

System with one solution: intersecting lines
$$x - y = -1$$
$$2x - y = 3$$

Some systems of equations have no solutions or infinite solutions. Consider the examples at right.

System with no solution: parallel lines
$$x + y = 3$$
$$x + y = 4$$

Notice that the Equal Values Method would yield $3 = 4$, which is never true. When the lines are graphed, they are parallel. Therefore, the system has **no solution**.

In the third set of equations, the second equation is just the first equation multiplied by 2. Therefore, the two lines are really the same line and have **infinite solutions**.

System with infinite solutions: coinciding lines
$$x + y = 3$$
$$2x + 2y = 6$$

Review & Preview

5-57. Determine the coordinates of each point of intersection without graphing.

a. $y = -x + 8$
$y = x - 2$

b. $y = -3x$
$y = -4x + 2$

Chapter 5: Systems of Equations

209

5-58. Change each equation below into $y = mx + b$ form.

    a. $y - 4x = -3$ b. $3y - 3x = 9$

    c. $3x + 2y = 12$ d. $2(x - 3) + 3y = 0$

5-59. Mailboxes Plus sends packages overnight for $5 plus $0.25 per ounce. United Packages charges $2 plus $0.35 per ounce. Mr. Molinari noticed that his package would cost the same to mail using either service. How much does his package weigh?

5-60. Solve for x.

    a. $\frac{2}{3} = \frac{x}{4}$ b. $\frac{2}{3} = \frac{x}{4} + \frac{x}{3}$

    c.   How are these problems the same and how are they different?

5-61. This problem is a checkpoint for solving equations. It will be referred to as Checkpoint 5.

Solve each equation.

    a. $3x + 7 = -x - 1$ b. $1 - 2x + 5 = 4x - 3$

    c. $-2x - 6 = 2 - 4x - (x - 1)$ d. $3x - 4 + 1 = -2x - 5 + 5x$

Check your answers by referring to the Checkpoint 5 materials located at the back of your book.

Ideally, at this point you are comfortable working with these types of problems and can solve them correctly. If you feel that you need more confidence when solving these types of problems, then review the Checkpoint 5 materials and try the practice problems provided. From this point on, you will be expected to do problems like these correctly and with confidence.

Chapter 5 Closure   What have I learned?

Reflection and Synthesis

The activities below offer you a chance to reflect about
what you have learned during this chapter. As you work,
look for concepts that you feel very comfortable with,
ideas that you would like to learn more about, and topics
you need more help with.

①   WHAT HAVE I LEARNED?

Doing the problems in this section will help you to evaluate which types of
problems you feel comfortable with and which ones you need more help with.

Solve each problem as completely as you can. The table at the end of this
closure section provides answers to these problems. It also tells you where you
can find additional help and where to find practice problems like them.

CL 5-62. Solve each equation.

    a. $3(2x-1)+7=-44$ b. $6(2x-5)=-(x+4)$

CL 5-63. Solve for the indicated variable.

    a. $2x+5y=10$ (solve for y)   b. $3(x+2)=y-6$ (solve for x)

CL 5-64. Examine the tile pattern below. Then complete parts (a) through (c) that follow.

    a.   Draw Figure 1 and Figure 5.

    b.   Make an $x \rightarrow y$ table for the
        pattern.

            Figure 2   Figure 3   Figure 4

    c.   Make a complete graph. Include points for Figures 0 through 5.

CL 5-65. Use the table at right to
complete parts (a) and (b)
below.

x	−5	−3	−1	1	3	5	7
y			−3	1		9	

    a.   Complete the table.

    b.   Find the rule ($y =$?).

CL 5-66. For each pair of lines below, solve the system first by graphing and then algebraically using the Equal Values Method. Explain how the graph confirms the algebraic result.

  a. $y = 7x - 5$ and $y = -2x + 13$ b. $y = 3x - 1$ and $y = 3x + 2$

CL 5-67. To rent a jet ski at Sam's costs $25 plus $3 per hour. At Claire's, it costs $5 plus $8 per hour. At how many hours will the rental cost at both shops be equal?

  a. Write an equation that represents each shop's charges. What do your variables represent?

  b. Solve the problem. Show your work.

CL 5-68. Solve each equation.

  a. $\frac{x+1}{3} = \frac{x+2}{5}$ b. $\frac{x}{3} + \frac{x}{4} + 1 = \frac{x}{2}$

CL 5-69. For each of the problems above, do the following:

  • Draw a bar or number line that represents 0 to 10.

  • Color or shade in a portion of the bar that represents your level of understanding and comfort with completing that problem on your own.

If any of your bars are less than a 5, choose *one* of those problems and complete one of the following tasks:

  • Write two questions that you would like to ask about that problem.

  • Brainstorm two things that you DO know about that type of problem.

If all of your bars are a 5 or above, choose *one* of those problems and do one of these tasks:

  • Write two questions you might ask or hints you might give to a student who was stuck on the problem.

  • Make a new problem that is similar and more challenging than that problem and solve it.

You have several tools and references available to help support your learning – your teacher, your study team, your math book, and your Toolkit, to name only a few. At the end of each chapter you will have an opportunity to review your Toolkit for completeness as well as to revise or update it to better reflect your current understanding of big ideas.

The main elements of your Toolkit should be your Learning Logs, Math Notes, and the vocabulary used in this chapter. Math words that are new to this chapter appear in bold in the text. Refer to the lists provided below and follow your teacher's instructions to revise your Toolkit, which will help make it a useful reference for you as you complete this chapter and prepare to begin the next one.

Learning Log Entries

- Lesson 5.1.2 – Solving Equations with Fractions
- Lesson 5.2.1 – Points of Intersection
- Lesson 5.2.3 – Equal Values Method

Math Notes

- Lesson 5.1.1 – Linear Equations
- Lesson 5.1.2 – Equivalent Equations
- Lesson 5.2.1 – Solving Equations with Fractions (also known as the Fraction Buster Method)
- Lesson 5.2.2 – Systems of Equations Vocabulary
- Lesson 5.2.3 – The Equal Values Method
- Lesson 5.2.4 – Solutions to a System of Equations

Mathematical Vocabulary

The following is a list of vocabulary found in this chapter. Some of the words you have been seen in previous chapters. The words in bold are the words new to this chapter. Make sure that you are familiar with the terms below and know what they mean. For the words you do not know, refer to the glossary or index. You might also add these words to your Toolkit so that you can reference them in the future.

coefficient	constant term	**counterexample**
Equal Values Method	**equivalent**	**Fraction Buster Method**
growth	**linear equation**	**point of intersection**
solution	**standard form**	**system of equations**
term	variable	*y*-intercept
$y = mx + b$ **form**		

Answers and Support for Closure Problems
What Have I Learned?

Note: MN = Math Note; LL = Learning Log

Problem	Solution	Need Help?	More Practice
CL 5-62.	a. -8 b. 2	Lessons 2.1.8 and 2.1.9 MN: 2.1.8 and 2.1.9 LL: 2.1.9	Problem 5-22
CL 5-63.	a. $y = -\frac{2}{5}x + 2$ b. $x = \frac{1}{3}y - 4$	Lesson 5.1.1 MN: 5.1.1	Problems 5-2, 5-3, 5-4, 5-6, 5-31, and 5-58
CL 5-64.	a. Figure 1 Figure 5 b. 	Section 3.1 MN: 3.2.1 LL: 3.1.6	Problems 3-1, 3-18, 3-58, and 3-84

b.

x	1	2	3	4	5
y	4	7	12	19	28

c.

Note: In this course, tile patterns will represent elements of continuous relationships and will be graphed with a continuous line or curve.

Problem	Solution	Need Help?	More Practice
CL 5-65.	Missing y-values: $-11, -7, 5, 13$ $y = 2x - 1$	Lesson 4.1.4 MN: 4.1.7	Problems 5-29 and 5-35

Problem	Solution	Need Help?	More Practice
CL 5-66.	a. The lines intersect at the point $(2, 9)$.	Lessons 5.2.2 and 5.2.3 MN: 5.2.2, 5.2.3, and 5.2.4	Problems 5-8, 5-23, 5-25, 5-28, 5-32, 5-33, 5-36, 5-44, 5-45, and 5-57
	b. There is no solution to the system of equations, because the lines are parallel.		
CL 5-67.	a. $y = 25 + 3x$ and $y = 5 + 8x$; x represents the number of hours rental, and y represents the cost. b. After 4 hours of ski rental, the cost at both shops will be equal.	Lessons 5.2.2 and 5.2.3 MN: 5.2.2, 5.2.3, and 5.2.4	Problems 5-32, 5-33, 5-36, 5-41, 5-43, 5-44, 5-52, 5-55, and 5-59
CL 5-68.	a. $\frac{1}{2}$ b. -12	Lesson 5.1.2 MN: 5.2.1	Problems 5-7, 5-11, 5-13, 5-16, 5-18, 5-49, and 5-40

5.3 How can I use it? What is the connection?

Mid-Course Reflection Activities

The activities in this section review several major topics you have studied so far. As you work, think about the topics and activities that you have done during the first half of this course and how they connect to each other. Also think about which concepts you are comfortable using and those with which you need more practice.

As you work on this activity, keep these questions in mind:

What mathematical concepts have you studied in this course so far?

What do you still want to know more about?

What connections did you find?

5-ML.   SOLUTIONS MEMORY LANE

Have you ever heard someone talk about "taking a trip down memory lane"? People use this phrase to mean taking time to remember things that have happened in the past, especially events that a group of people shared.

As you follow your teacher's directions to visit your mathematical "memory lane," think about all the work with algebra that you have done and what you have learned in your math class so far this year. Your Toolkit should be a useful resource to help you with this activity.

So far in this course, you have learned different ways the solution can appear in a problem. You have learned a lot about what it means to "solve." The exact nature of the solution changes based on whether there are one or two variables and one or two equations in the problem or situation.

Show what you know about the different representations of a solution by doing the following activity with your team.

Problem continues on next page. →

Core Connections, Course 3

5-ML.   *Problem continued from previous page.*

1.   First, work with your team to brainstorm the different ways that you have shown solutions in this course.

2.   Pick or create a problem from the first five chapters that you think can best demonstrate your understanding of each of the different representations of a solution.

3.   Work with your team to show how to solve each of the situations that you have selected.

4.   Obtain poster-making materials from your teacher. Create a poster that clearly shows each different representation of a solution that you and your team have found.

Copy the problems that you have selected onto the poster and show the solutions in as many ways as you can. Be sure to organize and label your work clearly for others to understand it.

5.   Use color or other means to show any connections that you see between each of the representations of a solution.

5-GW.   SITUATIONS GALLERY WALK

In this activity, you will apply what you know about linear situations to answer some challenging questions in real-life situations. The information in each question, parts (a) through (e) below, describes a different situation. All of the situations are linear. That is, when they are graphed, they are lines.

Based on the given information, answer the questions in each problem. Show your answers completely and explain your strategies for answering the questions. You may answer these problems in any order, but make sure you answer each one completely before moving to another problem.

Work together as a team. The more you listen to how other people see the connections and share your own ideas, the more you will know at the end of this challenge. Stick together and be sure to talk through every idea.

Each person will turn in his or her own paper at the end of the activity, showing solutions and explanations to each problem. Your work does *not* need to be identical to your teammates' work, but you should have talked and agreed that all explanations are correct. You will also make a team poster of one situation that your teacher chooses for your team.

Problem continues on next page. →

Problem continued from previous page.

a. SAVING MONEY

Julia has $325 in her savings account. She just got a new job and will be saving money every month. If she always deposits the same amount, how much money will be in her account after she has been saving for five years? (Assume she never spends money from this account.)

Number of Months	Money in Account
...	...
7	$780
8	$845
9	$910
...	...

b. POPULATION GROWTH

The $x \rightarrow y$ table, graph, rule, and words below each describe a different town. Based on the information you are given about each town's population, decide which town is growing the fastest. Explain how you know.

Population of Town

Year	Number of People
1975	32,000
1979	50,000
1980	54,500

Population of Town

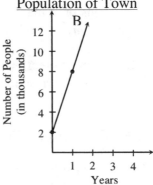

Population of Town C

If $x =$ year and $y =$ number of people, then:

$$y = 46000 - 5200x$$

Population of Town D

Town D is growing. Oddly, the same number of people moves to the town each year. Two years ago, the town had 9100 people. Now the town has 15,500 people.

Problem continues on next page. →

c. FUNDRAISING

The graph at right describes the money two clubs are earning from fundraising. In how many weeks will the two clubs have the same amount of money? Explain your thinking completely.

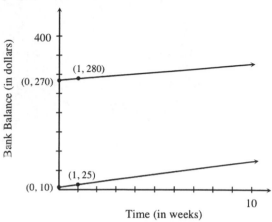

d. STORY TIME

The graph and $x \to y$ tables below describe a situation. Write a story that fits the given information. Show the connections between the information you are given and the information in your story. Your story must give meaning to the point of intersection.

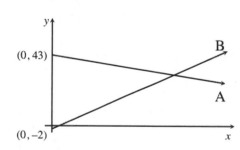

Line A		Line B	
x	*y*	*x*	*y*
⋮	⋮	⋮	⋮
8	11	4	22
9	7	5	28
10	3	⋮	⋮
⋮	⋮		

e. VIDEO RENTAL

Gina has a prepaid video rental card. She currently has a credit of $84 on the card.

The graph at right describes the amount of money there was on the card recently. Use this information to determine:

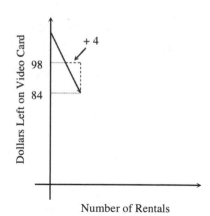

- How much one video rental costs.

- How many more videos can Gina rent before the card is used up.

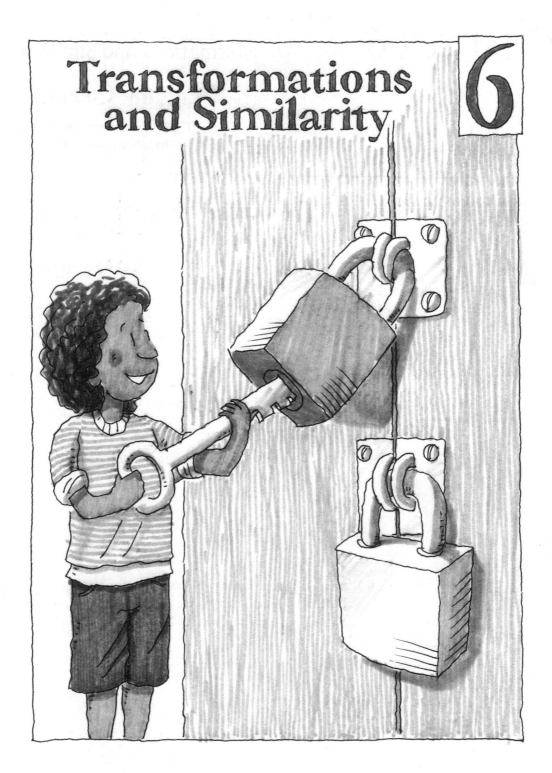

Transformations and Similarity

6

CHAPTER 6   Transformations and Similarity

You may not often take the time to think about how you move objects around as you go about daily life. Many of the movements you make in a given day involve changing directions. In Section 6.1, you will investigate different kinds of motion on a coordinate graph. You will learn how to give directions to slide, flip, turn, and stretch flat shapes. You will also learn how to show where the shapes will be after a series of moves.

In Section 6.2, you will use mathematics you already know to investigate how shapes change size. You will also determine the unknown length of a side in a figure with given information about the lengths of other sides in the figure and in related figures.

Guiding Questions

Think about these questions throughout this chapter:

How can I visualize it?

How can I describe the motion?

How can I transform it?

How do they compare?

What is the relationship?

In this chapter, you will learn how to:

➢ Transform shapes by flipping, turning, and sliding them on a coordinate graph.

➢ Describe movement on a graph using coordinates and expressions.

➢ Compare shapes and use similarity to find missing side lengths of polygons, especially triangles.

Chapter Outline

Section 6.1 You will use a technology tool to move a shape on a coordinate graph using slides, flips, and turns, and will use integers to describe those moves.

Section 6.2 This section will introduce similarity and congruence for polygons.

6.1.1 How can I move a shape on a grid?

Rigid Transformations

How can you describe the movement of a figure on a flat surface when it is not moving in a straight line? For example, when you need to move a loose puzzle piece into the puzzle (as shown at right), how can you describe the way its position changes?

Today you will explore mathematical ways of sliding, turning, and flipping an object without changing its size or shape. These types of movements are called **rigid transformations**. You will solve challenge problems as you explore the transformations.

6-1. KEY-IN-THE-LOCK PUZZLES

Are you ready for a puzzle challenge? You will use the technology tool "Rigid Transformations" (also available at www.cpm.org/students/technology). Your job will be to move the key to the keyhole to unlock the door, using the transformation buttons shown at right.

You will need to tell the computer about how you want the key to move. For example, how far to the left or right and how far up or down do you want the key to slide? In which direction do you want your key to flip?

Your Task: For each puzzle, move the key to the keyhole. Remember that to unlock the door, the key must fit exactly into the keyhole and not be upside down. Also note that your key will not be able to move through walls.

Be sure to record your moves on the Lesson 6.1.1 Resource Page.

Discussion Points

In what direction does the key need to move?

How can we get the key to fit the keyhole?

What information do we need to give the computer so that it moves the key into the lock?

6-2.   Describe what moves you could use to create the transformation of the original image shown at right.

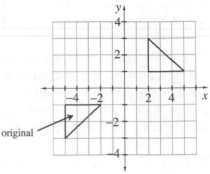

6-3.   Review what you know about graphs as you complete parts (a) through (d) below.

a.   Find the equation of the line graphed at right.

b.   What are its x- and y-intercepts?

c.   On your own graph paper, graph the line.

d.   On the same set of axes, graph a line that is *parallel* to the line graphed at right and that goes through the *origin* $(0, 0)$. Find the equation of this new line.

6-4.   Which equation below has *no* solution? Explain how you know.

a. $4(x+1) = 2x+4$

b. $9-5x+2 = 4-5x$

6-5.   Rena says that if $x = -5$, the equation below is true. Her friend, Dean, says the answer is $x = 3$. Who is correct? Justify your conclusion.

$$9(x+4) = 1+2x$$

6-6.   Find the rule for the pattern represented at right.

Figure 1

Core Connections, Course 3

6-7.   Homer the Hungry Hippo is munching on the
         lily pads in his pond. When he got to the
         pond, there were 30 lily pads, but he is eating
         5 lily pads an hour. Henrietta the Hungrier
         Hippo found a better pond with 38 lily pads!
         She eats 7 lily pads every hour.

   a.   If Homer and Henrietta start eating at the same time, when will their ponds
         have the same number of lily pads remaining?

   b.   How many lily pads will be left in each pond at that time?

Rigid Transformations on a Coordinate Graph

Have you ever had trouble giving directions? Sometimes describing where something is or how it has moved is difficult. For this reason, people often use coordinate graphs like the one shown at right. Coordinate graphs help you describe directions with words like "left" and "down." They can also help you measure distances.

Today you will work with your team to describe movement on a coordinate graph. You will also look at ways to describe where an object is on the grid before and after a transformation. As you work, use the questions below to help start math discussions with your team members.

Is there a different way to get the same result?

Did we give enough information?

How can we describe the position?

6-8.   While solving the key challenge in Lesson 6.1.1, Rowan made more than one move to change his key from point *A* to point *B* and from point *C* to point *D*, as shown on the graph at right. Both of these keys are shown as triangles on the Lesson 6.1.2 Resource Page.

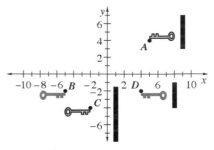

Your Task: With your team, describe how Rowan could have moved each key from the starting position to the ending position using slides (also called **translations**), turns (also called **rotations**), and/or flips (also called **reflections**).

- Make sure you provide enough detail to describe the moves completely.

- Try to find more than one way he could have moved each key.

- Be ready to justify your ideas with the class.

6-9.   **WHERE DOES IT LAND?**

Felicia found a copy of a puzzle like the one in problem 6-1, but the lock is missing. All she has are the starting points and the moves to unlock the lock. This time her key is shaped like a triangle.

The points are at A(−5, 0), B(−5, 3), and C(−1, 0).

Step 1:   Translate 4 units to the right and 2 units up.

Step 2:   Reflect across the x-axis.

Step 3:   Rotate counter-clockwise 90° about point (3, −2).

Help Felicia find out where the lock is by following her steps. The following questions are designed to help you.

a. With your team, set up your own coordinate graph on graph paper. The questions below will help.

   • How many quadrants (regions) should the graph have? Should it be a graph with only the first quadrant? Or a graph with four quadrants?

   • How should the axes be scaled? How many units should you use for each side length of a grid square?

b. Plot triangle *ABC* to represent the key.

c. Follow Step 1 to translate the triangle. Name the new location of each vertex, or corner, of the triangle in the form (x, y).

d. Complete Step 2. Sketch the triangle in its new position and label the coordinates of each vertex.

e. Where does Felicia's triangle end up? Complete Step 3 on the graph and label the coordinates of each vertex.

6-10.   Now compare the triangle in problem 6-9 that you have after Step 3 with the original triangle. How do the lengths of the sides compare? How do the sizes of the angles compare?

6-11.   Could Felicia's team have used different steps to "unlock" her puzzle in problem 6-9? In other words, could she have used different moves and still have the key end up in the same final position?

- If it is possible, list a new set of steps that would move her key from the same starting location to the same final position.

- If it is not possible, explain why not.

6-12.   On graph paper, draw a coordinate graph with *x*- and *y*-axes. Graph shapes A, B, and C as described below.

a.   Shape A is a triangle with vertices $(1,1)$, $(3,3)$, and $(2,4)$.

b.   Shape B is a square with vertices $(2,-1)$, $(4,-1)$, $(2,-3)$, and $(4,-3)$.

c.   Shape C is a rectangle with vertices $(-3,1)$, $(-3,4)$, $(-1,4)$, and $(-1,1)$.

6-13.   On the same grid you used in problem 6-12, translate triangle A four units right and three units up to create triangle D. Write the coordinates of the new vertices.

6-14.   Graph each equation below on the same set of axes and label the point of intersection with its coordinates.

$$y = 2x + 3 \qquad\qquad y = x + 1$$

6-15.   Shooter Marilyn is the Spartans' best free-throw shooter. She normally makes three out of every four shots. In an upcoming charity event, Shooter will shoot 600 free-throws. If she makes over 400 baskets, the school wins $1000. Should the Spartans expect to win the cash for the school? Show and organize your work.

6-16.   Examine the tile pattern shown at right.

Figure 1   Figure 2   Figure 3

a.   On graph paper, draw Figure 0 and Figure 4.

b.   How many tiles will Figure 10 have? Justify your answer.

6-17.   GETTING IN SHAPE

Frank weighs 160 pounds and is on a diet to gain two pounds a week so that he can make the football team. John weighs 208 pounds and is on a diet to lose three pounds a week so that he can be on the wrestling team in a lower weight class.

a.   If Frank and John can meet these goals with their diets, when will they weigh the same, and how much will they weigh at that time?

b.   Clearly explain your method.

6.1.3 How can I describe it?

Describing Transformations

In Lesson 6.1.2, you used words and coordinate points to describe how a triangle moved on a graph. These expressions described the starting place, the motion, and the point where the triangle ended up. Today, you will write similar expressions to describe transformations on a grid.

6-18.   Rosa changed the position of quadrilateral *ABCD* to that of quadrilateral *WXYZ*. "*How did the coordinates of the points change?*" she wondered.

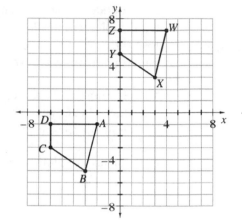

a.   Describe how Rosa transformed *ABCD*. Was the shape translated (slid), rotated (turned), or reflected (flipped)? Explain how you know.

b.   How far did *ABCD* move? In which direction?

c.   Point *B* became point *X*. What are the coordinates of points *B* and *X*? Name them using (x, y) notation.

d.   How did the *x*-coordinate of point *B* change? How did its *y*-coordinate change? For each coordinate, write an equation using addition to show the change.

e.   Visualize translating *WXYZ* 10 units to the right and 12 units up. Where will point *X* end up? *Without counting on the graph*, work with your team to find the new coordinates of point *Y*. Write equations using addition to show the change.

6-19.   Rosa translated a different shape on a grid. Use the clues below to figure out how her shape was moved.

a.   The point $(4, 7)$ was translated to $(32, -2)$. Without graphing, describe how the shape moved on the grid.

b.   Another point on her original shape was $(-16, 9)$. After the translation, where did this point end up? For each coordinate, write an equation using addition to show the change.

6-20.   Rowan transformed quadrilateral *CDEF* below to get the quadrilateral *PQRS*.

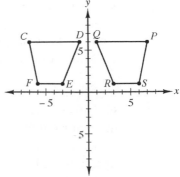

a.   Describe how Rowan transformed the quadrilateral. Was the shape translated, rotated, or reflected? Explain how you know.

b.   Rowan noticed that the *y*-coordinates of the points did not change. What happened to the *x*-coordinates? Compare the *x*-coordinate of point *D* with the *x*-coordinate of point *Q*. Do the same with points *E* and *R* and with points *F* and *S* and with points *C* and *P*. What do you notice?

c.   Can you describe the change to all of the *x*-coordinates with addition like you did in problems 6-18 and 6-19? If not, what other operation could you use? Explain.

d.   What parts of quadrilateral *CDEF* are the same as quadrilateral *PQRS*? How can you show that the corresponding angles are the same measure and the parallel sides remain parallel?

6-21.   Imagine that Rowan reflected quadrilateral *CDEF* from problem 6-20 across the *x*-axis instead. What do you think would happen to the coordinates in that case?

a.   First visualize how the quadrilateral will reflect across the *x*-axis.

b.   Set up a four-quadrant coordinate graph on graph paper and plot quadrilateral *CDEF* from problem 6-20.

c.   Reflect quadrilateral *CDEF* across the *x*-axis to get quadrilateral *JKLM*.

d.   Compare the coordinates of point *C* with point *J*, point *D* with point *K*, point *E* with point *L*, and point *F* with point *M*. What do you notice? How can you use multiplication to describe this change?

6-22.   In problem 6-20, Rowan noticed that multiplying the *x*-coordinates by –1 reflects the shape across the *y*-axis.

a.   Test this strategy on a triangle formed by the points *A* (–3,5), *B*(1,2), and *C*(0,8). Before you graph, multiply each *x*-coordinate by –1. What are the new points?

b.   Graph your original and new triangle on a new set of axes. Did your triangle get reflected across the *y*-axis?

6-23.   In the last three lessons, you have investigated rigid transformations: reflections, rotations, and translations. What happens to a shape when you perform a rigid transformation? Do the side lengths or angles in the figure change? Do the relationships between the lines (parallel or perpendicular) change? Why do you think reflections, rotations, and translations are called rigid transformations?

6-24.   Stella used three steps to move the key on the graph at right from *A* to *B*. On your graph paper, draw the key at *A*. (A triangle can be used to represent the key.) Then follow the steps Stella wrote below. What was her last move?

1. Slide the key to the right 3 units and up 6 units.

2. Reflect the key across the line *x* = 4.

3. ???

6-25.   **Additional Challenge:** Do you think there is a way to use translations to create a reflection or a rotation? Or can reflections be used to move a shape in the same way as a rotation? To investigate these questions, begin by making a graph like the one below. Then complete parts (a) through (c).

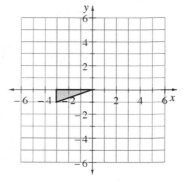

a. Reflect (flip) the triangle across the *x*-axis. Then reflect the new triangle over the *y*-axis.

b. Rotate the original triangle 180° around the point (0,0). What do you notice?

c. Is there a way to use more than one reflection step so that at the end, the triangle looks like it was translated (slid)? If so, describe the combination of moves you would use.

6-26.   LEARNING LOG

In your Learning Log, describe what the terms *translate*, *rotate*, and *reflect* mean in your own words. For each term, demonstrate the movement with a diagram. Title this entry "Rigid Transformations" and include today's date.

METHODS AND MEANINGS

Rigid Transformations

Rigid transformations are ways to move an object while not changing its shape or size. Specifically, they are translations (slides), reflections (flips), and rotations (turns). Each movement is described below.

A **translation** slides an object horizontally (side-to-side), vertically (up or down), or both. To translate an object, you must describe which direction you will move it, and how far it will slide. In the example at right, Triangle A is translated 4 units to the right and 3 units up.

A **reflection** flips an object across a line (called a **line of reflection**). To reflect an object, you must choose a line of reflection. In the example at right, Triangle A is reflected across the *x*-axis.

A **rotation** turns an object about a point. To rotate an object, you must choose a point, direction, and angle of rotation. In the example at right, Triangle A is rotated 90° clockwise (↻) about the origin (0,0).

6-27.   Erin started with one corner of a figure located at $(-4,5)$ and
        translated it to end at $(6,8)$. To find out how far the shape
        moved horizontally, she decided to find the difference between
        the two x-coordinates. She wrote: $6-(-4)$.

a.   When Erin simplified $6-(-4)$, she got 2 as her answer. Is
     this correct? If not, what is the correct simplification?

b.   Write another expression to find out how far the shape moved vertically
     ($\updownarrow$). Simplify both expressions and describe the translation in words.

c.   Describe each of the translations below.

   i. $(3,-2) \rightarrow (5,-9)$ ii. $(-1,4) \rightarrow (6,-2)$

   iii. $(0,0) \rightarrow (-4,-7)$ iv. $(-2,-9) \rightarrow (2,9)$

6-28.   On graph paper, set up x- and y-axes for a four-quadrant graph. Then draw a
        triangle with vertices at $(1,1)$, $(5,1)$, and $(6,3)$. Label this triangle T.

a.   Translate (slide) the triangle left 3 units and down 4 units. Label this
     triangle A and list the vertices.

b.   Reflect triangle T across the y-axis. Label this triangle B and list the
     vertices.

c.   Are triangles T, A, and B **congruent** (that is, do they have the same shape
     and size)? Explain.

6-29.   Change each equation below into $y = mx + b$ form.

a. $y - 4x = -3$ b. $3y - 3x = 9$

c. $3x + 2y = 12$ d. $2(x - 3) + 3y = 0$

Core Connections, Course 3

6-30.   Solve the problem below by defining a variable and then writing and solving an equation.

The perimeter of a triangle is 31 cm. Sides #1 and #2 have equal length, while Side #3 is one centimeter shorter than twice the length of Side #1. How long is each side?

6-31.   Simplify each expression.

a. $\frac{73}{100} \cdot (-\frac{2}{7})$

b. $0.4 \cdot 0.3$

c. $5\frac{1}{9} + 8\frac{2}{5}$

d. $-1.2 + (-\frac{3}{5})$

6-32.   Each part (a) through (d) below represents a different tile pattern. For each, find the pattern of growth and the number of tiles in Figure 0.

a.   b.

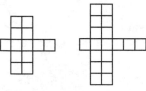

Figure 2   Figure 3   Figure 4

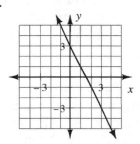

c. $y = 3x - 14$

d.

x	−3	−2	−1	0	1	2	3
y	18	13	8	3	−2	−7	−12

6.1.4 What can I create?

Using Rigid Transformations

In the last several lessons, you have described translations using coordinates. You have also developed strategies for determining where an object started when you know how it was translated and its final position. In this lesson, you will continue to practice transforming objects on a coordinate graph by translating (sliding), rotating (turning), and reflecting (flipping). As you work, visualize what each object will look like after the transformation. Use the graph to check your prediction.

6-33.   BECOMING AN ARTIST

Have you ever seen directions for drawing a cartoon figure such as a face? Usually these directions start by helping you to put some basic shapes together to form an outline. Then they give you ideas for how to finish the drawing. An example showing how you could draw a dinosaur is at right.

Your Task: Obtain Lesson 6.1.4A Resource Page from your teacher. On it, shapes A, B, and C are provided for you. Follow the directions below to create a design. Whenever one of the shapes is mentioned below, start with the original shape on the left side of the paper. The final result of each step is part of the outline of the design.

Once you have finished following all of the directions, describe the picture that is formed. Then use the outline to create a cartoon drawing, complete with color and other details.

- Draw a rectangle with vertices $(5,0)$, $(9,0)$, $(9,8)$, and $(5,8)$.

- Translate circle A so that its center is at $(7,6)$. Describe how the shape moved.

- Rotate (turn) triangle C 180° clockwise about the point $(-6,3)$. Record the coordinates of the new vertices. Then add 15 to each x-coordinate and graph the final result. What transformation does "adding 15" represent?

Problem continues on next page. →

236   *Core Connections, Course 3*

6-33.   *Problem continued from previous page.*

- Reflect (flip) triangle B across the *y*-axis. Record the new coordinates of the vertices. Describe how the coordinates have changed from the original shape.

- A new shape, triangle D, has vertices at $(-7,13)$, $(-8,11)$ and $(-6,11)$. Translate triangle D so that its top vertex is at $(7,4)$. Describe this translation with words.

- Translate triangle C to the right 11 units. Then reflect the result across the horizontal $(\leftrightarrow)$ line that goes through $y = 3$. Record the new coordinates for triangle C.

- Translate circle A so that the *x*-coordinates increase by 13 units and the *y*-coordinates increase by 11 units. Record the coordinates of the center of circle A in its new position.

6-34.   CREATE A DESIGN

Now create your own design using basic shapes A through F on the Lesson 6.1.4C Resource Page. Write complete directions at the bottom of your resource page (such as those in problem 6-33) for creating your design. Make sure you provide all of the necessary information.

6-35.   **Additional Challenge:** Visualize a pattern of squares covering a coordinate graph as show at right. What transformations could you make to move the whole pattern so that the squares and lines in the pattern line up exactly over other squares and lines?

6-36.   Sketch the graph at right on your paper.

a.   Write directions to translate the original triangle to make the new triangle.

b.   What are the coordinates of the vertices (corners) of the new shape?

c.   On your graph, reflect the original triangle across the *y*-axis. What are the coordinates of the new triangle?

6-37.   Make a table and graph for the rule $y = -3x + 1$.

6-38.   Solve the system of equations below using the Equal Values Method.

$$a = 12b + 3$$
$$a = -2b - 4$$

6-39.   Ms. Cai's class is studying a tile pattern. The rule for the tile pattern is $y = 10x + 8$. Kalil thinks that Figure 12 of this pattern will have 108 tiles. Is he correct? Justify your answer.

6-40.   Angel is picking mountain blueberries for a delicious pie. She can pick $\frac{1}{6}$ cup of blueberries in 2 minutes. If she needs $2\frac{1}{2}$ cups of blueberries for the pie, how long will it take her to pick the berries?

6-41.   Juan thinks that the graph of $6y + 12x = 4$ is a line.

a.   Solve Juan's equation for *y*.

b.   Is this equation linear? That is, is its graph a line? Explain how you know.

c.   What are the pattern of growth and *y*-intercept of this graph?

6.2.1 What if I multiply?

Multiplication and Dilation

Remember that when an object is translated, rotated, or reflected, it stays the same size and shape even though it moves. For this reason, these types of movements are called rigid transformations. In this lesson, you will explore a new transformation that changes how the object looks. As you work today, ask these questions in your team:

What parts of the shape are changing? What parts stay the same?

6-42.   When all of the x- or y-coordinates of each vertex of a shape are changed by adding or subtracting the same numbers, the shape translates (slides) to a new position on the coordinate graph. You learned in Lesson 6.1.3 that when one of the coordinates of the vertices (either the x- or y-coordinate) is multiplied by –1, the shape is reflected over the y-axis or the x-axis, respectively.

How do you think the shape will change when both the x- and y-coordinates are multiplied by some number? Use the directions below to help you answer this question.

a.   Plot the following points on graph paper: $(2,1)$, $(3,1)$, $(5,5)$, $(2,5)$. Connect the points to make a quadrilateral.

b.   Without graphing, predict how you think the figure would change if the x- and y-coordinates were multiplied by 2 and then plotted.

c.   Test your prediction by doubling the coordinates from part (a) and plotting them on your graph paper. Was your prediction correct?

d.   With your team members, look at the figure you just graphed. Transforming a graphed shape by multiplying each coordinate by the same number is called a **dilation**. With your team, discuss how this figure compares to the original. Be specific about changes in side length and area!

6-43.   INVESTIGATING DILATIONS

The students in Ms. Stanley's class were studying what happens to the graph of a shape when both coordinates are multiplied by the same number. They came up with these questions:

- *"What happens when each coordinate is multiplied by one-half?"*
- *"What changes when the coordinates are multiplied by 1?"*
- *"What happens when both of the coordinates are multiplied by –1?"*
- *"What happens when the coordinates are multiplied by –2?"*

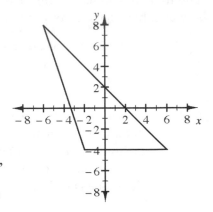

a. Use the shape at right to investigate the questions above. Use graph paper to make the dilations.

b. How did the figure change in each of the investigations? Compare the side lengths, the angles, and the line relationships. Explain what your team learned about the three questions you investigated.

6-44.   In problem 6-43, you investigated questions about multiplying coordinates that were posed by other students.

a. With your team, write a different question about the effect of multiplying the coordinates of a shape on a grid. This question might start with, *"What happens when you multiply…"*

b. Write a **conjecture** — that is, an educated guess based on the evidence in the last two problems — to answer your question.

c. On graph paper, investigate your question, and see if your conjecture is supported, by multiplying the coordinates of the shape in problem 6-43 as you described in your question. What happened? Was your conjecture correct?

6-45.   LEARNING LOG

In your Learning Log, explain how multiplying the coordinates of a shape affects the shape. How does the size of the shape change (or not change)? How do the angles of the shape change (or not change)? Do these results depend on the multiplier that is chosen? Be as specific as you can and include examples to demonstrate your thinking. Title your entry "Dilations" and include today's date.

Core Connections, Course 3

6-46.   Louis is dilating triangle *ABC* at right. He multiplied each *x*-coordinate and *y*-coordinate of triangle *ABC* by –2.

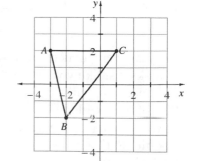

    a.   What are the new coordinates of the points?

    b.   Graph Louis' new triangle.

    c.   Describe how triangle *ABC* changed.

6-47.   On the same set of axes, graph the two rules shown at right. Then find the point(s) of intersection, if one (or more) exists.

$$y = -x + 2$$
$$y = 3x + 6$$

6-48.   Evaluate the expression $6x^2 - 3x + 1$ for $x = -2$.

6-49.   When Ms. Shreve solved an equation in class, she checked her solution and found that it did not make the equation true! Examine her work below and find her mistake. Then find the correct solution.

$$5(2x - 1) - 3x = 5x + 9$$
$$10x - 5 - 3x = 5x + 9$$
$$7x - 5 = 5x + 9$$
$$12x = 4$$
$$x = \frac{1}{3}$$

6-50.   Determine if the statement below is true or false. Justify your conclusion.

$$2(3 + 5x) = 6 + 5x$$

6-51.   Complete the missing entries in the table below. Then write the rule.

IN (*x*)	2	10	6	7	–3		–10	100	*x*
OUT (*y*)	4	28	16			10			

6.2.2 How do shapes change?

Dilations and Similar Figures

Have you ever wondered how different mirrors work? Most mirrors show you a reflection that looks just like you. But other mirrors, like the mirrors commonly found at carnivals and amusement parks, reflect back a face that is stretched or squished. You may look taller, shorter, wider, or narrower. These effects can be created on the computer if you put a picture into a photo program. If you do not follow the mathematical principles of proportionality when you enlarge or shrink a photo, you may find that the picture is stretched thin or spread out, and not at all like the original. Today you will look at enlarging and reducing shapes using dilations to explore why a shape changes in certain ways.

6-52.   UNDOING DILATION

In Lesson 6.2.1, you looked at dilations and multiplied each of the coordinates of a shape to change its size. Now you will explore how to undo dilations.

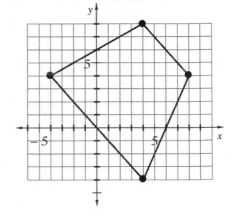

Charlie multiplied each coordinate of the vertices of a shape by 4 to create the dilated shape at right.

a.   If Charlie multiplied to find this shape, what operation would undo his dilation? Why?

b.   On a Lesson 6.2.2A Resource Page, undo the dilation on the graph above. Label the vertices of Charlie's original shape. How does the shape compare to the dilated shape?

6-53.   Alana was also working with dilations. She
wondered, *"What would happen if I multiplied
each coordinate of a shape by $\frac{1}{3}$?"* On the
Lesson 6.2.2A Resource Page, graph and connect
the points below to form her dilated shape. Be
sure to connect them in the order given.

$$(-1,-1) \quad (-1,1) \quad (1,2) \quad (2,-1)$$

a.   Alana graphed this shape by multiplying each of her original coordinates by
$\frac{1}{3}$. What do you think Alana's shape looked like before the dilation? Make
a prediction.

b.   On the same graph, undo the dilation to show Alana's original shape. List
the coordinates of the vertices of Alana's original shape.

c.   What did you do to each coordinate to undo the dilation? How did the
shape change?

d.   Why do you think the shape changed in this way?

6-54.   With your team, look carefully at Alana's dilated and original shapes in
problem 6-53 and describe how the two shapes are related. Use the questions
below to help you.

  •   How are the sides of the small and large shape related?

  •   How many of the small sides does it take to measure the
      corresponding (matching) side of the large shape? Is this true for all
      of the sides?

  •   Compare the four angles of the smaller shape to those of the larger
      shape. What can you say for sure about one matching pair of these
      angles? What appears to be true about the other three pairs?

6-55.   CHANGING SHAPE

When you multiplied each coordinate of a
shape by the same constant, you saw that
sometimes the shape became smaller and
sometimes it became larger. In this chapter,
you moved shapes on a graph without
changing their size or shape by rotating,
reflecting, and translating them. In what other
ways can you change a shape?

Your Task: Work with your team to make predictions about what you could do
to the coordinates of the shape above to make it look stretched or squished, and
what actions will keep the shape the same. Make predictions for the situations
presented below. You will test these predictions in problem 6-56.

Discussion Points

What do you think will change if both the x- and y-coordinates of the points
  P, Q, R, and S are multiplied by the same number, such as 4?

What do you think will happen if only the x-coordinates are multiplied by 3?

What do you think will happen if just the y-coordinates are multiplied by 2?

What do you think will happen if the x- and y-coordinates
are multiplied by different numbers, like 2 for x and 3 for y?

6-56.   Test the predictions your team made in problem 6-55. On the Lesson 6.2.2B
Resource Page, graph each of the shapes described below.

a.   Dilate each coordinate of shape *PQRS* by multiplying each x-coordinate
and each y-coordinate by 4. Graph the dilated shape on the same graph
using a color other than black.

b.   Go back to the original shape, and this time multiply only the x-coordinates
by 3. Leave the y-coordinates the same. Find, graph, and connect the new
coordinates.

c.   What happened to the shape in part (b)? Why did this happen?

d.   Look at the predictions your team made in problem 6-55. Do you still
agree with your predictions? Revise your predictions if necessary, based on
your work so far. What do you think will happen if you multiply only the
y-coordinates of the vertices by a number? Be ready to explain your
reasoning.

6-57.   **Similar figures** are figures that have the same shape, but not necessarily the
same size. One characteristic of similar shapes is that the sides of one shape are
each the same number of times bigger than the corresponding sides of the
smaller shape.

Which pairs of shapes that you have worked with in this lesson are similar and
which are not? Justify your answer using specific examples.

METHODS AND **M**EANINGS

MATH NOTES

Corresponding Parts of Similar Shapes

Two figures are **similar** if they have the same
shape but not necessarily the same size. For example,
all semi-circles are similar, as are all squares, no matter
how they are oriented. Dilations create similar figures.

To check whether figures are similar, you need
to decide which parts of one figure **correspond**
(match up) to which parts of the other. For
example, in the triangles at right, triangle *DEF* is
a dilation of triangle *ABC*. Side *AB* is dilated to
get side *DE*, side *AC* is dilated to get side *DF*,
and side *BC* is dilated to get side *EF*. Side *AB*
corresponds to side *DE*, that is, they are
corresponding sides. Notice that vertex *A*
corresponds to vertex *D*, *C* to *F*, and *B* to *E*.

Not all correspondences are so easily seen.
Sometimes you have to rotate or reflect the shapes
mentally so that you can tell which parts are the
corresponding sides, angles, or vertices. For
example, the two triangles at right are similar, with
R corresponding to *X*, *S* to *Y*, and *T* to *Z*. You can
get triangle *XYZ* from triangle *RST* by a dilation of
$\frac{1}{2}$ followed by a 90° counter-clockwise (↺) turn.

Shapes that are similar and have the same size are called **congruent**.
Congruent shapes have corresponding sides of equal length and
corresponding angles of equal measure. Rigid transformations
(reflections, rotations, and translations), along with dilations with a
multiplier of 1 or -1, create congruent shapes.

6-58.   Create a large coordinate graph on graph paper and graph the triangle at right. Multiply the *y*-coordinate of each point by 4. Then graph the new shape. Make sure you connect your points. List the points for the new shape. Are the two figures similar? Why or why not?

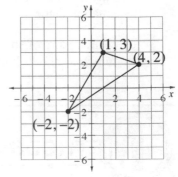

6-59.   Lashayia is famous for her delicious brownies, which she sells at football games. The graph at right shows the relationship between the number of brownies she sells and the amount of money she earns.

   a.   How much should she charge for 10 brownies? Be sure to demonstrate your reasoning.

   b.   During the last football game, Lashayia made $34.20. How many brownies did she sell? Show your work.

6-60.   Figure 3 of a tile pattern has 11 tiles, while Figure 4 has 13 tiles. The pattern grows at a constant rate.

   a.   Write an equation to represent this situation.

   b.   Which figure number will contain 1015 tiles?

6-61.   Normally, the longer you work for a company, the higher your salary per hour. Hector surveyed the people at his company and placed his data in the table below.

Number of Years at Company	1	3	6	7
Salary per Hour	$7.00	$8.50	$10.75	$11.50

a.   Use Hector's data to estimate how much he makes, assuming he has worked at the company for 12 years.

b.   Hector is hiring a new employee who will work 20 hours a week. How much should the new employee earn for the first week?

6-62.   Mr. Greer solved the equation as shown below. However, when he checked his solution, it did not make the original equation true. Find his error and then find the correct solution.

$$4x = 8(2x - 3)$$
$$4x = 16x - 3$$
$$-12x = -3$$
$$x = \frac{-3}{-12}$$
$$x = \frac{1}{4}$$

6-63.   The box plot below shows the different grades (in percents) that students in Ms. Sanchez's class earned on a recent test.

a.   What was the median score on the test? What were the highest and lowest scores?

b.   Did most students earn a particular score? How do you know?

c.   If Ms. Sanchez has 32 students in her class, about how many students earned a grade of 80% or higher? About how many earned more than 90%? Explain how you know.

d.   Can you tell if the scores between 80% and 90% were closer to 80% or closer to 90%? Explain.

6.2.3 Are they similar?

Identifying Similar Shapes

Have you ever noticed how many different kinds of cell phones there are? Sometimes you might have a cell phone that is similar to one of your friends' cell phones because it is the same brand, but it might be a different model or color. Occasionally, two people will have the exact same cell phone, including brand, model, and color. Sorting objects into groups based on what is the same about them is also done in math. As you work with your team to sort shapes, ask the following questions:

How do the shapes grow or shrink?

What parts can we compare?

How can we write the comparison?

6-64.   WHICH SHAPES ARE SIMILAR?

If two shapes appear to have the same general relationship between sides, how can you decide for sure if the shapes are similar? Work with your team to:

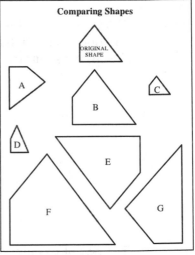

- Carefully cut out the original shape and shapes A through G from one copy of the Lesson 6.2.3 Resource Page.

- Decide how each shape is related to the original shape. (Each person should use an uncut copy of the resource page and the team's cut out shapes to help decide.)

- Compare the angles and the sides of shapes A through G to the original shape.

a. Which shapes are similar to the original shape? Give specific reasons to justify your conclusions.

b. Now look only at the shapes that are similar to the original shape. What do these shapes have in common? What is different about them? Be specific.

c. When two shapes are similar, the **scale factor** is the number you multiply the length of the side of one shape by to get the length of the corresponding side of the new shape. What is the scale factor between the original shape and shape E? Is each side of the shape enlarged the same number of times? Use a ruler to help you decide, if needed.

d. What is the scale factor between the original shape and shape C? Why is it less than 1?

Core Connections, Course 3

6-65.   Shapes that are similar but do not grow or shrink are called **congruent** shapes.

   a.   Which shape from problem 6-64 is exactly equal to the original shape in every way?

   b.   Record the pairs of shapes below that appear to be congruent to each other.

   c.   Get a piece of tracing paper from your teacher and use it to check that the shapes you identified as congruent have exactly the same size and shape. Were you correct? If not, why not?

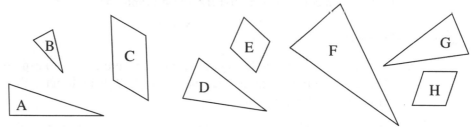

6-66.   Quan enlarged shape Q to make shape P, below. Are his shapes similar? If they are similar, identify the scale factor (multiplier). If they are not, demonstrate that at least one pair of sides does not share the scale factor.

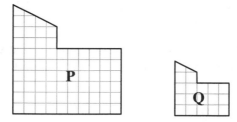

6-67.   Draw each of the shapes in problem 6-66 on graph paper. Color-code the corresponding sides on each shape using the colors suggested by your teacher.

   a.   Compare the green sides of each shape. What do you notice about those sides?

   b.   Compare each of the other five sides of shape P with their corresponding sides on shape Q. What do you notice about those pairs of sides?

   c.   Imagine enlarging shape P to make a new shape R that has a base 25 units long. If shape R is similar to shape P, predict the length of the shorter vertical side of shape R *without drawing the shape*. What is the scale factor in this situation?

6-68. Using the triangle shown at right as the original figure, *predict* which of the scale factors below would enlarge (make bigger) or reduce (make smaller) the shape. (Do not actually make a new shape.)

$$\frac{5}{3} \qquad \frac{3}{4} \qquad \frac{7}{6} \qquad \frac{2}{3}$$

12 units

original

12 units

After you write down your prediction, decide which scale factor each member of your team will use. Then copy the original figure on graph paper and draw a similar triangle using your scale factor.

a. Show your new triangle to your teammates and check your predictions. Which scale factors made the triangle larger? Which made the triangle smaller? Is there a pattern?

b. Which parts of the new triangles remained the same as the original triangle? Which parts changed? How do you know?

c. Each of the new triangles is similar to the original triangle used to create it. Compare the corresponding (matching) sides and angles to each other. Describe the relationship or explain why you think there is no relationship.

d. What scale factor could you use to create a triangle that is congruent to the original? Explain.

e. **Additional Challenge:** Find a scale factor that will make a similar shape that is larger than the original but has a scale factor less than 2.

6-69. LEARNING LOG

In your Learning Log, explain how to determine when shapes are similar. To decide if two shapes are similar, what do you need to know about the side lengths? The angles? Title your entry "Finding Similar Shapes" and include today's date.

Core Connections, Course 3

6-70.   Which of the shapes at right appear to be similar? Explain how you know.

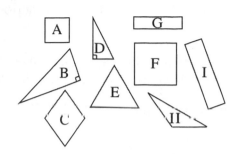

6-71.   A local deli sells 6-inch sub sandwiches for $2.95. Now the deli has decided to sell a "family sub" that is 50 inches long. If they want to make the larger sub price comparable to the price of the smaller sub, how much should it charge? Show all work.

6-72.   Represent the tile pattern below with a table, a rule, and a graph.

Figure 1   Figure 2   Figure 3

6-73.   How many solutions does each equation below have? How can you tell?

    a. $4x - 1 + 5 = 4x + 3$

    b. $6t - 3 = 3t + 6$

    c. $6(2m - 3) - 3m = 2m - 18 + m$

    d. $10 + 3y - 2 = 4y - y + 8$

6-74.   Simplify each expression below.

    a. $-2\frac{3}{10} - 1\frac{2}{5}$

    b. $3 \div -\frac{5}{4}$

    c. $\frac{3}{4} + 5\frac{7}{8}$

    d. $5\frac{1}{6} \cdot (-\frac{7}{9})$

6-75.   Look carefully at the key at right. Which of the keys below could you create by spinning (rotating) the original key? Which keys could you create by flipping (reflecting) the original key?

original

    a.   b.   c.   d.

6.2.4 What sequence makes them the same?

Similar Figures and Transformations

So far in this chapter you have investigated transformations and similar figures. Recall that reflections, rotations, and translations are all special cases of transformations that are called rigid transformations. Today you will investigate how to use transformations to show that two figures are similar.

6-76.   Copy the graph at right.

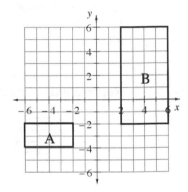

   a.   Do you think the figures are similar? Why or why not?

   b.   Describe a sequence of transformations (reflections, rotations, translations, and dilations) to change Figure A to Figure B.

   c.   How does your sequence of transformations prove that the figures are similar?

6-77.   Figures that are congruent are the same shape and the same size. You can also say they have a scale factor of 1. Which transformation(s) can you use to show that two figures are congruent? Which transformation(s) will cause figures that are not congruent, but similar?

6-78.   Angelina and Vee have each made a challenge for you. Begin with Figure A at right, and then follow the steps of their transformations to find the coordinates of the new figure, Figure B. Record your work on graph paper.

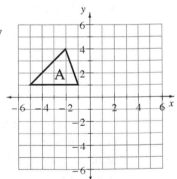

   a.   Angelina's steps:

   •   Reflect the triangle across the x-axis.

   •   Rotate the triangle about the origin counter-clockwise (↺) 90°.

   •   Dilate the figure by a scale factor of $\frac{1}{2}$ (multiply the coordinate of each point by $\frac{1}{2}$).

Problem continues on next page. →

6-78.   *Problem continued from previous page.*

    b. Vee's steps:

- Translate the triangle 4 units right and 3 units down.
- Rotate the triangle clockwise (↻) 180° about its top vertex (point).
- Reflect the triangle across the line $x = 3$.

    c. Were your resulting figures congruent, similar, or neither? Explain.

6-79.   With your team, find a sequence of transformations that will transform Figure C to become Figure D.

6-80.   On your paper, sketch the graph at right.

    a. Write directions for translating the original triangle to make the new triangle.

    b. What are the coordinates of the vertices (corners) of the new shape?

    c. On your graph, reflect the original triangle over the *y*-axis. What are the coordinates of the new triangle?

6-81.   Hannah thinks the solution to the system below is (−4, −6). Wirt thinks the solution is (20, 10).

$$2x - 3y = 10$$
$$6y = 4x - 20$$

    a. Is Hannah correct?   b. Is Wirt correct?

    c. What do the answers to (a) and (b) tell you about the lines in the problem?

6-82.   Figure 2 of a tile pattern is shown at right. If the pattern grows linearly and if Figure 6 has 18 tiles, then find a rule for the pattern.

Figure 2

6-83.   Solve the following equations for x, if possible. Check your solutions.

a. $-(2-3x)+x=9-x$

b. $\frac{6}{x+2}=\frac{3}{4}$

c. $5-2(x+6)=14$

d. $\frac{1}{2}x-4=-3-\frac{1}{3}x$

6-84.   Kevin found the box plot below in the school newspaper.

Number of hours spent watching TV each week

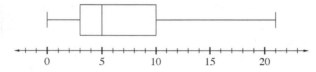

a.   Based on the plot, what percent of students watch more than 10 hours of television each week?

b.   Based on the plot, what percent of students watch less than 5 hours of television each week?

c.   Can Kevin use the box plot to find the mean (average) number of hours of television students watch each week? If so, what is it? Explain your reasoning.

6-85.   Solve each equation. Show all work.

a. $0.85x=200$

b. $\frac{7}{6}x=140$

6.2.5 What do similar shapes tell us?

Working With Corresponding Sides

Graphic artists often need to make a shape larger to use for a sign. Sometimes they need to make a shape smaller to use for a bumper sticker. They have to be sure that the shapes look the same no matter what size they are. How do artists know what the side length of a similar shape should be? That is, does it need to be larger or smaller than the original?

6-86.　With your team, find the scale factor between each pair of similar shapes. That is, what are the sides of each original shape multiplied by to get the new shape?

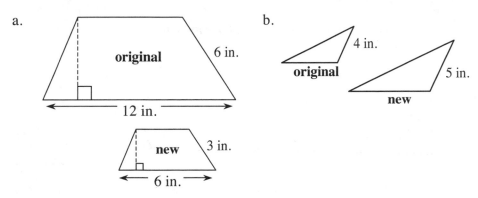

6-87.　It may have been easier to recognize the scale factor between the two shapes in part (a) of problem 6-86 than it was to determine the scale factor between the two shapes in part (b). When sides are not even multiples of each other (like the sides labeled 4 in. and 5 in. in part (b), it is useful to have another strategy for finding the scale factor.

Your Task: Work with your team to describe a strategy for finding the scale factor between any two shapes. Refer to the questions below to begin your discussion.

Discussion Points

How can we use pairs of corresponding sides to write the scale factor?

Will the scale factor between the shapes be more or less than 1?

Does it matter which pair of corresponding sides we use?

6-88.   A study team was
         working together to
         find the scale factor
         for the two similar
         triangles at right.

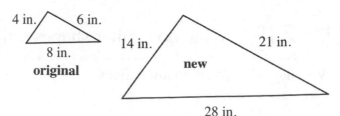

- Claudia set up the ratio $\frac{14}{4}$ to find the scale factor.

- Issac set up the ratio $\frac{28}{8}$ to find the scale factor.

- Paula set up the ratio $\frac{21}{6}$ to find the scale factor.

a.   What did the students do differently when they found their scale factors?

b.   Do the triangles have more than one scale factor? If not, show how they
     are the same.

c.   Why does it make sense that the ratios are equal?

6-89.   Alex was working with the two
         triangles from problem 6-86,
         but he now has a few more
         pieces of information about the
         sides. He has represented the
         new information and his scale
         factor in the diagram reprinted
         at right. Sketch his diagram on
         your own paper.

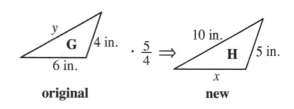

a.   Use the scale factor to find the length of the side labeled x. Show your
     work.

b.   Since Alex multiplied the side lengths of triangle G to get triangle H, he
     needs to undo the enlargement to find the side labeled y. What math
     operation would he use to undo the enlargement? Write an expression and
     be prepared to explain your reasoning. If you are able, simplify the
     expression to find y.

c.   If triangle H had been the original triangle and triangle G had been the new
     triangle, how would the scale factor change? What would the new scale
     factor be? Explain.

6-90.   For the pairs of similar shapes below, find the lengths of the missing sides. Be
         sure to show your calculation. You can choose which shape is "new" and
         which is "original" in each pair. Assume the shapes are all drawn to scale. The
         shapes in part (b) are parallelograms and the shapes in part (d) are trapezoids.

a.

b.

c.

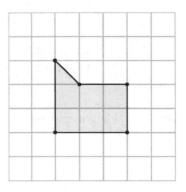

d.

6-91.   **Additional Challenge:** On graph paper, copy
         the figure shown at right.

    a.   Find the area of the shape.

    b.   Enlarge the shape by a scale factor of 2,
          and draw the new shape. Find the area.

6-92. Sketch the two similar triangles at right on your own paper. Find the scale factor and the missing side lengths.

6-93. Alex and Maria were trying to find the side labeled *x* in problem 6-92. Their work is shown below.

Alex: *"I noticed that when I multiplied by 3, the sides of the triangle got longer."*

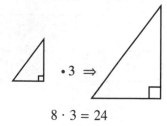

$8 \cdot 3 = 24$

Maria: *"I remember that when we were dilating shapes in Lesson 6.2.2, my shape got bigger when I divided by $\frac{1}{3}$."*

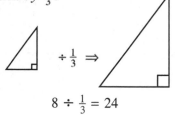

$8 \div \frac{1}{3} = 24$

a. Look at each student's work. Why do both multiplying by 3 and dividing by $\frac{1}{3}$ make the triangles larger?

b. Use Alex and Maria's strategy to write two expressions to find the value of *y* in problem 6-92.

6-94. Consider these two equations:

$$y = 3x - 2$$
$$y = 4 + 3x$$

a. Graph both equations on the same set of axes.

b. Solve this system using the Equal Values Method.

c. Explain how the answer to part (b) agrees with the graph you made in part (a).

6-95.   Hollyhocks are tall, slender, flowering plants that grow in many areas of the U.S. Here are the heights (in inches) of hollyhocks that are growing in a park: 10, 39, 43, 45, 46, 47, 48, 48, 49, 50, and 52.

   a.   Find the median.

   b.   Find the quartiles.

   c.   Make a box plot of the data.

6-96.   Use the graph at right to add points to the table below.

   a.   Write the rule in words.

   b.   Explain how to use the table to predict the value of y when x is −8.

6-97.   Use these following directions to create a mystery letter. On a piece of graph paper, draw a four-quadrant graph. Scale each axis from 6 to −6. Plot these points and connect them in order to create a rectangle: $(2,1)$, $(2,4)$, $(3,4)$, $(3,1)$. Be sure to connect the last point to the first point. Then follow the directions in parts (a) through (c) below.

   a.   Rotate the rectangle 90° clockwise (↻) about the point $(2,1)$ and draw the rotated rectangle.

   b.   Reflect the new rectangle over the line $y = 2$ and draw the reflected rectangle.

   c.   Name the letter of the alphabet that your graph resembles.

6.2.6 How do I find a missing side?

. . . .

Solving Problems Involving Similar Shapes

Architects create scaled plans for building houses. Artists use sketches to plan murals for the sides of buildings. Companies create smaller sizes of their products to display in stores. Each of these models is created to show all of the information about the real object, without being the actual size of the object. Today you will work with your team to find strategies that you can use when you are missing some of the information about a set of similar shapes. As you work, look for more than one way to solve the problem.

6-98.   MODEL TRAINS

Kenen loves trains, especially those that run on narrow-gauge tracks. (The gauge of a track measures how far apart the rails are.) He has decided to build a model train of the Rio Grande, a popular narrow-gauge train.

Use the following information to help him know how big his model should be:

- The real track has a gauge of 3 feet (36 inches).

- His model railroad track has a gauge of $\frac{3}{4}$ inches.

- The Rio Grande train he wants to model has driving wheels that measure 44 inches high.

Your Task: With your team, discuss what you know about the model train Kenen will build. What scale factor should he use? What will be the height of the driving wheels of his model? Be prepared to share your strategies with the class.

6-99.   Heather and Cindy are playing "Guess My Shape." Heather has to describe a shape to Cindy accurately enough so that Cindy can draw it without ever seeing the shape. Heather gives Cindy these clues:

   Clue #1:   The shape is similar to a rectangle with a base of 7 cm and a height of 4 cm.

   Clue #2:   The shape is five times larger than the shape it is similar to.

a.   Has Heather given Cindy enough information to draw the shape? If so, sketch the shape on your paper. If not, write a question to ask Heather to get the additional information you need.

b.   Use what you know about similar shapes to write a set of "Guess My Shape" clues to describe each of the mystery shapes below. Your clues should be complete enough for someone in another class to be able to read them and draw the shape. Be sure to include at least one clue about the relationship between the mystery shape and a similar shape.

   i.   SHAPE A: Triangle   *ii.*   SHAPE B: Parallelogram

6-100.   Nick enlarged figure A at right so that it became the similar figure B. His diagrams are shown at right.

a.   Write all of the ratios that compare the corresponding sides of figure B to figure A.

b.   What is the relationship between these ratios? How do you know?

c.   Use two different ways to find the value of *x* in this quadrilateral. Does your solution seem reasonable? Be ready to share your strategies with the class.

6-101.   Fatima solved for p in the diagram of similar triangles below and got $p = 30$. Looking at her answer, she knows she made a mistake. What would make Fatima think that her answer is wrong?

6-102.   LEARNING LOG

In your Learning Log, write a description about how to find the missing side of a similar shape. Be specific about your strategy and include a picture with labels. Put today's date on your entry and title it "Finding Missing Sides of Similar Shapes."

6-103.   For each expression below:

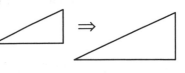

- Sketch and label a pair of similar shapes (like those at right or in problem 6-92) that would result in each calculation.

- Rewrite the expression so that the operation is multiplication.

- Calculate the value of the expression.

a. $6 \div \frac{1}{2}$ b. $4 \div \frac{2}{3}$

6-104.   Sketch the triangle below. Then redraw it with sides that are $\frac{1}{3}$ as long as the sides of the original.

a.   Calculate the perimeters of both triangles.

b.   Calculate the areas of both triangles.

c.   What is the relationship between the perimeters of the triangles?

6-105.   Lucy and Marissa each designed a box plot to represent this data set:

16 18 19 19 25 26 27 32 35

Their plots are shown below. Which plot is scaled correctly and why? Explain the mistakes in the incorrect plot.

a.   b.

6-106.   Draw a coordinate graph, and then plot and connect the following points: $A(-3,1)$, $B(-1,3)$, $C(4,2)$, $D(2,0)$.

a.   What is the shape you created?

b.   Reflect the shape across the x-axis. List the coordinates of the new points.

c.   Multiply each coordinate of the original shape by 3. Graph the dilated shape. What are the new coordinates of the points?

6-107.   Examine the diagram at right. The smaller triangle
is similar to the larger triangle. Write and solve a
proportion to find x. It may be helpful to draw the
two triangles separately.

6-108.   SEQUENCES OF TRANSFORMATIONS

a.   A figure is rotated and reflected. What can you say about the new figure in
relation to the original figure?

b.   A figure is translated, reflected, and then dilated. What can you say about
the new figure in relation to the original figure?

6-109.   This problem is a checkpoint for multiple representations of linear equations. It
will be referred to as Checkpoint 6.

For each situation given below, complete the Representations of Patterns Web
by finding the missing $x \rightarrow y$ table, graph, and/or rule. Since there are many
possible patterns, it is not necessary to create one.

a.

Figure 1   Figure 2   Figure 3

b. $y = -3x + 7$

c.

x	0			3	
y	1			10	

d.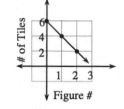

Check your answers by referring to the Checkpoint 6 materials located at the
back of your book.

Ideally, at this point you are comfortable working with these types of problems
and can solve them correctly. If you feel that you need more confidence when
solving these types of problems, then review the Checkpoint 6 materials and try
the practice problems provided. From this point on, you will be expected to do
problems like these correctly and with confidence.

Chapter 6 Closure   What have I learned?

Reflection and Synthesis

The activities below offer you a chance to reflect about
what you have learned during this chapter. As you work,
look for concepts that you feel very comfortable with,
ideas that you would like to learn more about, and topics
you need more help with.

①   SUMMARIZING MY UNDERSTANDING

This section gives you an opportunity to show what you know about certain
math topics or ideas. Your teacher will give you specific directions for exactly
how to do this and will provide you with instructions about how to summarize
your understanding of transformations and undoing transformations. In this
activity, you will use a triangle to review transformations.

Predict and Order: Predict how each
transformation will change or move the shape.
Select an order for the four transformations
and predict what the new coordinates of the
vertices will be after each step.

Tracy Triangle's Transformation Travels

Apply Transformations: Follow the
transformation steps you described
on the graph. Use color and written descriptions to show how each
transformation alters the shape and its position on the coordinate graph. Check
that the coordinates you predicted were correct.

Tracy Triangle's Transformative Travels	Tracy Triangle's Transformative Travels
Add 5 to each x-coordinate.	Multiply each y-coordinate by -1.
Tracy Triangle's Transformative Travels	**Tracy Triangle's Transformative Travels**
Multiply each coordinate by 2.	Add -8 and then 3 to each x-coordinate. Add 9 and -4 to each y-coordinate.

Undo Transformations: To get the triangle back to the original position, undo
your transformations. You may choose to undo *each* transformation step or to
find a new series of steps to return the shape to its original position. Using
color, symbols, and written descriptions, show how each transformation
changes the shape's size and position on the coordinate graph.

②   **WHAT HAVE I LEARNED?**

Doing the problems in this section will help you
to evaluate which types of problems you feel
comfortable with and which ones you need
more help with.

Solve each problem as completely as you can.
The table at the end of this closure section
provides answers to these problems. It also tells you where you can find
additional help and where to find practice problems like them.

CL 6-110.   Priscilla and Ursula went fishing. Priscilla brought a full box of 32 worms
and used one worm every minute. Ursula brought a box with five worms
and decided to dig for more before she began fishing. Ursula dug up two
worms per minute. When did Priscilla and Ursula have the same number of
worms? Show how you know.

CL 6-111.   Copy the graph at right on your paper.
You will need a second graph for List II.
Complete each list of transformation steps
you could use to move triangle B back to
where it started at position A, and show
each transformation on your graph.

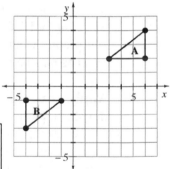

List I	List II
1. Rotate triangle B 180° about point (−1,−1)	1. Reflect triangle B across the y-axis
	2. ?
2. ?	3. ?

CL 6-112.   Neatly graph the points $(-2,9)$, $(-3,7)$ and $(-5,10)$ on a four-quadrant
graph. Connect them to make a triangle. Then, for each transformation
described below:

- Write and simplify an expression to find the new coordinates.

- Check your answer on your graph.

a.   Slide the triangle right 4 units and down 6 units.

b.   Reflect the triangle across the y-axis.

CL 6-113. The shapes at right are similar.

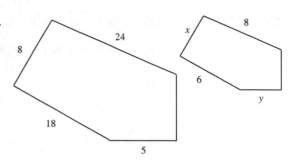

a. What is the scale factor?

b. Find the sides labeled x and y.

CL 6-114. As Khan and Jorman practice for college entrance tests, their scores increase. Khan's current score is 750 and is rising 8 points per week. Jorman's current score is 650 but is growing by 30 points per week. Write an equation or system of equations to determine when Jorman will catch up with Kahn. Be sure to define your variable(s).

CL 6-115. Solve each equation.

a. $3(2+x)=4-(x-2)$

b. $\frac{x}{2}+\frac{x}{3}-1=\frac{x}{6}+3$

CL 6-116. Samantha is dilating triangle ABC at right. She multiplied each x-coordinate and y-coordinate of triangle ABC by -2.

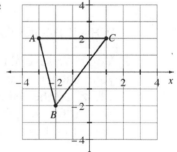

a. Graph Samantha's new triangle.

b. Describe how triangle ABC changed.

CL 6-117. A trapezoid has a perimeter of 117 cm. The two shortest sides have the same length. The third side is 12 cm longer than one short side. The final side is 9 cm less than three times one short side. How long is each side of the trapezoid?

Define a variable and write an equation to represent this problem. Solve your equation and write your answer in a complete sentence.

CL 6-118.   For each of the problems in this section of closure, do the following:

- Draw a bar or number line like the one below that represents 0 to 10.

I am completely confused.

I totally get it!

0   2   4   6   8   10

- Color or shade in a portion of the bar that represents your current level of understanding and comfort with completing that problem on your own.

If any of your bars are less than a 5, choose *one* of those problems and do one of the following tasks:

- Write two questions that you would like to ask about that problem.
- Brainstorm two things that you DO know about that type of problem.

If all of your bars are a 5 or above, choose one of those problems and do one of these tasks:

- Write two questions you might ask or hints you might give to a student who was stuck on the problem.
- Make a new problem that is similar and more challenging than that problem and solve it.

③   WHAT TOOLS CAN I USE?

You have several tools and references available to help support your learning – your teacher, your study team, your math book, and your Toolkit, to name only a few. At the end of each chapter you will have an opportunity to review your Toolkit for completeness as well as to revise or update it to better reflect your current understanding of big ideas.

The main elements of your Toolkit should be your Learning Log, Math Notes, and the vocabulary used in this chapter. Math words that are new to this chapter appear in bold in the text. Refer to the lists provided below and follow your teacher's instructions to revise your Toolkit, which will help make it a useful reference for you as you complete this chapter and prepare to begin the next one.

Learning Log Entries
- Lesson 6.1.3 – Rigid Transformations
- Lesson 6.2.1 - Dilations
- Lesson 6.2.3 – Finding Similar Shapes
- Lesson 6.2.6 – Finding Missing Sides of Similar Shapes

Math Notes

- Lesson 6.1.3 – Rigid Transformations
- Lesson 6.2.2 – Corresponding Parts of Similar Shapes
- Lesson 6.2.6 – Scale Factor

Mathematical Vocabulary

The following is a list of vocabulary found in this chapter. Some of the words you have been seen in previous chapters. The words in bold are the words new to this chapter. Make sure that you are familiar with the terms below and know what they mean. For the words you do not know, refer to the glossary or index. You might also add these words to your Toolkit so that you can reference them in the future.

congruent	**conjecture**	**corresponding parts**
dilation	**enlarge**	linear equation
point of intersection	**reduce**	**reflection**
rigid transformation	**rotation**	**scale factor**
similar figures	system of equations	**translation**
y-intercept		

Answers and Support for Problems
What Have I Learned?

Note: MN = Math Note, LL = Learning Log

Problem	Solution	Need Help?	More Practice
CL 6-110.	Let w = # worms and t = time in minutes. $w = 32 - t$ and $w = 2t + 5$ 9 minutes	Lessons 5.2.2 and 5.2.3 MN: 5.2.2, 5.2.3, and 5.2.4	Problems 5-32, 5-33, 5-36, 5-41, 5-43, 5-44, 5-52, and 5-59
CL 6-111.	List I: 2. Translate (slide) triangle B right 4 units and up 3 units. List II: 2. Reflect triangle B across the *x*-axis. 3. Translate triangle right 2 units and up 1 unit.	Lesson 6.1.1 MN: 6.1.3 LL: 6.1.3	Problems 6-1, 6-2, 6-8, 6-9, 6-18, 6-22, 6-24, 6-25, 6-27, 6-36, and 6-79

Problem	Solution	Need Help?	More Practice
CL 6-112.	a. x: $-2+4=2$, y: $9-6=3$; $(2,3)$ x: $-3+4=1$, y: $7-6=1$; $(1,1)$ x: $-5+4=-1$, y: $10-6=4$; $(-1,4)$ b. y-coordinates remain the same. x: $-2\cdot(-1)=2$; $(2,9)$ x: $-3\cdot(-1)=3$; $(3,7)$ x: $-5\cdot(-1)=5$; $(5,10)$ 	Lesson 6.1.1 MN: 6.1.3 LL: 6.1.3	Problems 6-20, 6-25, 6-28, 6-33, 6-78, 6-80, 6-97, and 6-106
CL 6-113.	a. Divide by 3 or multiply by $\frac{1}{3}$ b. $x=\frac{8}{3}$ or $2\frac{2}{3}$ $y=\frac{5}{3}$ or $1\frac{2}{3}$	Lesson 6.2.3 MN: 6.2.2 and 6.2.6	Problems 6-64, 6-66, 6-68, 6-70, 6-77, 6-78, 6-87, 6-88, 6-91, and 6-92
CL 6-114.	$x=$ number of weeks $750+8x=650+30x$ approximately 5 weeks ($x\approx 4.5$)	Lessons 5.2.2 and 5.2.3 MN: 5.2.2, 5.2.3, and 5.2.4	Problems 6-7 and 6-17
CL 6-115.	a. $x=0$ b. $x=6$	Lessons 2.1.8 and 2.1.9 MN: 2.1.8 and 2.1.9 LL: 2.1.9	Problems 6-5, 6-49, 6-62, and 6-83
CL 6-116.	a. b. The sides are twice as long and the triangle is reflected over both the x- and y-axes.	Lessons 6.2.1 and 6.2.2 MN: 6.2.2 and 6.2.6	Problems 6-34, 6-43, 6-46, 6-52, 6-53, 6-54, and 6-86
CL 6-117.	$x=$ length of short side $x+x+(x+12)+(3x-9)=117$ The side lengths are 19 cm, 19 cm, 31 cm, 48 cm	MN: 1.1.3	Problem 6-30

Slope and Association

CHAPTER 7

Slope and Association

Previously you used histograms and box plots to answer statistical questions involving a single piece of data. In this chapter, you will learn how to use scatterplots to find relationships between *two* different measures for a set of objects. For example, you could analyze amounts of fertilizer and plant height to answer a question like, *"If I give a plant more fertilizer, will it grow taller?"*

In Section 7.2, you will examine races called triathlons to discover when rates are the same or different. You will also measure of the steepness of lines, a concept called slope, for situations, tables, and graphs.

Finally, you will look at how to make predictions about future events from existing data using trend lines and equations. You will learn about the concept of association that helps describe the relationship between two pieces of data.

Guiding Questions

Think about these questions throughout this chapter:

What would a graph of this data look like?

Can I make a prediction?

Is there a relationship?

What is slope?

What information is needed to find the equation of a line?

In this chapter, you will learn how to:

> ➢ Create scatterplots that show the relationship between two variables.
> ➢ Identify associations between sets of data and represent the relationship with a trend line.
> ➢ Measure the steepness of a line by using slope.
> ➢ Find the slope of a line given its equation, its graph, or any two points on the line.
> ➢ Find the equation of a trend line to fit linear data.

Chapter Outline

Section 7.1 In this section, you will first create and interpret circle graphs. You will also learn how to make graphs that compare two sets of data. Then, you will use scatterplots and linear graphs to make observations and predictions about the data based on correlations.

Section 7.2 Here, you will compare ratios and rates using different representations, including numbers, tables, and graphs. You will find out how to measure the steepness of a line on a graph.

Section 7.3 In this section, you will find equations of lines that fit data and will use them to make predictions based on trends.

7.1.1 How can I represent the data?

Circle Graphs

Data can be found everywhere in the world. When scientists conduct experiments, they collect data. Advertising agencies collect data to learn which products consumers prefer. In previous courses, you developed histograms and box plots to represent the center and spread of data. How can you represent data that is non-numerical or that cannot be represented on a number line? Today you will look at a data display that is used for data that comes in categories or groups. As you work, keep these questions in mind:

What portion is represented?

Should I use a fraction or a percent?

Am I measuring in percents or degrees?

7-1.   HUMAN CIRCLE GRAPH

Get a shape card from your teacher. Look at your shape and decide if your shape is a parallelogram, another form of a quadrilateral, a triangle, or some other shape. Follow your teacher's directions to create a linear model and **circle graph**. Then answer the questions below.

a.   Your class built a circle graph with your bodies. How can this model be drawn on paper? Work with your team to sketch a picture of your class circle graph showing the portion of your class that held parallelograms, other quadrilaterals, triangles, and other polygons. Be sure to label each section with the category of shape it represents and with an estimated percentage or angle measure.

b.   Approximately what portion of the class held triangles? Write your answer as a percent. Then estimate the measure of the **central angle** on the graph for that portion. A central angle is an angle with its vertex at the center of a circle. Its sides are formed by two radii, and its measure is a portion of 360°.

c.   Was there a section of the circle that had a central angle of approximately 90°? If so, what type of figure is represented in that section?

7-2.   Nate and Rick are interested in buying a car. According to an ad in the paper, they found that there were 12 cars, 9 pickup trucks, 6 SUVs, and 3 minivans for sale in their price range.

   a. How many vehicles were in Nate and Rick's price range?

   b. What portion of the total does each type of vehicle represent?

   c. On the Lesson 7.1.1B Resource Page, create a circle graph of the vehicles in Nate and Rick's price range. Label each section of the graph with the type of vehicle along with the fraction or percent of the circle it represents.

   d. Calculate the central angle created by each section in the circle graph.

   e. Is there another way to represent this data? Is a box plot, stem-and-leaf plot, histogram, or bar graph an appropriate way to display this data? Why or why not?

7-3.   Circle graphs can be used to compare data at different points in time. Use the questions that follow to analyze the two circle graphs below.

Population of the Continents in 1950

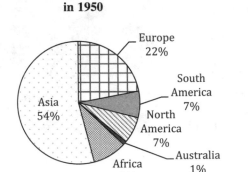

Predicted Population of the Continents in 2050

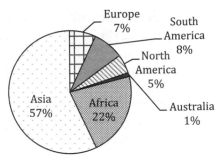

   a. According to the circle graphs, which continent had the largest population in 1950? Which has the largest predicted population in 2050? Do they represent the same percent of the world's population in both graphs?

   b. Which continent is predicted to have its percent of world population increase the most between 1950 and 2050? By what percent is it expected to increase?

   c. Which continent is expected to have its portion of the total population shrink the most between 1950 and 2050? By how much will its percentage of world population change?

   d. Is it reasonable to say that continents with a small percentage of the world population in 1950 will have a small percentage of the world populatation in 2050? What evidence from the graphs can you provide to justify your answer?

Core Connections, Course 3

7-4. The world's landmasses are divided into seven continents. The largest continent in terms of landmass is Asia, representing almost 30% of the earth's land area. In contrast, the smallest continent is Australia, at about 6% of the earth's land area. Use the circle graph at right to help you make the following comparisons.

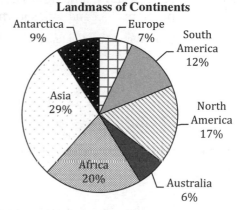

Landmass of Continents

a. Which continents are approximately the same size?

b. Which continent is about one-half the size of Asia?

c. Which continents together make up about half of the world's land mass?

7-5. The population of the world's people is not evenly divided over the earth's surface. In 2009, only 0.0002% of people in the world lived in Antarctica, while 60% of people lived in Asia.

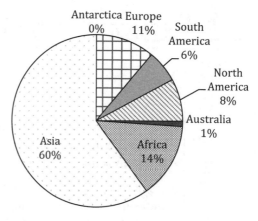

Population of the Continents in 2009

a. Where is the portion representing Antarctica's population? Explain.

b. What similarities and differences do you notice about the landmass and population circle graphs in problem 7-4 and this problem?

c. Is it reasonable to say that larger continents have larger populations? Why or why not?

7-6.   **Additional Challenge:** Take another look at the population graphs from problems 7-3 and 7-5, shown below.

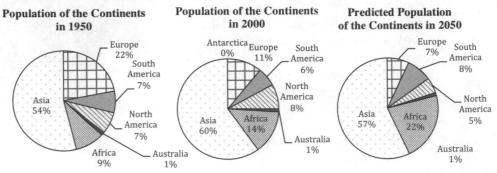

Population of the Continents in 1950

Population of the Continents in 2000

Predicted Population of the Continents in 2050

a. Note that Asia's population percentage goes from 54% to 60% to 57%. However, the population of Asia is not expected to shrink between 2000 and 2050. How could this be true?

b. What kind of graph could be used so that misunderstandings like the one in part (a) would not occur?

$\bigcirc$ETHODS AND MEANINGS

MATH NOTES

Circle Graphs

   A **circle graph** (sometimes called a **pie chart**) is similar to a bar graph in that it deals with categorical data (such as make of car or grade in school) and not continuous data (such as age or height).

   Each category of data is put into its own sector of the circle. The measure of the central angle bounding the sector is proportional to the percent of elements of that type of the whole. For example, if Central Schools has 40% of its students in elementary school, 35% in middle school, and 25% in high school, then its circle graph would have a central angle of 144° (0.4 times 360°) for the sector showing the elementary school, 126° for the sector showing the middle school, and 90° for the sector showing the high school.

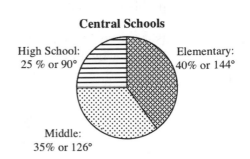

Central Schools

High School: 25 % or 90°

Elementary: 40% or 144°

Middle: 35% or 126°

7-7.   Answer the following questions about the graph below.

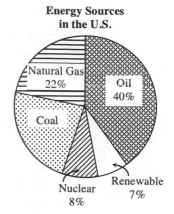

Energy Sources
in the U.S.

a.   According to the graph, what percent of the energy in the United States comes from coal?

b.   Which two sources of energy equal about one-third of the total energy for the United States?

c.   What combination of energy sources provides about half of the total energy for the United States?

7-8.   A group of classmates surveyed how other students travel to school. The results of the survey are shown in the table at right. Make a circle graph showing the results of the survey using percents.

Mode of Transportation	Number of Students
Bus	90
Ride Bike	30
Ride in Car	75
Walk	45

7-9.   Solve each equation below for the indicated variable.

a. $4x - 2 + y = 6 - 2x$ for y

b. $4x - 2 + y = 6 - 2x$ for x

c. $3(6 - x) + 2x = 15$ for x

7-10.   Find the solution for each system of equations below, if a solution exists. If there is not a single solution, explain why not. Be sure to check your solution, if possible.

a. $x + 4y = 2$
     $x + 4y = 10$

b. $2x + 4y = -10$
     $x + 2y = -5$

7-11.   Graph the following points on a coordinate grid: $A(-3,-3)$, $B(3,0)$, $C(3,6)$, $D(-3,6)$. Connect the points as you plot them. Then connect point A to point D.

    a.   Describe the shape you have created.

    b.   Identify the angles at points C and D.

    c.   Record the coordinates of the new points if you were to translate the original points three units left and five units up.

7-12.   Use proportions to solve each of the problems below.

    a.   At the zoo, three adult lions together eat 250 pounds of food a day. If two more adult lions joined the group and ate food at the same rate as the original three, how much food would the zoo need to provide all five lions each day?

    b.   Byron can read 45 pages in an hour. At that rate, how long would it take him to read the new 700-page Terry Cotter book?

    c.   What is the unit rate of pounds of food per lion in part (a)?

7.1.2 Is there a relationship?

Organizing Data in a Scatterplot

In Lesson 7.1.1, you looked at single data sets, such as world population. Often, you need to compare two measurements to answer a question or to see a connection between two types of data. For example, comparing the odometer reading of a car to the price of a car can help determine if these factors are related. In this lesson, you will study scatterplots, a new tool for visually presenting data, as a way to relate two sets of measurements. You will be asked to analyze the data to see if you can make predictions or come to any conclusion about the relationships that you find.

As you work with your team today, use these focus questions to help direct your discussion:

How can I organize data?

Can I use this data to make a prediction?

What does a point represent?

Is there a connection between the two variables?

7-13.   HOW MUCH IS THAT CAR?

Nate and Rick were discussing cars again. Nate claimed that cars with lower odometer readings were more expensive than cars with higher odometer readings. His evidence was that his car with 23,000 miles was worth more than Rick's car with 31,000 miles. To investigate Nate's claim, the boys collected data from several car advertisements and found the information in the table at right.

Nate's Data from Car Ads

Odometer Reading (thousands of miles)	Price (thousands of $)
35	$38
55	$16
6	$50
28	$30
50	$26
31	$35
15	$28
99	$10
99	$13

Does the information in the table support Nate's claim? That is, do you believe Nate's claim that cars with a lower odometer reading cost more money?

7-14. Melissa looked at the data from problem 7-13 and said, *"I need to be able to see the data as a picture. I cannot tell if there is a relationship from the lists of numbers."* She decided to use a box plot. Her box plots for odometer reading and price are shown below. Do these pictures help you decide if Nate is correct? Why or why not?

Odometer Reading
(thousands of miles)

Price
(thousands of dollars)

7-15. Melissa wondered if a coordinate graph could help determine if there was a relationship in Nate's data from problem 7-13.

a. Follow the directions below to create a scatterplot of the data for Melissa.

- Set up a graph showing Odometer Reading on the *x*-axis and Price on the *y*-axis.

- Label equal intervals on each axis so that all of the data will fit on the graph.

- Plot the data points from problem 7-13.

b. Describe the scatterplot you just created. What do you notice about how the points are placed on the graph? Do you see any patterns?

c. Place an additional point on your graph for Nate's car that has an odometer reading of 23,000 miles. Explain your strategy for deciding where to put the point.

d. When a relationship exists, one way to help show a trend in the data is to place a line or curve that, in general, represents where the data falls. This line, sometimes called a **line of best fit**, does not need to touch any of the actual data points. Instead, it shows where the data generally falls. The line is a mathematical model of the data. Models of data help you describe the data more easily and help you make predictions for other cars with different mileages.

With your team, decide where a line of best fit could be placed that would best model the data points. Are there any limits to where your line makes sense?

Problem continues on next page. →

7-15.   *Problem continued from previous page.*

    e. Using the line of best fit, can you predict the price of a car with an odometer reading of 80,000 miles? If so, explain how the line of best fit helps. If not, explain why it is not helpful.

    f. Based on the scatterplot, would you agree with Nate's claim that cars with a higher odometer reading cost less? Use the scatterplot to justify your answer.

7-16.   Sometimes what you know about relationships can help you predict what data will look like when it is graphed. For each situation below:

- Look at the scatterplots and use your experience to decide which statement fits each scatterplot.

- Decide if there is a relationship between the data. That is, as one quantity changes, does the other change in a predictable way?

- If there is a relationship, describe it in a sentence.

- If there is no relationship, explain why you think there is not one.

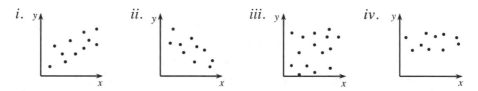

    a. How fast a dog can run and the length of the dog's fur.

    b. A person's age and his or her body temperature.

    c. A child's age and the size of his or her feet.

    d. Outdoor temperature and the percent of people wearing long-sleeved shirts.

METHODS AND MEANINGS

Line of Best Fit

MATH NOTES

   A **line of best fit** is a straight line drawn through the center of a group of data points plotted on a scatterplot. It represents a set of data for two variables. It does not need to intersect each data point. Rather, it needs to approximate the data. A line of best fit looks and "behaves" like the data, as shown in the example at right.

7-17.   HOW MUCH IS THAT CAR?

Nate and Rick were still talking about cars. Nate claimed that cars with more horsepower were more expensive than cars with less horsepower. His reason was that his 300-horsepower sports car was worth more than Rick's 120-horsepower small economy car. To investigate Nate's claim, the boys looked up information about their friends' cars. The table at right shows their results.

Rick and Nate's Data

Horsepower	Price (Thousands $)
500	$38
160	$16
453	$23
505	$23
228	$30
311	$26
335	$15
197	$40

a.   Does the information in the table support Nate's claim that cars with more horsepower cost more? Is there a relationship between horsepower and the price of a car?

b.   Set up a graph and plot the points from the table. Now do you believe Nate's claim? Explain your reasoning.

7-18.   Look at the scatterplots and use your experience to decide which statement fits each scatterplot. If there is a relationship, describe it in a sentence.

i.   *ii.*   *iii.*   *iv.*

a.   A city's average daytime temperature in January and its latitude. Recall that the equator is at 0° latitude and the poles are at 90° latitude.

b.   Weight of a car and its speed in a traffic jam on the freeway.

c.   Number of pets a student has at home and his or her grades.

d.   Cost of a person's home and the value of his or her car.

7-19.   Match the system of equations in the left column with its solution in the right column.

a. $6x - y = 4$
     $3x + y = 5$ 1. $(0, -4)$

b. $x = y + 4$
     $2x + 3y = -12$ 2. $(3, 7)$

c. $5x - 2y = 1$
     $y = 2x + 1$ 3. $(1, 2)$

7-20.   Use the rectangle at right to answer the following questions.

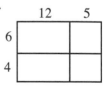

a.   Find the area of the entire rectangle. Explain how you found your solution.

b.   Calculate the perimeter of the figure.

7-21.   Evaluate each expression below for a when $a = \frac{2}{3}$, if possible.

   a. $24a$ b. $3a$ c. $\frac{a}{0}$ d. $\frac{0}{a}$

7-22.   The school library has 6500 titles in its collection of books, magazines, and reference materials. The librarian is presenting information about the library to the parent association, and she made the graph at right.

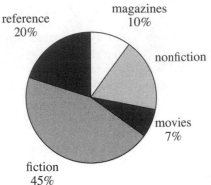

   a.   According to the graph, what percent of the collection are nonfiction books?

   b.   Could the librarian have presented this information in a histogram? Why or why not?

   c.   How many of the books in the library are fiction?

7.1.3 What is the relationship?

Identifying and Describing Association

When is it reasonable to make a prediction? For example, when you know the height of a tree, can you predict the size of its leaves? Or if you know the outdoor temperature for the day, can you predict the number of glasses of water you will drink during the day?

In Lesson 7.1.2, you found that some data sets were related and others were not. In this lesson, you will look at different situations and decide if they show relationships that allow you to make predictions. As you work with your team today, use these focus questions to help direct your discussion:

> When one value goes up, what happens to the other one?

> Is there a relationship between one measurement changing and the other changing?

> Can I make a prediction?

7-23. The students in Mr. Carle's science class have been experimenting with different factors that they think may affect how tall a plant will grow. Each team planted seeds in several pots using different experimental conditions.

With your team, read the questions that the students investigated. Write a team prediction (hypothesis) for the results for each experiment. Assume that all other variables are controlled (meaning that they will not affect the experimental outcome). Write your hypothesis so that it indicates a directional relationship between the independent and dependent variables.

a. Does the amount of fertilizer affect the plant height?

b. Does how deep the seed is planted in each pot affect the plant height?

c. Does the number of seeds in each pot affect the plant height?

d. Does the size of the pot affect the plant height?

e. Does the number of hours of sunlight per day affect the plant height?

7-24.   After three weeks, the teams measured the
         heights of their plants and recorded the data.
         The Team 1 data table and the question Team 1
         investigated are included below. On graph
         paper, make a scatterplot for the data gathered.
         Be sure that you:

- Clearly label your axes.

- Mark the scale at equal intervals.

- Title your graph appropriately (such
  as with the experimental question).

Team 1: Does the amount of fertilizer affect the plant height?

Amount of fertilizer over 3 week period (ml)	5	10	15	20	25	30
Height of plant (cm)	14	17	21	31	33	40

7-25.   Your teacher will assign your team one of the remaining sets of data. Prepare a
         scatterplot poster for your assigned set of data. Be sure your graph has a title
         and that the axes are correctly labeled. Also make sure that the points on your
         graph will be easily seen from across the room.

Team 2: Does the depth of seed in each pot affect the plant height?

Depth of seed in pot (cm)	3	6	9	12	15	18
Height of plant (cm)	24	21	18	12	6	0

Team 3: Does the number of seeds in each pot affect the plant height?

Number of seeds planted in pot	1	2	3	4	5	6
Height of plant (cm)	21	24	27	21	25	20

Team 4: Does the size of the pot affect the plant height?

Diameter of pot (cm)	3	6	9	12	15	18
Height of plant (cm)	21	20	16	20	22	17

**Team 5: Does the number of hours of sunlight per day affect the plant
height?**

Amount of light per day (hours)	1	3	5	7	9	11
Height of plant (cm)	3	10	11	24	30	34

7-26.   Examine your scatterplot for Team 1 from problem 7-24. Also look at the
         scatterplot posters created by your classmates for Teams 2 through 5. Then
         answer the following questions.

    a.   For each of the graphs of data, does there appear to be a relationship?
         Describe the relationship by completing the appropriate sentence below.

             As _____ gets larger, then _____ gets _____.
                                      OR
             There appears to be no relationship between _____ and _____ .

    b.   DIRECTION OF ASSOCIATION

         In a scatterplot, if there appears to be no relationship between the variables,
         then the points in the scatterplot have **no association**. But if one variable
         generally increases as the other variable increases, there is said to be a
         positive association. If one variable generally decreases as the other
         variable increases, there is said to be a **negative association**. See some
         examples below.

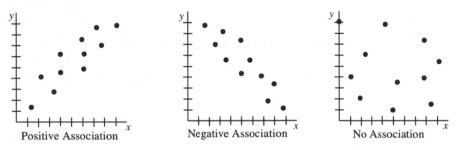

         Positive Association   Negative Association   No Association

         Review each of the graphs of the plant-experiment data and decide on the
         direction of the association. That is, decide if there is a positive
         association, a negative association, or no association.

                                               Problem continues on next page. →

7-26. *Problem continued from previous page.*

    c. FORM OF ASSOCIATION

When there is a positive or negative association, the shape of the pattern is called the **form** of the association. Associations can have a **linear form** or a **non-linear form**, and the form can be made up of **clusters** of data. See some examples below.

Negative **linear** association (for example, gas mileage decreases as the weight of cargo on a truck increases)

Negative **non-linear** association (for example, temperature of a cup of coffee decreases over time)

Positive **linear** association with **clusters** (for example, height increases as shoe size increases; one cluster is mostly girls and the other cluster is mostly boys)

Review each of the graphs of the plant-experiment data that has an association, and decide on the form of the association. That is, decide if it is linear or non-linear, and whether it has clusters or no clusters.

    d. OUTLIERS

An **outlier** is a piece of data that does not seem to fit into the pattern. Do there appear to be any outliers in any of the example scatterplots above?

    e. Now go back and look at your team predictions (hypotheses) for each question in problem 7-23. Were your predictions accurate? Explain your reasoning.

7-27.   When there is an association, predictions can be made. One way to help make predictions is to draw a line (or curve) of best fit for the data.

a.   Find your graph of Team 1's data from problem 7-24. Work with your team to draw a *straight* line that models (represents) the trend of the data on this graph. The line does not need to intersect each of the points, and the line does not need to pass through the origin.

b.   Now use your line of best fit to predict the height of the plant when 12 milliliters of fertilizer are given to the plant over a 3-week period.

c.   What is the *y*-intercept? Interpret the *y*-intercept in this situation.

7-28.   LEARNING LOG

In this Learning Log entry, describe how a graph can help you tell if there is an association between two sets of data. That is, what does it look like if there is an association? What does it look like if there is no association? What are the forms an association might have? What does an outlier look like? Title this entry "Associations" and label it with today's date.

METHODS AND MEANINGS

Describing Association – Part 1

An association (relationship) between two numerical variables can be described by its form, direction, strength, and outliers.

If one variable increases as the other variable increases, there is said to be a **positive association**. If one variable increases as the other variable decreases, there is said to be a **negative association**. If there is no relationship between the variables, then the points in the scatterplot have **no association**. An example of each situation is illustrated below.

Positive Association   Negative Association   No Association

When there is a positive or negative association, the shape of the pattern is called the **form** of the association. Associations can have a **linear form** or a **non-linear-form**, and the form can be made up of **clusters** of data. See some examples below.

Negative **linear** association (for example, gas mileage decreases as the weight of cargo on a truck increases)

Negative **non-linear** association (for example, temperature of a cup of coffee decreases over time)

Positive **linear** association with **clusters** (for example, height increases as shoe size increases; one cluster is mostly girls and the other cluster is mostly boys)

7-29.   For each scatterplot below, determine if there is an association between the
         points. Label each graph as showing a positive association, negative
         association, or no association. If there is an association, write a sentence
         describing it.

a.

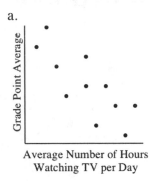

Average Number of Hours
Watching TV per Day

b.

Age

c.

Length of Hair

7-30.   Make a graph of Team 2's data from problem 7-25.

    a.   Draw a *straight* line that models the trend of the data on this graph.
         Remember, the line does not need to intersect each of the points.

    b.   Use your line of best fit to predict the height of the plant when the seed is
         planted 14 cm deep.

    c.   What is the *y*-intercept? Interpret the *y*-intercept in this situation.

7-31.   During a given week, the museum had attendance as
         shown in the table at right.

    a.   Numerically summarize the center and spread of
         attendance by finding the median and
         interquartile range (IQR).

    b.   The museum management needs to tell the
         staff members their work schedules a week in
         advance. The museum wants to have approximately one staff member for
         every 150 visitors. How many staff members should be scheduled to work
         each week? Explain your reasoning.

    c.   Why is a scatterplot *not* an appropriate display of this data?

Day	Attendance
1	870
2	940
3	731
4	400
5	861
6	680
7	593

7-32.   Simplify each expression.

a. $\frac{2}{3}(0.8)$ b. $\frac{4}{3} \cdot \frac{3}{7}$ c. $-\frac{5}{6} \cdot \frac{4}{7}$ d. $-\frac{4}{5} \cdot (-1\frac{1}{3})$

7-33.   Solve each equation below for x. Check your solution.

a. $\frac{3x}{4} - 2(4 + 2x) = -\frac{1}{2}x + \frac{1}{4}$ b. $\frac{-5}{3}x + \frac{2}{5} - \frac{1}{3}x + 1 = 0$

7-34.   The figures at right are similar. Describe a sequence of transformations that will exhibit the similarity between them. Transform KITE to LOWR.

7.2.1 What is the equation of the line?

$y = mx + b$ Revisited

Previously, you developed ways to find the growth of a line using its rule, table, and graph. You also learned how the y-intercept is present in each of the representations. In this lesson, you will enhance your study of lines and will develop ways to find the equation of a line using different pieces of information about the line, such as two points that are on it. Today's lesson will help you review connections you made in previous chapters by challenging you to find equations for lines from multiple representations.

7-35.   THE LINE FACTORY

Congratulations! You have recently been hired to work at the city's premiere Line Factory. People from all over the country order lines from your factory because of their superior quality and excellent price.

Lately, however, the Line Factory is having a serious problem: Too many customers have placed orders and then have received lines different from the ones they wanted. The factory has hired your team to correct this problem.

Your Task: Review the recent orders below and decide if there is anything wrong with each customer's order. If the order is correct, then pass it on to your production department with a rule, a table, and a graph (on graph paper). If the order is incorrect, explain to the customer how you know the order is incorrect and suggest corrections.

- **Customer A** wants a line with a y-intercept of $(0, -3)$ and that grows by 4. She ordered the line $y = -3x + 4$.

- **Customer B** wants the line graphed at right. He ordered the line $y = 3x + 2$.

- **Customer C** wants a line that passes through the points $(2, -4)$ and $(5, 2)$. She ordered the line $y = 2x - 8$.

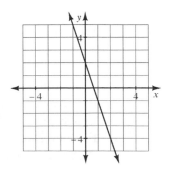

Problem continues on next page. →

7-35. *Problem continued from previous page.*

- **Customer D** wants the line that is represented by the table below.

IN (x)	−3	−2	−1	0	1	2	3
OUT (y)	−4	−1	2	4	7	10	13

- **Customer E** ordered the line $2x - y = 4$ and wants the line to grow by 2 and pass through the point $(5, 6)$.

- **Customer F** wants a line that starts at $(0, 1)$, grows first by 3, and then grows by 5.

7-36. For the customer order that your team is assigned, prepare a team poster with your analysis from problem 7-35. Every team poster should include:

- The original customer order, complete with any given table, rule, graph, or statements.

- An explanation of any errors your team found in the order. If your team did not find any errors, the poster should justify this fact as well.

- Suggestions for how the customer can fix his or her order. You may want to suggest an equation that you suspect the customer wanted. If no mistake was made, then write a note to the company's production department with a rule, a table, and a graph for the order.

Review & Preview

7-37. Would you expect a scatterplot comparing "speed of a car" and "time it takes to drive 10 miles" to show a positive association, a negative association, or no association? Explain your thinking.

7-38. Okie is a western lowland gorilla living at the Franklin Park Zoo near Boston, MA. He loves to finger paint! Many of his paintings have been sold because their colors are so interesting. One painting was sold for five times the amount of a second, and a third was sold for $1500. If the total sale was for $13,500, how much did the most expensive painting sell for?

Define a variable and then write and solve an equation to solve the problem. Remember to write your answer as a complete sentence.

7-39.   Mt. Rose Middle School collected canned food to donate to a local charity. Each classroom kept track of how many cans it collected. The number of cans in each room were: 107, 55, 39, 79, 86, 62, 65, 70, 80, and 77. The principal displayed the data in the box plot below.

a.   What is the range of the data? Are there any outliers?

b.   The main office staff collected 55 cans, the counseling staff collected 74 cans, and the custodial staff collected 67 cans.

On graph paper, make a new box plot that includes this data. Clearly label the median and the upper and lower quartiles.

7-40.   The trapezoids at right are similar shapes.

a.   What is the scale factor between shape B and shape A?

b.   Find the lengths of the missing sides.

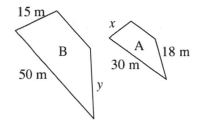

7-41.   MORE OR LESS

Judy has $20 and is saving at a rate of $6 per week. Ida has $172 and is spending at a rate of $4 per week. After how many weeks will each have the same amount of money?

a.   Write an equation using x and y for Judy and Ida. What does x represent? What does y represent?

b.   Solve this problem using any method you choose.

7-42.   Simplify the following expressions.

a. $-\frac{3}{4}-\frac{2}{5}$

b. $\frac{7}{8}-\frac{2}{3}$

c. $\frac{1}{3}-\frac{5}{6}$

d. $1\frac{2}{3}+(-\frac{2}{5})$

e. $\frac{4}{7}-(-\frac{3}{8})$

f. $-4\frac{1}{2}+3\frac{1}{9}$

Can you imagine swimming 1.5 km (just less than a mile), getting dressed as fast as you can, hopping on a bicycle to race 40 km (almost 25 miles), then getting off your bike to run 10 km (just over 6 miles)? Athletes who compete in Olympic distance triathlons do exactly that! In the 2008 Summer Olympic Games, Jan Frodeno of Germany won the gold medal by finishing the triathlon in 1 hour, 48 minutes and 53.28 seconds. Frodeno did not finish the swimming section in first place, though. In fact, he was not even one of the first ten people to finish that part of the race. While Frodeno may not have been the fastest swimmer, what mattered most was his overall rate.

As you compare rates today, you will learn a new way to describe the growth rate of a line called **slope**. As you investigate rates of change, use the following questions to facilitate mathematical discussions with your team:

> How can I use the graph to figure out which racer is faster?
>
> How can we find the unit rate for each racer?
>
> What if the line does not pass through $(0,0)$?

7-43.   BIKING THE TRIATHLON

The second part of the triathlon is a bicycle race. Since participants do not start the bicycle race until they complete the swimming portion, the bicyclists have varying starting times.

The graph at right shows information about four bicyclists during a 20-minute portion of a race.

a.   Based on the graph, list the bicyclists from slowest to fastest. How can you tell?

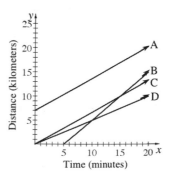

Problem continues on next page. →

7-43.   *Problem continued from previous page.*

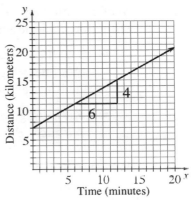

b.   Lydia wants to describe each bicyclist's rate in kilometers per minute for an article in the school paper. To do this, she sketched triangles like the one for line A on the graph at right.

Where do the 4 and 6 come from on Racer A's triangle? What do they represent?

c.   These numbers can be written as a rate in kilometers per minute to describe the distance the bicyclist rides as time passes. The fraction $\frac{4}{6}$ represents how the graph of the line goes up 4 units for every 6 units that it moves to the right. The number $\frac{4}{6}$ is called the **slope** of the line.

On the Lesson 7.2.2 Resource Page, find the slope of each of the other three lines.

d.   Did the slopes in part (c) confirm your ranking from slowest to fastest in part (a)? If not, review your slopes and your comparison of rates based on the graph to find any mistakes.

7-44.   Look at your "Biking The Triathlon" Resource Page from problem 7-43. Slope can also be thought of as a unit rate.

a.   Remember that a unit rate compares the change in one quantity to a one-unit change in another quantity. Find the unit rate for each of the triathlon bicyclists. Make sure you label the units.

b.   Write each of the bicyclists' rates as a decimal rounded to the nearest one-hundredth of a kilometer per minute. When you order the bicyclists' rates, do you get the same results as in problem 7-43?

7-45.   While comparing the rates from problem 7-43, a study team is struggling to decide how to tell which athlete is moving faster.

- Leo thinks that because athlete A's line is highest on the graph, he is traveling faster.

- Kara disagrees. *"He starts first, but racer B is moving faster."*

Which person do you agree with? Look at the graph of bicyclists A and B at right and discuss this with your team. Be prepared to explain your reasoning to the class.

7-46.   In Chapter 4 (problems 4-8 through 4-10), you looked at how tile patterns grow. You examined how the growth rate could be seen in the table, graph, and rule for the pattern. One of the patterns that you looked at and its graph are shown below.

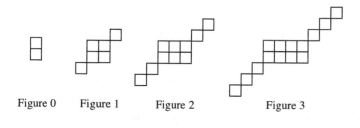

Figure 0   Figure 1   Figure 2   Figure 3

a.   What is the growth rate for this pattern? How can you tell?

b.   What is the slope of the line on the graph? How does this value compare to the growth rate for the pattern?

7-47. Mr. Regnier's class has been struck with hiccups! Three of the students track their number of hiccups over time. Assume each student hiccups at a constant rate.

Student I

Time (in min)	Number of Hiccups
2	8
4	16
7	28

Student II

Student III

a. Which student has the most hiccups per minute? Justify your answer.

b. Find the slope that describes the rate of hiccups for each student. What does the slope tell you about each student?

c. If you graphed a line for the student who hiccups 4 times per minute, would the line be steeper, less steep, or the same steepness as the line in the graph for Student II? Explain your reasoning.

7-48. **Additional Challenge:** CHANGING LINES

Lupe is a manager of an assembly line at a manufacturing company that makes cars. The speed at which the cars are usually built is represented by the graph at right.

Lupe has decided to increase the number of cars built each day and has written directions for her employees. How would each of her directions below change the number of cars built each day? Explain how you know.

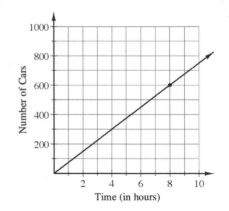

a. Build 200 cars every 4 hours.

b. Build 75 cars every hour.

c. Build 500 cars every 5 hours.

d. Decrease the time it takes to make each car.

7-49.   Compare the graphs of lines A, B, and C at right.

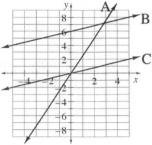

a.   Which line has the greatest slope?
     Justify your answer.

b.   What is the *y*-value of line A when $x = 2$?

c.   Compare the slopes of lines B and C.

7-50.   Lydia drew a graph of four athletes in the final part of the triathlon, the 10 km
         run. She found the slope of each runner's line. Her results are listed below.

         Runner A: slope $= \frac{2}{6}$ Runner B: slope $= \frac{3}{7}$

         Runner C: slope $= \frac{5}{12}$ Runner D: slope $= \frac{4}{10}$

         List the runners from slowest to fastest.

7-51.   If a car is parked on the side of the road and not moving, what is its speed?
         What would it look like on a graph of time and distance?

7-52.   The class advisor was helping students plan an end-of-
         year trip. The students were surveyed about their choices.
         The results are shown in the circle graph at right.

a.   What percent of the students chose the water park?

b.   Which two results are very close?

c.   Write a recommendation to the class advisor regarding what the next step
     would be.

7-53.   Solve this problem by defining a variable, writing an equation, and solving it. Write your solution in a sentence.

The number of students attending the fall play was 150 fewer than three times the number of adults. Together, students and adults purchased 1778 tickets. How many students attended the fall play?

7-54.   The figures below are similar. Use the information given about the lengths of the sides to solve for x and y.

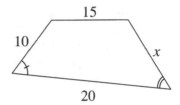

7.2.3   How can I find the slope ratio?

Slope in Different Representations

In Lesson 7.2.2, you learned about how to use a number to describe the steepness of a line. Today, you will work with different representations of lines and look for how the slope can be found in each representation. As you work with your study team today, keep the following questions in mind.

What is being compared to find the slope ratio?

What would it look like in another representation?

7-55.   A planting manual printed the graphs below so that gardeners could predict the height of trees after planting. Jill wants to figure out the rate that each tree will grow.

She remembers that slope is a ratio of the vertical change to the horizontal change between any two points on a line. The units for the vertical change are the same as the *y*-axis, and the units for the horizontal change are the same as the *x*-axis. Finding the slope for each graph will allow her to compare the change in height to the change in time.

a. On a Lesson 7.2.3 Resource Page, draw and label a slope triangle on the line in graph (*i*). Then write the slope ratio. How fast does the tree in graph (*i*) grow?

b. Can you find the slope on graph (*ii*) just by looking at the line? Why or why not? When it is difficult to read the slope on a graph, look for points where the line appears to pass through **lattice points** (where the grid lines intersect). Then use those points to create a slope triangle and find the slope for graph (*ii*).

Slope Triangle

c. On the resource page, use lattice points to draw a slope triangle for each of the lines in graphs (*iii*) and (*iv*). Then label each slope triangle with its dimensions and calculate the slope ratio.

i.

ii.

iii.

iv.

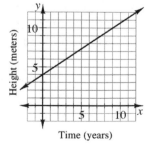

7-56. Three different students looked at the line graphed at right, and each drew a different slope triangle. Their slope triangles are labeled A, B, and C in the graph at right.

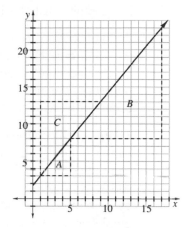

a. Find the length of the horizontal and vertical sides of each slope triangle A, B and C on the Lesson 7.2.3 Resource Page. What is the relationship between triangles A, B, and C? Explain your answer. Using what you learned in Chapter 6 about the ratios of side lengths of similar figures may be helpful.

b. Find each slope using the slope triangles.

c. The numbers in the slope ratios found by the students are all different. Does this mean that the slope of the line changes depending on which points you pick? Discuss this with your team and be ready to share your reasoning with the rest of the class.

d. Another student said her slope triangle goes up 20 units for every 16 units to the right. Where could her slope triangle be? Draw a possible slope triangle for this student.

e. Simplify each of the four slope ratios and compare them. Describe what you find.

7-57.   IS SEEING BELIEVING?

Did you know that a bank will pay you money
(called **interest**) when you place your money in a
savings account? The amount you receive is a
portion of the amount you deposit. The interest rate
often varies with each bank.

Thomas and Ryan have each invested the same amount of money in different
bank accounts that earn **simple interest**. Simple interest means the same
amount of interest is added for each time period. In this case, the interest is
added each week. Thomas and Ryan decided to compare their rate of earnings
by graphing how much interest each of them has earned over time. Their
graphs are shown below.

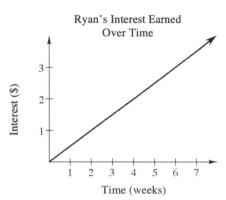

a.   When you look at the graphs, which investment seems to be growing
fastest? Explain how you decided.

b.   The tables for Thomas'
and Ryan's accounts are
shown at right. Which
table reflects Thomas'
interest? Which one
reflects Ryan's interest?
How do you know?

Time (in weeks)	Interest Earned ($)	Time (in weeks)	Interest Earned ($)
1	0.60	2	1.00
4	2.40	3	1.50
7	4.20	6	3.00
10	6.00	12	6.00

c.   Use the tables to find the rate of *interest earned (in dollars)* to *time (in
weeks)* for each of them. Whose money is growing faster?

d.   Did your answers from parts (a) and (c) agree? If not, compare the tables
and graphs with your team to find out why the line that is less steep actually
represents the bank account that grows faster. Be ready to share your ideas
about why the graphs look the way they do.

Core Connections, Course 3

7-58.   The students in a study team are now arguing about who has graphed the steepest line. Assume that they set up their axes with the same scale. Here is some information about their lines:

Lucy: slope = $\frac{7}{5}$ Bree: slope = $\frac{5}{7}$

Cliff: slope = $\frac{14}{10}$ Geetha: slope = $\frac{12}{10}$

Can you use the slopes of their lines to visualize how each of the lines would look on a graph? Discuss their lines with your team, and then settle their argument without graphing. Explain completely who has the steepest line and who has the least steep line.

7-59.   Which lines on the graph at right and on your resource page appear to have the same slope? Which line or lines are steepest? First, make a prediction. Then check your prediction by finding the slope of each line in the graph on the Lesson 7.2.3 Resource Page.

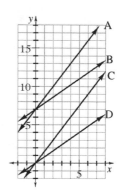

7-60.   LEARNING LOG

What is slope? How is it calculated? In your Learning Log, sketch a graph of a line and explain how to find its slope. How would the slope be different if the line was steeper? Explain as completely as you can. Title this entry "Slope and Steepness" and include today's date.

———— Review & Preview ————

7-61.   Graph the points in the table at right and draw a line. Then, find three different ratios to describe the slope of this line.

x	y
0	1
2	6
5	13.5
−2	−4
−4	−9

7-62.   Find the slope of each line below.

a.   b.   c.

7-63.   For each equation below, solve for x and check your answer.

a. $10(0.02x - 0.01) = 1$ b. $\frac{1}{3}x - 6 = 8$

c. $\frac{x}{3} + 1 = \frac{x}{4} - 1$ d. $0.9x - 2.1 + 0.9 = 0.2(5 - x)$

7-64.   Write and solve an equation for the situation below. Define any variables and write your solution as a sentence.

Jennifer has a total of four-and-a-half hours to spend on the beach swimming and playing volleyball. The time she spends playing volleyball will be twice the amount of time she spends swimming. How long will she do each activity?

7-65.   When Yoshi graphed the lines $y = 2x + 3$ and $y = 2x - 2$, she got the graph shown at right.

a.   One of the lines at right matches the equation $y = 2x + 3$, and the other matches $y = 2x - 2$. Which line matches which equation?

b.   Yoshi wants to add the line $y = 2x + 1$ to her graph. Predict where it would lie and sketch a graph to show its position. Justify your prediction.

c.   Where would the line $y = -2x + 1$ lie? Again, justify your prediction and add the graph of this line to your graph.

7-66.   Solve each of the following equations. Be sure to show your work and check your answers.

a. $2(3x - 4) = 22$ b. $6(2x - 5) = -(x + 4)$

c. $2 - (y + 2) = 3y$ d. $3 + 4(x + 1) = 159$

7.2.4 What else can slope tell you?

More About Slope

In recent lessons, you have learned how to find the slope of a line. You have also learned how slope describes the rate of change and the steepness of a line on a graph. In this lesson, you will learn about other information that the slope of a line can tell you.

7-67.   Which is steeper: a line with a slope of $\frac{2}{5}$ or a line with a slope of $\frac{5}{2}$? How do you know? Explain.

7-68.   Compare the two lines in the graph at right.

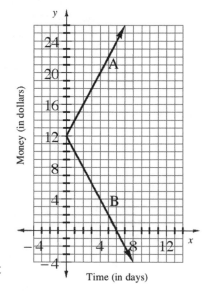

a.   How are the two lines the same? How are they different?

b.   Each line on this graph describes how much money a person has in his or her wallet over time (in days). Explain what is happening to the amount of money each person has. Be specific.

c.   To describe how person A's amount of money is changing, the unit rate (slope) represents the amount that is added each day. Since the value of money is increasing, the slope is positive. But what should you do when the value is decreasing? How should the decrease be reflected in the rate (slope)? Discuss this with your team.

d.   Remember that the slope ratio compares how the change on the y-axis compares to the change on the x-axis. Lines that go up from left to right show positive rates of change, or **positive slopes**, while lines that go down from left to right show negative rates of change, or **negative slopes**.

Find the slope of each line in the graph.

7-69.   WHAT IF IT DOES NOT GROW?

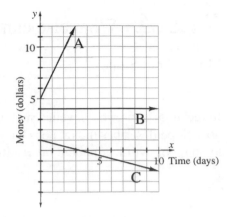

The graph at right shows three different lines.

a.   Describe each line in words. Is it increasing or decreasing? Quickly or slowly?

b.   Line B is different from the other two lines. As the x-value increases, what happens to y?

c.   Slope is a comparison of $\frac{\text{change in } y}{\text{change in } x}$. Pick two points on line B. How can you use a number to represent the change in y between these two points? Use this number or the change in y to write a slope ratio for line B.

d.   Recall that the units for the "change in y" are the same as the y-axis, and that the units for the "change in x" are the same as for the x-axis. What are the rates of growth for lines A and C? Be sure to include units.

e.   Express the rates in part (d) as unit rates.

7-70.   PERSONAL TRAINER

To prepare for biking long distances, Antoine has
been trying to keep a steady pace as he bikes.
However, since his hometown has many hills, he
ends up biking faster and slower during different
parts of his ride.

To track the distance and time when he trains
for the triathlon, Antoine purchased a special watch
that tells him how far he has traveled at specific
time intervals. With the push of a button, he can set
it to record data. Then, at the end of his
workout, the watch gives him a list of the data.

Antoine's Data

Time (minutes)	Distance (miles)
3	0.5
5	1
8	2
12	3
16	4.5
19	6

a.   On his first bike ride around town, he
recorded several times and distances.
These measurements are shown in the table
at right. According to the table, does he
appear to be traveling at a constant rate?
Explain your reasoning.

b.   Draw and label a graph that extends to
40 minutes on the *x*-axis and to at least
15 miles on the *y*-axis. Plot Antoine's time
and distance data on the graph. What type of graph is this?

c.   Draw a trend line that best represents Antoine's data. Then extend it to
predict about how long it will take him to bike 10 miles (his normal long
distance workout).

d.   What is Antoine's general rate during his bike ride? Find the slope (rate of
change) of the trend line you drew in part (c) to determine his general rate.

METHODS AND MEANINGS

Slope of a Line

The **slope** of a line is the ratio of the change in y to the change in x between any two points on the line. To find slope, you compute the *ratio* that indicates how y-values are changing with respect to x-values. Essentially, slope is the unit rate of change, because it measures how much y increases or decreases as x changes by one unit. If the slope is positive (+), the y-values are increasing. If it is negative (–), the y-values are decreasing. The graph of a line goes up for positive slopes and down for negatives slopes as the line moves across the graph from left to right.

$$\text{slope} = \frac{\text{vertical change}}{\text{horizontal change}} = \frac{\text{change in } y\text{-values}}{\text{change in } x\text{-values}}$$

Some textbooks write this ratio as $\frac{\text{rise}}{\text{run}}$.

In the graph at right, the slope of line A is $\frac{5 \text{ dollars}}{2 \text{ hours}}$ because for every 2 hours the line increases horizontally, the line increases 5 dollars vertically. Since y increases by $\frac{5}{2}$ dollars when x increases by

1 hour, the unit rate is $\frac{\frac{5}{2} \text{ dollars}}{1 \text{ hour}}$ or 2.5 dollars per hour.

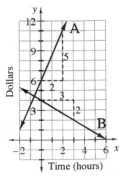

To find the slope of line B, notice that when x increases by 3 hours, y *decreases* by 2 dollars, so the vertical change is –2 dollars and the slope is written as $-\frac{2 \text{ dollars}}{3 \text{ hours}}$ or $-\frac{2}{3}$ dollars per hour.

It is important to notice that horizontal lines do not increase or decrease vertically, so they are described with a slope of 0. The slope of a vertical line is undefined. This is because the horizontal change is 0, resulting in a slope of $\frac{y}{0}$, which is undefined.

slope = 0

slope is undefined

7-71.   For each pair of slope ratios, decide if they are equivalent (=), or if one slope is greater. If the slopes are not equal, use the greater than (>) or less than (<) symbol to show which is greater.

   a. $\frac{6}{7}$, $\frac{5}{6}$ 　　　　　b. $\frac{3}{2}$, $\frac{15}{10}$ 　　　　　c. $\frac{12}{10}$, $\frac{7}{5}$

7-72.   Describe the associations in the two graphs below. Remember to describe the form, direction, and outliers.

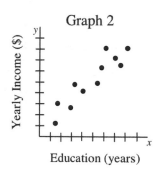

7-73.   Ella and her study team are arguing about the slope of the line in the graph at right. They have come up with four different answers: $\frac{3}{4}$, $-\frac{4}{3}$, $-\frac{3}{4}$, and $\frac{4}{3}$. Which slope is correct? Justify your answer.

7-74.   Solve each of the following equations.

   a. $\frac{1}{6}x + \frac{2}{3} = \frac{1}{4}x - \frac{1}{3}$ 　　　　　b. $0.15(w+2) = 0.3 + 0.2w$

   c. $\frac{8x}{6} = \frac{72}{54}$ 　　　　　d. $3(2x-7) = 5x + 17 + x$

7-75. Salami and More Deli sells a 6-foot sandwich for parties. It weighs 8 pounds. Assume the weight per foot is constant.

a. How much does a sandwich 0 feet long weigh?

b. Draw a graph showing the weight of the sandwich (vertical axis) compared to the length of the sandwich (horizontal axis). Label the axes with appropriate units.

c. Use your graph to estimate the weight of a 1-foot sandwich.

d. Write a proportion to find the length of a 12-pound sandwich.

7-76. Find the area of the entire rectangle in each diagram below. Show all work.

a.

48 ⬛
102

b.

13
x $+7$

c.

20
32   13

d.

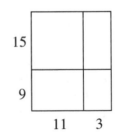
15
9
11   3

7.2.5 Can I connect rates to slopes?

Proportional Equations

In Chapter 1, you identified proportional relationships in both tables and graphs. Today you will look at the connection between slope and graphs of a proportional relationship.

7-77.   POLITICAL POLL

Mr. Mears was running for mayor of Atlanta. His campaign managers were eager to determine how many citizens of Atlanta would vote for him in the upcoming election. They decided to pay a respected, impartial statistical company to survey potential voters (a process called "polling") to find out how many people would probably vote for Mr. Mears.

One afternoon, pollsters called 100 random potential voters in Atlanta to ask them how they would vote in the election. During that survey, 68 people indicated that they would vote for Mr. Mears.

a.   If the pollsters had instead called 50 randomly selected potential voters, predict how many of them would have said that they would vote for Mr. Mears.

b.   Do you suppose that this relationship is proportional? Why or why not?

c.   Carina's neighborhood has 327 potential voters. If voting in her neighborhood is similar to that of the poll, how many neighbors will probably vote for Mr. Mears? Complete the table at right.

Number of Potential Voters	Number of Votes Expected for Mr. Mears
50	34
100	68
327	x

d.   Make a graph of the data Carina has collected, and draw a line through the points. Should your line go through the origin? How do you know?

e.   What is the equation of the line in $y = mx + b$ form?

f.   Use the equation to help Carina figure out how many people will probably vote for Mr. Mears if 350,125 people vote in the election. What do x and y represent in your equation?

g.   What information would the unit rate give Carina? What is the unit rate? How does the unit rate compare to the slope?

7-78.   In two minutes, Stacie can write her name 17 times.

   a.   Use a proportion (write equivalent ratios) to find how long it will take Stacie to write her name 85 times.

   b.   Make a graph of this situation. Which piece of information is on the dependent axis?

   c.   Another name for the slope in a proportional relationship is the **constant of proportionality**. Find the constant of proportionality and write an equation in $y = mx + b$ form for Stacie's situation. What do x and y represent in this situation?

   d.   Use the equation to find how many minutes it will take Stacie to write her name 85 times.

   e.   What is the advantage of the equation in part (d) compared to the proportion (equivalent ratios) in part (a)? What is the advantage of the proportion?

   f.   What is the unit rate at which Stacie writes her name?

7-79.   Beth and her father have a large model railroad in their basement. Beth figured out that the equation $y = \frac{260}{3} x$ relates the length of an item on her model railroad to the length of the real thing, where x is the size on the model and y is the real object's size. Beth's uncle has a different model railroad in his home. It has a different scale. He put together the following table for Beth.

	Height on Model Railroad (inches)	Height of Real Object (inches)
Human	0.94	60
Tree	4.70	300
Apartment Building	7.52	480

   a.   In decimal notation, what is the unit rate for Beth's railroad? For her uncle's railroad? Make sure you show units on your unit rate.

   b.   On which model would a horse be taller? Use the unit rates to justify your answer without making any calculations.

7-80.   Eight of 29 students in your class want to attend the Winter Ball.

   a.   Find the constant of proportionality, and then write an equation in
        $y = mx + b$ form. What do x and y represent?

   b.   If your class represents the entire school, how many of the 1490 students
        will probably attend the dance? Solve your equation from part (b).

Methods and Meanings

Proportional Equations

A proportional relationship can be seen in a table or a graph, as
you saw in Section 1.2 of Chapter 1. The equation for a proportion is
$y = kx$, where k is the **constant of proportionality**, or the slope of the
line. The starting point of the linear equation is always zero, because a
proportional relationship always passes through the origin.

The constant of proportionality, when written as a fraction with a
denominator of 1, is the **unit rate**.

For example, if the constant of proportionality (the slope) is
$\frac{\$7.00}{3 \text{ pounds chicken}}$, then the equation relating weight to cost is $y = \frac{7}{3}x$, where
x is the weight (lbs) and y is the cost ($).

The unit rate is $\frac{\$\frac{7}{3}}{1 \text{ pound chicken}} \approx \$2.33$ per pound.

Review & Preview

7-81.   Aja and Emilie were riding their skateboards. They knew that they could ride
         3 miles in 20 minutes.

   a.   How far can the girls ride in 45 minutes?

   b.   If y represents the distance in miles and x represents the time in minutes,
        write an equation to represent the distance traveled for any time.

7-82.   Joe is downloading songs from the Internet. He can download them at a rate of 8 songs every 10 minutes. Jasmine, who is also downloading songs, can download at a rate of 12 songs every 15 minutes. Who is downloading songs faster?

7-83.   Reflect quadrilateral ABCD across the line $y = -2$. Write the new coordinate points.

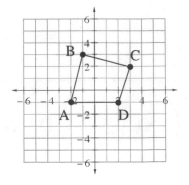

7-84.   Copy and complete each of the Diamond Problems below. The pattern used in the Diamond Problems is shown at right.

a.   b.   c.   d.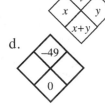

7-85.   On graph paper, graph the line that goes through the points $(-6, 3)$ and $(-3, -1)$.

a.   What is the slope of the line?

b.   What is the y-intercept?

c.   Find the equation of the line.

7-86.   Mr. Crow, the head groundskeeper at High Tech Middle School, mows the lawn along the side of the gym. The lawn is rectangular, and the length is 5 feet more than twice the width. The perimeter of the lawn is 250 feet.

a.   Define a variable and write an equation for this problem.

b.   Solve the equation that you wrote in part (a) and find the dimensions of the lawn.

c.   Use the dimensions you calculated in part (a) to find the area of the lawn.

7.3.1   How can I use an equation?

•••

Using Equations to Make Predictions

Previously, you have learned to find and extend patterns in data and to make predictions using rules, equations, and graphs. Today you will apply these mathematical tools to a real situation in which your data does not make a perfect pattern.

7-87.   AURÉLIE'S BIKE RIDE

To prepare for a 30-mile ride for charity, Aurélie has been biking every weekend. To predict how long the charity event will take her to complete, Aurélie has been keeping track of her time and distances. She tries to ride at a constant pace, but of course that is not easy to do.

a.   Would a box plot, scatterplot, or histogram be most useful in helping Aurélie make a prediction?

b.   Considering that Aurélie is trying to predict how long it will take to complete the ride, which is the independent variable and which is the dependent variable? Make a scatterplot.

Aurélie's Data

Weekend	Time (minutes)	Distance (miles)
Feb 6	68	7
Feb 13	88	17
Feb 20	35	3.5
Feb 27	150	25
Mar 6	104	14
Mar 13	80	11

c.   Use a line of best fit to predict how long it will take Aurélie to complete the charity ride. Remember that the line does not need to intersect each of the points and that the line does not need to pass through the origin to model the data.

7-88.   USING AN EQUATION TO MAKE PREDICTIONS

Sometimes it is more convenient and more accurate to use an equation to make a prediction rather than making a prediction by reading a graph.

a.   Choose two points that lie on your line of best fit. These points can be given data points or lattice points on the coordinate grid. Use these two points to calculate the slope of your line of best fit. What does the slope mean in terms of Aurélie's bike riding?

b.   What is the y-intercept of your line of best fit? What does the y-intercept mean in terms of Aurélie's training?

c.   Write the equation of the line of best fit in $y = mx + b$ form. Identify your variables.

d.   Use your equation to predict how long the charity ride would take Aurélie to complete. How did your prediction compare to the prediction you made from the graph in part (c) of problem 7-87?

7-89.   Westland Workers Union's Health and Wellness Department started a voluntary lunchtime running club. Members kept track of how much they ran each week for exercise and how much their resting heart rate dropped over several weeks. Their data is in the table at right. Note that a negative heart rate change is actually a *gain* in heart rate.

Average Distance Run per Week (miles)	Resting Heart Rate Change (beats per minute)
5	6
3	4
1	–2
7	–1
4	2
8	8
5	4.5
6	8

a.   Make a scatterplot of the data.

b.   Describe the association.

c.   Draw a line of best fit for the data. Find the equation of the line of best fit.

d.   Use the equation to predict the heart rate change for an employee who ran 10 miles a week.

e.   Interpret the slope and y-intercept in this situation.

7-90. **LEARNING LOG**

In your Learning Log, describe how to find the equation of a line in $y = mx + b$ form from a graph of points. Include an example of how to calculate the slope from two points. Title this entry "Line From Data Points" and label it with today's date.

─────────── Review & Preview ───────────

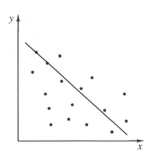

7-91. Anthony has added a line of best fit to the scatterplot at right. Do you agree with where he put the line? Explain your reasoning.

7-92. Graph $y = -\frac{1}{2}x + 6$. Find its x- and y-intercepts.

7-93. Graph a line that goes through the points $(0, 3)$ and $(2, -1)$. What is the slope of the line?

7-94. How many yearbooks should your school order? Your student government surveyed three homeroom classes, and 55 of 90 students said that they would definitely buy a yearbook. If your school has 2000 students, approximately how many books should be ordered? Show and organize your work.

7-95. Find the perimeter and area of each triangle below.

a.
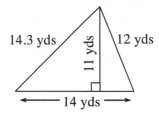
14.3 yds   11 yds   12 yds
14 yds

b.

20 ft   12 ft   15 ft
25 ft

7-96. Graph the lines $y = -4x - 3$ and $y = -4x + 1$ on graph paper.

a.   Where do they intersect?

b.   Solve this system using the Equal Values Method.

c.   Explain how your graph and algebraic solution relate to each other.

7.3.2 How can I describe the association?

Describing Association Fully

You have already seen that form, direction, and outliers can be used to describe an association. Today you will complete the description of an association by considering strength.

7-97. Do you remember the "Newton's Revenge" roller-coaster problem from Chapter 1? You will now return to the problem, using your knowledge of $y = mx + b$ to solve it. The problem (problem 1-24) is summarized below.

Newton's Revenge, the new roller coaster, has a tunnel that thrills riders with its very low ceiling. The closest the ceiling of the tunnel ever comes to the seat of the roller-coaster car is 200 cm. Although no accidents have been reported yet, it is said that very tall riders have stopped riding the roller coaster.

a. To help determine whether the tunnel is safe for any rider, no matter how tall, you collected data in problem 1-24. The height and reach were both measured in centimeters. Use the data from the class at the right. Which is the dependent variable? As you plot the data, consider whether the plot is useful for making predictions. If not, can you change the plot to make it more useful?

b. Work with your team to draw a straight line that models the data on this graph. Use two points from the line that you drew to calculate the slope. Then find the equation of this line. Identify the variables.

Height (cm)	Reach (cm)
166.4	127
169	133
172.8	133
179	139
170	139
183	137
162.5	121
165	126
157.5	128
165	123
169	132
156	119

7-98. Once you have an equation that can best represent the data in problem 7-97, you will be able to use the equation to verify that the roller coaster is safe. The amusement park wants Newton's Revenge to be safe for tall riders. For example, remember that one of the tallest NBA players in history was Yao Ming, who is 7 feet 6 inches (about 228.6 cm) tall. Is the roller coaster safe for him? Explain.

7-99.   The slope and *y*-intercept can sometimes give you more information about the situation you are studying, but sometimes their interpretation makes no sense.

   a.   What is the slope of the line of best fit in Newton's Revenge? Interpret the slope in this problem situation. Does your interpretation make sense?

   b.   Interpret the *y*-intercept in this situation. Does your interpretation make sense?

   c.   Make a conjecture about why your interpretation for the *y*-intercept does not make sense in a real-world situation, but can still be part of the equation to model this situation.

7-100.   STRENGTH OF ASSOCIATION

   Although considering the direction of an association (positive or negative) is important in describing it, it is just as important to consider the **strength of the association**. Strength is a description of how much scatter there is in the data away from the line of best fit. Some examples are below.

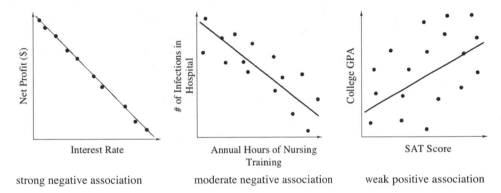

strong negative association   moderate negative association   weak positive association

   a.   Fully describe the association in "Newton's Revenge" (problem 7-97), considering the form, direction, strength, and outliers. See the Math Notes box in Lesson 7.1.3 to review some of these terms.

   b.   Look back at Aurélie's scatterplot from the previous lesson (problem 7-87). Fully describe the association between the distance she bikes and the time it takes her.

7-101.   LEARNING LOG

   Make an entry in your Learning Log. Title it "Describing Association" and label it with today's date. What are the four things you need to consider when describing an association? Give examples of each item. What information does an equation give you? When might an equation be more useful than a graph? What additional information does the slope tell you about the association?

MᴇTHODS AND MᴇANINGS

Describing Association – Part 2

Although considering the direction of an association (positive or negative) is important in describing it, it is just as important to consider the **strength** of the association. Strength is a description of how much scatter there is in the data away from the line of best fit. Examples are shown below.

strong negative association

moderate negative association

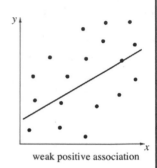

weak positive association

An **outlier** is a piece of data that does not seem to fit into the pattern. There is one obvious outlier in the association on the graph at right.

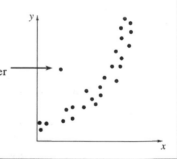

outlier ⟶

Review & Preview

7-102. At a family reunion, each family member recorded his or her age and height.

a. Fully describe the association.

b. Copy the scatterplot and draw the trend line. Does your *y*-intercept make sense in this problem situation?

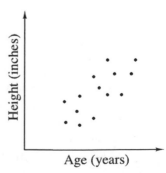

Age (years)

Core Connections, Course 3

7-103. Marissa's older sister was discussing purchasing a car with her summer job earnings. Marissa collected data from her friends at her job.

Age of Car (years)	Avg. Miles per Gallon
9	34
2	30
5	30
1	35
4	34
10	28
9	27
3	40
8	29

a. Marissa would like to know the typical age of her friends' cars. What kind of graphical display should she use?

b. Marissa wants to convince her dad that newer cars are more fuel-efficient. What kind of graph(s) should Marissa make to convince her dad?

c. Make a scatterplot of the data.

d. Fully describe the association.

e. Draw a line of best fit on the data. Find the equation of the line of best fit.

f. Use the equation to predict what the correct mileage for a 7-year-old car should be.

g. Interpret the slope and *y*-intercept in this situation.

7-104. When Malcolm hops 10 times down the hallway, he travels 12 feet. How many times would he need to hop to travel to his class, 90 feet away?

7-105. Jeff and Liz are each saving money for college. Their savings are shown in the graph at right.

a. Based on the graph, who is saving money fastest? Justify your answer.

b. What is the slope of each line? What does the slope tell you about this situation?

7-106. Simplify and solve the following equations.

a. $\frac{1}{4}x + \frac{1}{10} = -\frac{3}{20}x - \frac{7}{10}$

b. $3x + 4.5 = 4.5x - 18$

c. $\frac{1}{12}x - \frac{1}{12} = \frac{1}{8}x + \frac{1}{6} - \frac{1}{6}x$

d. $6.25x + 7.5 - 2.5x = 3.75x - 8.75$

7.3.3 What if the data is not numerical?

Association Between Categorical Variables

In previous lessons, you described the association between two numerical variables, such as the amount of fertilizer used and the height of the plant. Some variables, however – such as gender, eye color, names of countries, or weather conditions – are not numerical. Since the data are in categories, non-numerical variables are called **categorical variables**. Another type of categorical variable occurs when numerical variables are lumped into categories, such as in age groups. Today you will look for relationships in variables that are not numerical.

7-107. The experiments students did with plants and different growing conditions in Lesson 7.1.3 caught the attention of a local farmer. He was interested in whether the type of soil made a difference in the height of his corn crop. He planted 2500 stalks of corn and collected the following data. This type of table is called a **frequency table** because it shows counts, or frequencies, in each of the cells of the table.

	Height of Corn (ft)				
	0-3 ft	**3-4 ft**	**4-6 ft**	**7-8 ft**	**Total**
Sandy Soil	150	200	575	750	1675
Clay Soil	225	150	200	250	825
Total	375	350	775	1000	2500

a. Make a conjecture about the effect of soil type on the height of the corn.

b. The table of data on corn height used counts because it counted the number of stalks of corn. When analyzing categorical data, percents are much easier to analyze. But first, you need to determine the independent variable so that you can determine, "Percent of what?" What is the independent variable in this situation?

c. Create a second table that contains the data above but as percentages instead of counts. The percentage should be the count for each height category out of the total number for that soil type. For example, the height of the bar for 0-3 ft will be 9.0%, because $\frac{150}{1675}$ is 0.090. The third row of the table is not needed in this case.

7-108.   The farmer is interested in the height of his corn for each of the two soil types. A straightforward way to compare the effect of the independent variable is to make a different bar graph for each independent variable.

   a.   Make a bar graph for the sandy soil. The horizontal axis should be the height categories. The vertical axis will represent the percent of the corn in sandy soil that grew to that height.

   b.   Make a similar bar graph for the other independent variable.

   c.   Is the height of corn associated with the soil type? That is, does the soil type have an impact on height? Report your conclusions to the farmer.

   d.   Why did you make a bar graph instead of a histogram for the height of the corn?

7-109.   The nutrition staff at CPM Diabetic Institute is interested in the impact of three new energy bars on blood sugar levels. The staff conducted a study on 1000 volunteers and collected the following data.

	Mighty Bar	Force Bar	Strength Bar
Lower Blood Sugar	30	91	66
Higher Blood Sugar	120	409	284

   a.   Complete the table by computing row and column totals. What is the independent variable?

   b.   A **relative frequency table** displays the percents in a table instead of a bar graph. Change the frequency table at the beginning of this problem to a relative frequency table by changing the counts to percents. For example, the 30 Mighty Bars that lowered blood sugar will be displayed as 20%.

   c.   Use your data from the relative frequency table to make a bar graph for each of the independent variables. The horizontal axis should be the dependent variable.

   d.   Is there an association between blood sugar level and the choice of energy bar?

7-110. An unusually severe increase in gasoline prices may have motivated full-sized pickup truck buyers to purchase a highly fuel-efficient vehicle. Purchase behavior was collected in one area for one year and reported below.

	Low Fuel Prices	High Fuel Prices
Number of Highly Fuel Efficient Trucks Purchased	392	442
Number of Ordinary Cars and Regular Trucks Purchased	36,929	42,255

a. Complete the row and column totals. What is the independent variable?

b. Create a relative frequency table. Is there an association between fuel prices and the number of highly fuel-efficient trucks purchased?

7-111. Researchers have determined that teenagers' memories are negatively affected by getting less than 10 hours of sleep. Being good scientists, the math students at North Middle School were skeptical, so they did their own study. They asked 300 students to memorize 10 objects. The next day, each student was asked how much sleep he or she got and then was asked to list the ten items. The results are below.

	Remembered all 10 items?		
	Yes	No	TOTAL
Less than 7 hours sleep	6	149	155
7-9 hours sleep	11	109	120
At least 10 hours sleep	5	20	25
TOTAL	22	278	300

Make a relative frequency table to determine if there is an association between hours of sleep and memory.

Core Connections, Course 3

7-112. Ruthie did a survey among her classmates comparing the time spent playing video games to the time spent studying. The scatterplot of her data is shown at right.

Playing Video Games

a. What association can you make from her data?

b. Use an ordered pair (x, y) to identify any outliers.

7-113. Sao can text 1500 words per hour. He needs to text a message with 85 words. He only has 5 minutes between classes to complete the text. Can he do it in 5 minutes?

7-114. Where would the point $(11, -18)$ be after each transformation described below?

a. Reflect $(11, -18)$ across the x-axis, and then reflect that point across the y-axis.

b. Translate $(11, -18)$ 5 units to the right and 3 units down.

7-115.   This problem is a checkpoint for solving equations with fractions and decimals (Fraction Busters). It will be referred to as Checkpoint 7.

Solve each equation or system of equations.

a. $\frac{1}{5}x + \frac{1}{3}x = 2$

b. $x + 0.15x = \$2$

c. $\frac{x+2}{3} = \frac{x-2}{7}$

d. $y = \frac{2}{3}x + 8$
$y = \frac{1}{2}x + 10$

Check your answers by referring to the Checkpoint 7 materials located at the back of your book.

Ideally, at this point you are comfortable working with these types of problems and can solve them correctly. If you feel that you need more confidence when solving these types of problems, then review the Checkpoint 7 materials and try the practice problems provided. From this point on, you will be expected to do problems like these correctly and with confidence.

Chapter 7 Closure   What have I learned?

Reflection and Synthesis

The activities below offer you a chance to reflect
about what you have learned during this chapter.
As you work, look for concepts that you feel very
comfortable with, ideas that you would like to learn
more about, and topics you need more help with.

①   SUMMARIZING MY UNDERSTANDING

This section gives you an opportunity to show what you know about certain
math topics or ideas. In this case, you will be solidifying some of your ideas
about slope.

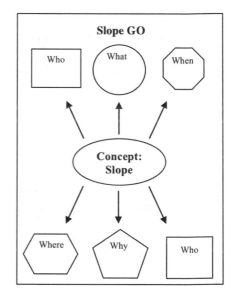

Obtain the Chapter 7 Closure GO
Resource Page (pictured at right) from
your teacher. Follow the directions
below to demonstrate your
understanding of slope.

Part 1:   Answer the question provided
in each section of the Slope
GO. On the resource page,
work with your team to write
six "Who, What, When,
Where, Why, How?"
questions about slope.

Part 2:   Follow your teacher's
directions to pair up with
students in another team and
trade GO questions to answer.

Part 3:   Be ready to contribute your team's ideas to a class discussion. On
your own paper, make note of new ideas about slope.

WHAT HAVE I LEARNED?

Doing the problems in this section will help you to evaluate which types of problems you feel comfortable with and which ones you need more help with.

Solve each problem as completely as you can. The table at the end of this closure section provides answers to these problems. It also tells you where you can find additional help and where to find practice problems like them.

CL 7-116. Graph the following data on a scatterplot.

a. Does the graph show either a positive or a negative association?

b. Does there appear to be a connection between height and spelling ability?

c. Does greater height cause better spelling ability?

d. What other factors could create the association you see?

Height (Inches)	Test Scores (Percent)
24	3
56	86
72	98
49	50
18	0
36	12
70	90
66	81
61	75
34	25
59	80
57	77
64	88

CL 7-117. Complete the table and find the rule.

x	6	$\frac{1}{2}$	−6	8	−12	3	$\frac{2}{3}$
y				18		3	

CL 7-118. For the following examples, tell whether there is positive association, negative association, or no association.

    a.   The number of inches of rain per hour and the height of water in a reservoir.

    b.   The amount of food a person eats and how many pets he or she has.

    c.   The height of a tree and the amount of nutrients it gets.

    d.   The number of hours spent hiking in the mountains and the amount of water left in your water bottle.

CL 7-119. Answer the following questions for the graph at right.

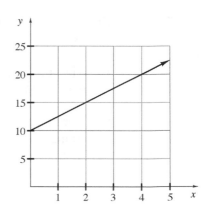

    a.   What is the slope of the line?

    b.   What is the y-intercept?

    c.   What is a rule for the line?

CL 7-120. Solve the following equations.

    a. $0.75x - 0.5 = x + 1.5$ b. $x - 2 = -\frac{1}{6}x + \frac{1}{3}$

    c. $3(x + 2) - 3 = 3x - 2$ d. $5(x - 1) = 5(2x - 3)$

CL 7-121. Ryan and Janelle are driving from different locations to meet at Mammoth Lakes. When they each stopped for lunch, they called each other on their cell phones. Ryan had traveled 245 miles in $3\frac{1}{2}$ hours. Janelle had driven 260 miles in 4 hours.

    a.   How fast was each person driving?

    b.   If Janelle originally started 575 miles from Mammoth Lakes and continues traveling at the same rate (from part (a)), how many more hours will it take her to arrive at her destination?

CL 7-122.   Graph a line that goes through the points $(-2,1)$ and $(4,-2)$.

a.   What is the slope of the line?

b.   Graph a line that is parallel to this line.
       What is the slope of the parallel line?

CL 7-123.   Describe a set of transformations that will move
Triangle A on the graph at right to match up with
Triangle B.

CL 7-124.   For each of the problems above, do the following:

•   Draw a bar or number line that represents 0 to 10.

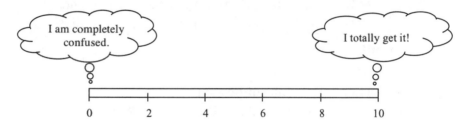

•   Color or shade in a portion of the bar that represents your level of
     understanding and comfort with completing that problem on your own.

If any of your bars are less than a 5, choose *one* of those problems and do
one of the following tasks:

•   Write two questions that you would like to ask about that problem.

•   Brainstorm two things that you DO know about that type of problem.

If all of your bars are a 5 or above, choose one of those problems and do one
of these tasks:

•   Write two questions you might ask or hints you might give to a student
     who was stuck on the problem.

•   Make a new problem that is similar and more challenging than that
     problem and solve it.

③ WHAT TOOLS CAN I USE?

You have several tools and references available to help support your learning –
your teacher, your study team, your math book, and your Toolkit, to name only
a few. At the end of each chapter you will have an opportunity to review your
Toolkit for completeness as well as to revise or update it to better reflect your
current understanding of big ideas.

The main elements of your Toolkit should be your Learning Log, Math Notes,
and the vocabulary used in this chapter. Math words that are new to this
chapter appear in bold in the text. Refer to the lists provided below and follow
your teacher's instructions to revise your Toolkit, which will help make it a
useful reference for you as you complete this chapter and as you work in future
chapters.

Learning Log Entries
- Lesson 7.1.3 – Associations
- Lesson 7.2.3 – Slope and Steepness
- Lesson 7.3.1 – Line From Data Points
- Lesson 7.3.2 – Describing Association

Math Notes
- Lesson 7.1.1 – Circle Graphs
- Lesson 7.1.2 – Line of Best Fit
- Lesson 7.1.3 – Describing Association – Part 1
- Lesson 7.2.4 – Slope of a Line
- Lesson 7.2.5 – Proportional Equations
- Lesson 7.3.2 – Describing Association – Part 2

Mathematical Vocabulary

The following is a list of vocabulary found in this chapter. Some of the words you have been seen in previous chapters. The words in bold are the words new to this chapter. Make sure that you are familiar with the terms below and know what they mean. For the words you do not know, refer to the glossary or index. You might also add these words to your Toolkit so that you can reference them in the future.

association	**categorical variable**	**central angle**
circle graph	**cluster**	**constant of proportionality**
form	**frequency table**	**lattice point**
line of best fit	linear equation	**linear (non-linear) form**
negative association	**negative slope**	**positive association**
positive slope	**outlier**	**simple interest**
slope	**strength (of an association)**	unit rate
$y = mx + b$	**y-intercept**	

Answers and Support for Closure Problems
What Have I Learned?

Note: MN = Math Note, LL = Learning Log

Problem	Solution	Need Help?	More Practice
CL 7-116.	a. Yes, positive b. Yes c. No d. The short people may be young and have not yet learned to spell.	Lessons 7.1.2 and 7.1.3 MN: 7.1.3 and 7.3.2 LL: 7.1.3	Problems 7-15, 7-16, 7-17, 7-18, 7-24, and 7-25

Problem	Solution	Need Help?	More Practice
CL 7-117.	<table><tr><td>6</td><td>$\frac{1}{2}$</td><td>−6</td><td>8</td><td>−12</td><td>3</td><td>$\frac{2}{3}$</td></tr><tr><td>12</td><td>−4.5</td><td>−24</td><td>18</td><td>−42</td><td>3</td><td>−4</td></tr></table> $y = 3x - 6$	Lesson 4.1.4 MN: 4.1.7	Problems 7-77 and 7-89
CL 7-118.	a. positive association b. no association c. positive association d. negative association	Lesson 7.3.2 MN: 7.1.3 and 7.3.2 LL: 7.1.3 and 7.3.2	Problems 7-16, 7-18, 7-26, 7-29, 7-72, 7-89, 7-100, 7-102, 7-103, and 7-112
CL 7-119.	a. 2.5 b. 10 c. $y = 2.5x + 10$	Lessons 7.2.2 and 7.2.3 MN: 7.2.4 LL: 7.2.3 and 7.3.1	Problems 7-77 and 7-89
CL 7-120.	a. $x = -8$ b. $x = 2$ c. no solution d. $x = 2$	Lessons 2.1.8 and 2.1.9 MN: 2.1.8 and 2.1.9 LL: 2.1.9	Problems 7-9, 7-33, 7-63, 7-74, and 7-106
CL 7-121.	a. Ryan: 70 mph, Janelle: 65 mph b. About 4.85 hours or 4 hours and 51 minutes	Lessons 7.2.2 and 7.3.1	Problems 7-43, 7-45, and 7-87
CL 7-122.	a. Slope $= -\frac{1}{2}$ b. Lines will vary but should have a slope of $-\frac{1}{2}$.	Lesson 7.2.1 LL: 7.3.1	Problems 7-35, 7-77, and 7-93
CL 7-123.	One possible answer is to reflect over the line $y = 2$ and then slide up 1 and left 1.	Lesson 6.1.1 MN: 6.1.3 LL: 6.1.3	Problems 7-11, 7-34, 7-83, and 7-114

Exponents and Functions

8

CHAPTER 8

In previous chapters you have investigated relationships that have a constant rate and can be represented as lines on a graph. Other relationships do not change at the same rate all of the time. In Section 8.1, you will investigate patterns of non-linear growth in tables, graphs, and expressions.

Following this work, you will look for patterns that will help you simplify complicated expressions with exponents. You will also learn how to represent very large and very small numbers more easily using scientific notation.

Finally, in this chapter, you will learn what a function is. You will explore several non-linear functions and learn how to describe them completely.

In this chapter, you will learn how to:

➤ Calculate compound interest.

➤ Determine whether a relationship grows linearly or exponentially.

➤ Rewrite expressions using exponents and scientific notation.

➤ Perform operations with numbers written in scientific notation.

➤ Determine if a relation is a function by looking at its table or graph.

Guiding Questions

Think about these questions throughout this chapter:

How is it changing?

What patterns can I see?

Is it a function?

How can I describe it?

Chapter Outline

Section 8.1 You will learn about compound interest and use patterns of growth to write expressions. You will analyze the patterns in tables, graphs, and expressions to compare linear and exponential growth.

Section 8.2 You will learn new ways to rewrite numbers and expressions involving exponents. You will also learn how to perform operations with these numbers and expressions.

Section 8.3 This section is devoted to special relationships called functions. You will learn how to distinguish functions from other relationships by examining their graphs and tables. Finally, you will investigate a variety of functions and learn how to describe them completely.

8.1.1   Is the graph linear?

Patterns of Growth in Tables and Graphs

Have you ever noticed that the sun rises earlier and sets later in the summer than it does in the winter? If you live north of the equator, you may have noticed that in December you often wake up for school while it is still dark. However, if you wake up at the same time of day in May, the sun is shining. The number of hours of sunlight in any one place changes during the year, unless you live directly at the equator. This is because the earth's tilt changes in comparison to the sun. The number of hours of daylight is approximately equal to the number of hours of darkness at just two times of year: the fall equinox and the spring equinox.

If you compared the average number of hours of daylight to the time of year on a graph, you would be able to see a pattern in how the number of hours of daylight changes. Today you will explore situations, tables, and graphs that change in different ways and build strategies for visualizing different patterns of growth. As you work with your team, ask each other these questions:

How does this grow?

What happens when one measurement changes?

How can we see the pattern of growth in the table?

8-1.   With your team, discuss each of the comparisons described below. Consider how the measurements are related and visualize what each relationship would look like on a graph. Sketch your predictions after you discuss your ideas with your team.

a.   The month of the year compared to the average daily hours of sunlight in the Northern Hemisphere.

b.   The number of months money has been invested compared to the total balance for a bank account that earns simple interest.

c.   The cost of an item that has had its price repeatedly increased by 50%.

d.   The length of the base of a rectangle that has an area of 24 square centimeters compared to its height.

8-2. Now that you have predicted what different graphs will look like, you will investigate how some of the measures are related. To start, consider this situation:

Oscar puts $1000 of principal in a bank account that earns 2% simple interest each month. He wants to track how his money is growing over time.

Oscar is using the formula at right to calculate how much interest he will earn on investments that are earning simple interest. He knows that simple interest is paid only on the original amount that was deposited (the principal). For an amount of money that was invested for two months, he wrote the equation below.

$$I = 1000(0.02)(2) = \$40.00$$

Formula for Simple Interest
$I = Prt$ where $\begin{array}{l} P = \text{Principal} \\ I = \text{Interest} \\ r = \text{Rate} \end{array}$

a. On the Lesson 8.1.1A Resource Page, complete the table to show the interest Oscar has earned after 1, 2, 3, 4, and 5 months. How do you find his new balance each month?

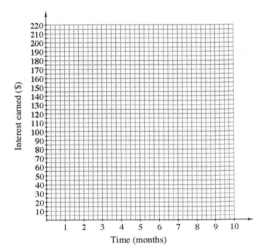

Months	Total Interest Earned	Bank Balance
0	$0	$1000
1		

b. Make a graph comparing months and interest on the resource page.

c. What patterns do you notice in the table and the graph? How can you see each pattern in the other representations (situation, table, graph)?

d. Use the patterns you have found to predict how long it will take before Oscar has $1800 in the bank. Justify your prediction.

e. Compare your graph from part (b) to the sketch you made in part (b) of problem 8-1. Did you predict that the graph would be a straight line? Explain why your prediction was correct, or any changes you would make and why.

8-3.   PROFIT, PROFIT, PROFIT

Anita bought a special baseball card for $8.00. Later, she decided to sell it, but she wanted to make a profit. She added 50% to the price she paid and sold the card to Brandon. When he decided to sell it, he also wanted to make a profit, so he added 50% to the price he paid for the card and sold it to Casey. Casey increased the price by 50% and sold the card to Eli, who increased the price another 50% when he sold it to Fernanda.

a.   On the Lesson 8.1.1B Resource Page, make a table and a graph of the new price after 1, 2, 3, 4, and 5 exchanges. How do you find the new price at each exchange?

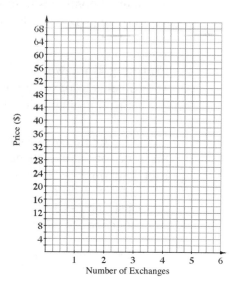

Exchanges	Increase in Price	New Price
0	$0	$8
1		

b.   What patterns do you notice in the table and the graph? Is the graph a straight line? How can you justify your conclusion based on the table or the graph?

c.   How does the graph you made in this problem compare to your sketch from part (c) of problem 8-1? Did you predict that the graph would curve?

d.   How much did Fernanda pay for the baseball card?

8-4.   In problems 8-2 and 8-3, one graph made a straight line while the other curved.

a.   How was the situation that created a straight line changing (growing)?

b.   Growth that creates a straight line shows constant change and is called **linear growth**. What made the graph in problem 8-3 curve? How did the growth show in the table and in the graph?

8-5.   Guillermo was studying the two different situations below. He knows that one is represented by a line on a graph but that the other is represented by a curve.

The Basketball Tournament: The first round of a basketball tournament starts with 16 teams that each play one game. The eight winning teams move on to Round 2, and the other teams are done competing. The tournament continues in this way until Round 4, the finals, where the last two teams play to determine the champion.

The Basketball Tournament	
Round	Number of Teams Left
1	16
2	8
3	4
4	2

Finishing Homework: You have 16 problems to finish at home tonight. You can finish 4 problems in 10 minutes.

Help Guillermo by explaining how you see the situations above changing over time. For each situation:

Finishing Homework	
Time Spent Working	Problems Left to Complete
0	16
10	12
20	8
30	4

a.   Describe to Guillermo how you see the values in the table changing.

b.   Explain whether the change is constant from one row to the next.

8-6.   Guillermo graphed the points for each table in problem 8-5 and sketched a trend line for each graph to show the pattern in the points. But he forgot to label his axes. Decide which graph matches the basketball tournament data and which graph matches the homework data. Explain how you know that they match.

Graph A

Graph B

METHODS AND MEANINGS

Simple Interest

Simple interest is interest paid only on the original amount of the principal at each specified interval (such as annually, or monthly). The formula to calculate simple interest is:

$$I = Prt \qquad \text{where} \qquad \begin{array}{l} P = \text{Principal} \\ I = \text{Interest} \\ r = \text{Rate} \\ t = \text{Time} \end{array}$$

Example: Theresa invested $1425.00 in a savings account at her local bank. The bank pays a simple interest rate of 3.5% annually. How much money will Theresa have after 4 years?

$$I = Prt \quad \Rightarrow \quad I = 1425(0.035)(4) = \$199.50$$
$$\Rightarrow \quad P + I = \$1425 + \$199.50 = \$1624.50$$

Theresa will have $1624.50 after 4 years.

8-7. Cassandra is calculating how much interest she will earn on investments that are earning simple interest. She knows that simple interest is paid only on the original amount that was deposited (the principal). For one amount of money that was invested for three years, she wrote the equation
$I = 500(0.025)(3) = \$37.50$.
Use what you know about simple interest to answer the following questions. Refer to the Math Notes box for this lesson if you need additional information.

a. In Cassandra's equation, identify the principal, interest, rate, and time.

b. Use this formula to calculate how much interest you would earn if you deposit $200 for 5 years at an annual (yearly) simple interest rate of 4%.

8-8.   Which is a better deal? Sabrina wants to buy a
         new digital camera. The one she wants is currently
         on sale for $300. She could borrow the money at a
         monthly interest rate of 4% simple interest and pay
         it off after 6 months. Her other option is to work
         for 6 months and then pay cash, but the camera
         will no longer be on sale and will cost $350.

         Which option will cost her the least money?
         Include calculations to justify your advice.

8-9.   Mighty Max started the wrestling season weighing 135 pounds. By the time the
         season ended, he weighed 128 pounds. What was the percent decrease in his
         weight? That is, what was his decrease in weight as a percent of his starting
         weight?

8-10.   Use the Distributive Property to rewrite each of the following expressions as a
         product. This process of rewriting a sum as a product is also called **factoring**.
         It is called *factoring* because you are writing the expression as multiplication of
         factors.

         a. $4x + 8$ b. $-45 - 5x$ c. $7x - 21$

8-11.   The school counselors are worried about the study habits of students who are
         involved in a lot of after-school activities. They randomly selected students at
         the school and gathered the following data. Consider the number of activities
         the independent variable.

# OF STUDENTS Hours of After-School Activities Per Week	Hours Spent Studying Per Week	
	Less Than 8 Hours	Eight or More Hours
Less Than 5 Hours	29	19
Five or More Hours	14	36

         a. Make a relative frequency table.

         b. Is there an association between the amount of time spent studying and
             number of after-school activities?

8-12.   Find the lengths of the missing
         sides on the similar shapes at right.

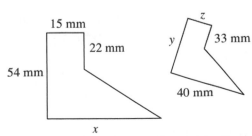

Core Connections, Course 3

$8.1.2$ How can I describe the growth?

Total Interest Earned	Money Owed
0	1000
20	1020
40	1040
60	1060

Compound Interest

So far in this course you have studied simple interest, which only pays interest on the amount invested. It might be used for informal loan arrangements made between parents and children or between friends. However, banks and other financial institutions calculate interest in a different way. They commonly use **compound interest**. You will learn more about this type of interest in this lesson.

In the last lesson, you explored how simple interest increases a bank balance. That growth can be seen in a table and a graph. You also saw that in another situation, where prices grow by 50% each time they increase, the amount added is not constant. In this lesson, you will learn about compound interest and how to create an expression to describe this non-linear growth. Continue to ask these focus questions in your team:

What patterns do we see?

How can we show the connection?

8-13.   Ms. Hartley won $20,000 in the lottery! She decided to spend half of it right away, and invest the other half of the money for her retirement.

The interest rate on the account Ms. Hartley chose is 5%. She calculated that after 10 years, based on simple interest, her account balance should be $15,000. However, the banker told her that after 10 years the account balance would be $16,289.

A financial adviser explained to her that the bank is paying her **compound interest**. That means that the bank is calculating the interest each year on the total of the principal and any interest she has earned so far, rather than just the $10,000. If Ms. Hartley leaves the money in the account for 30 years, her $10,000 will grow to more than $40,000.

To help Ms. Hartley see the difference between simple interest and compound interest, her adviser made the following tables for her.

Simple Interest		Compound Interest	
Years of Teaching	Account Balance	Years of Teaching	Account Balance
0	$10,000	0	$10,000
5	$12,500	5	$12,763
10	$15,000	10	$16,289
15	$17,500	15	$20,789
20	$20,000	20	$26,533
25	$22,500	25	$33,864
30	$25,000	30	$43,219

a.   Explain how you see the interest growing in the simple-interest table.

b.   Explain how the interest grows in the compound-interest table.

c.   After 30 years, how does the simple-interest balance compare to the balance in the compound-interest table?

8-14.   Compound interest is calculated on all of the money in an account at specific points in time. Each time interest is calculated, it is based on both the principal amount and any interest that was earned before. This is similar to how the price of the baseball card grew in problem 8-3. In that situation, each price increase was based on what the seller paid, not on what the card originally cost.

Mariana's grandfather invested $500 for her college tuition in a savings account when she was born. The account pays 5% compound interest every year.

a.   On the Lesson 8.1.2 Resource Page, complete the middle column of the table to show the account balance each year after the money was deposited. How do you find the new balance each year?

Time (years)	Balance ($)
0	500
1	525
2	551.25
3	
4	
5	
6	

·1.05
·1.05

b.   Use the information in this column to fill in the "Total Interest Earned" column in the table on the resource page. This will show the total interest earned since year 0 after any number of years. How do you calculate the total interest earned?

c.   On the resource page, make a graph of the year and total interest earned. Work with your team to show the growth in both the table and the graph.

•   What patterns do you see on the graph and in the table?

•   How does the interest increase?

8-15.   Mariana is curious how much money will be in her account when she is 18 and graduates from high school. She went back to the table she had created. As she looked at the numbers in the first two columns (years and balance), she noticed a pattern that she thought she could rewrite into a shortcut. Study the table and her work.

Time (years)	Balance ($)	
0	500	
1	525	$= 500 \cdot 1.05$
2	551.25	$= (500 \cdot 1.05) \cdot 1.05$
3	578.81	$= (500 \cdot 1.05 \cdot 1.05) \cdot 1.05$
4		

$\cdot 1.05$ $\cdot 1.05$ $\cdot 1.05$ $\cdot 1.05$

a.   As Mariana works down the table to fill in entries, what changes in Mariana's calculations? What patterns do you see in her work?

b.   In Mariana's calculation for 2 years, what does $(500 \cdot 1.05)$ represent? What is $(500 \cdot 1.05)$ equal to?

c.   How could you rewrite Mariana's balance at the end of any year in terms of the principal, $500? In words, generalize the pattern you see in the table.

d.   Based on this pattern, describe how you would find Mariana's balance after 18 years *without* first finding her balance at 17 years. Then, use your calculator to find out her balance in year 18.

8-16.   The pattern you described in words in part (c) of problem 8-15 can be rewritten in symbols using an exponent. For example, $4 \cdot 4 \cdot 4 \cdot 4 \cdot 4$ can be rewritten using an exponent like this:

$$4 \cdot 4 \cdot 4 \cdot 4 \cdot 4 = 4^5$$

Here, 4 is the **base** and 5 is the **exponent** (sometimes called a power). 4^5 is read, *"Four raised to the fifth power"* or *"Four multiplied by itself 5 times."*

a.   Write the numbers you multiplied in part (d) of problem 8-15 as an expression using an exponent.

b.   Write an expression to represent this situation:

A comic book is purchased for $6. It is resold 7 times, and each time it is resold the seller charges 15% more than he or she paid for it.

8-17.   Simplify each expression.

a. 5^3 b. 3^5 c. $\left(\frac{2}{3}\right)^4$ d. $(0.8)^3$

METHODS AND **M**EANINGS

MATH NOTES

Exponents

Bases and exponents can be used to rewrite expressions that involve repeated multiplication by the same number or variable. The expression a^n is written in **exponent form**. The **base**, a, is a factor that is raised to a power. The **exponent**, n, is sometimes called the power. It shows how many times the base is used as a factor.

In general, a^n means a multiplied by itself n times. For example,

$$2^4 \text{ means } 2 \cdot 2 \cdot 2 \cdot 2 .$$

The base is 2 and the exponent is 4.

8-18.   Rachel has been given $1000 to put into a savings account. She earns 2% simple interest every month. Rachel hopes to buy a car in two years. Help Rachel determine whether she will have enough money if the car will cost $1500.

8-19.   Copy and complete the table at right for powers of 10.

a.   Use the pattern in the completed table to decide how many zeros 10^7 will have. How many zeros will 10^{23} have?

b.   How would you tell someone to write 10^{50}? Do not actually write the number; just write a sentence telling someone how he or she would write it.

Powers of 10	Standard Form
10^0	
10^1	10
10^2	100
10^3	
10^4	
10^5	

8-20.   Jack noticed a sale on his favorite model of All-
         Terrain Vehicle (ATV). The salesperson said
         the company was cutting the price for that
         weekend, so Jack got an 8% discount.

   a.   If the usual price of the ATV was $4298,
        estimate how much the discount will be.
        Explain your reasoning.

   b.   Calculate the amount Jack did pay with the 8% discount.

   c.   If the store sold three of the ATVs that weekend, how much money was
        saved by the three customers combined?

8-21.   The choir is planning a trip to the water park,
         and the parents are trying to determine how
         much to charge each child. The cost to use a
         school bus is $350. Complete the table at
         right, graph your results, and then answer parts
         (a) and (b) below.

Number of Students on the Trip	Bus Cost per Student ($)
10	
15	
20	
35	

   a.   Think back to your work with proportions.
        Is this a proportional relationship?

   b.   Is there an association between the number of students and the cost per
        student? If so, describe it. Consider the form, direction, and outliers in
        your description.

8-22.   Simplify each expression.

   a. $-\frac{4}{5}+\frac{7}{12}$ b. $\frac{5}{9}+(-\frac{1}{4})$ c. $-\frac{3}{7}\cdot\frac{11}{12}$ d. $-1\frac{2}{3}\cdot\frac{4}{5}$

8-23.   Graph these points on a coordinate grid and connect them to make a triangle:
         $(0,1), (3,2), (2,4)$. Then:

   •   Dilate the shape by multiplying each coordinate by 2.

   •   List the coordinates of the new vertices.

   What do you notice about the sides of the two shapes?

8.1.3 What patterns can I see?

Total Interest Earned	Money Owed
0	1000
20	1020
40	1040
60	1060

Linear and Exponential Growth

Patterns in tables, graphs, and expressions give clues about the kind of growth that is being represented. Today, you will work with your team to identify whether a table, graph, or situation represents simple interest or compound interest based on the kind of growth that is shown. You will also compare the different kinds of interest in situations to see which one is a better deal. By the end of this lesson, you should be able to answer these questions:

> What are the patterns in the tables, graphs, and
> expressions for each kind of interest?
>
> What are the differences between the two kinds of interest?
>
> How does the pattern relate to how the amounts are growing?

8-24.   John needs to borrow $250. Moneybags Municipal Bank will charge him 8% simple interest each week to borrow the money. Scrooge Savings will charge him 6% compound interest each week. With your team, help John decide which loan is the better choice.

a.   Make a table for each bank. The tables should show the amount John owes after each week for 12 weeks.

b.   Graph both tables on the same set of axes.

c.   Which bank will charge him more if he pays the loan back in 12 weeks? Should he choose the same bank if he plans to pay back the loan in just 4 weeks?

d.   Simple interest is an example of **linear growth**, and compound interest is an example of **exponential growth**. Talk with your team about how you could explain to someone else the difference between the two kinds of growth.

8-25. The table at right represents the balance in Devin's bank account for the last five months. Has Devin been earning simple interest or compound interest? How do you know?

Time (months)	Balance ($)
0	257.50
1	263.25
2	269.00
3	274.75
4	280.50
5	286.25

8-26. Imari borrowed money from her uncle to buy a new bicycle. She made the graph at right to show how much interest she will need to pay him if she pays back the loan at different points in time.

a. About how much interest will Imari owe her uncle if she pays him back in 3 months? When will she owe him $40 in interest?

b. Is Imari's uncle charging her simple or compound interest? Justify your answer. How would the graph be different if he was charging her the other type of interest (simple or compound)?

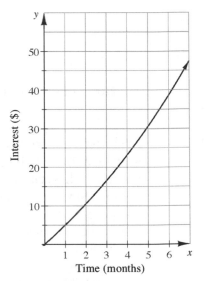

8-27. Tom has a choice between borrowing $250 from his grandmother, who will charge him simple interest, or borrowing $250 from the bank, which will charge him compound interest at the same percentage rate. He plans to pay off the loan in 8 months. He wrote the two expressions below to figure out how much he would owe for both loan options.

$$250(1.02)^8 \qquad\qquad 250 + 8(5.00)$$

a. What percent interest will he be charged? Where can you see the rate (percent) in each expression?

b. Which expression represents the amount he would owe his grandmother? Which one represents what he would owe the bank?

c. Evaluate each expression. Should he borrow the money from his grandmother or from the bank?

yea .

8-28.   **Additional Challenge:** Four years ago, Spencer borrowed $50 from his cousin, who charged him simple interest each year. If Spencer pays his cousin back $62 today, what annual interest rate did his cousin charge? Could you figure this out if he had been charged compound interest instead?

8-29.   LEARNING LOG

How can you describe the differences between simple and compound interest? In your Learning Log, write down what each kind of interest looks like in a table, on a graph, and in an expression. Be sure to answer the questions given at the beginning of the lesson (reprinted below). Title this entry "Simple and Compound Interest" and include today's date.

What are the patterns in the tables, graphs, and expressions for each kind of interest?

What are the differences between the two kinds of interest?

How does the pattern relate to how the amounts are growing?

METHODS AND MEANINGS

Compound Interest

MATH NOTES

Compound interest is interest paid on both the original principal (amount of money at the start) and the interest earned previously.

The formula for compound interest is: $A = P(1+r)^n$

where A = total amount including previous interest earned,
         P = principal,
         r = interest rate for each compounding period, and
         n = number of time periods

Example: Theresa has a student loan that charges a 1.5% monthly compound interest rate. If she currently owes $1425.00 and does not make a payment for a year, how much will she owe at the end of the year (12 months)?

$$A = P(1+r)^n \implies A = 1425(1+0.015)^{12}$$
$$\implies 1425(1.015)^{12} = 1425 \cdot 1.1956 = \$1703.73$$

Theresa will owe $1703.73 after 12 months (1 year).

8-30. Read this lesson's Math Notes box about compound interest, and then answer the questions below.

a. What does the $(1+r)$ represent in the formula? Why are the two quantities added together?

b. If Melanie invests $2500 at a 3% interest rate compounded annually, how much will she have at the end of four years?

8-31. Simplify each exponential expression.

a. 2^4 b. 3^6 c. 25^3

d. 4^2 e. 9^3 f. 5^6

g. What patterns do you see between the expressions in parts (a) through (f) that have equivalent simplified forms?

8-32. Copy and complete the table at right.

8-33. Write and solve an equation to solve the following problem. Be sure to define your variable and to state your answer in a complete sentence.

Jen, Carrie, and Fran are each thinking of a number. When you add their numbers together you get 207. Jen's number is 9 more than Carrie's, and Fran's number is 3 less than Jen's number. What is Fran's number?

Exponent Form	Factored Form	Standard Form
2^3	$2 \cdot 2 \cdot 2$	8
3^3		
	$4 \cdot 4 \cdot 4$	
		125
6^3		
7^3		
	$8 \cdot 8 \cdot 8$	
9^3		

8-34. Rotate the triangle at right 90° clockwise about the origin. State the coordinates of the new vertices.

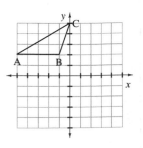

8-35. Daniel has $1200 in the bank. He is earning 3.5% compound interest each month. How much money will he have in the bank in one year? Is this example of linear or non-linear growth?

8.2.1 How can I rewrite it?

$$3^5 \cdot 3^2 = 3^7$$

Exponents and Scientific Notation

Earlier in this chapter you worked with expressions for interest problems. You could rewrite them in simpler ways by using multiplication in place of repeated addition, and by using exponents in place of repeated multiplication. Rewriting expressions in different forms can be a powerful tool for simplifying expressions and seeing patterns. In this lesson, you will develop strategies for how to rewrite expressions using exponents.

8-36.   Is 3^5 the same as $3 \cdot 5$? Explain.

8-37.   Exponents allow you to rewrite some multiplication problems in a simpler form. Some exponent expressions can also be simplified. Complete the table below on the Lesson 8.2.1 Resource Page, or copy and complete it on your own paper. Expand each expression into factored form and then rewrite it with new exponents as shown in the example.

Original Form	Factored Form	Simplified Exponent Form
$5^2 \cdot 5^5$	$(5 \cdot 5) \cdot (5 \cdot 5 \cdot 5 \cdot 5 \cdot 5)$	5^7
$2^2 \cdot 2^4$		
$3^7 \cdot 3^2$		
$x^3 \cdot x^5$		
$x^3 y^2 \cdot x y^2$		
$7^2 \cdot x^3 \cdot 7 \cdot x^2$		
$2 \cdot x^4 \cdot 3 \cdot x y^2$		

a.   Work with your team to compare the bases and exponents of the original form to the base and exponent of the simplified exponent form. Write a statement to describe the relationships you see.

b.   Visualize how you would expand $20^{12} \cdot 20^{51}$ in your mind. What would this expression be in a simplified exponent form? Describe your reasoning.

c.   One study team rewrote the expression $10^3 \cdot 5^4$ as 50^7. Is their simplification correct? Explain your reasoning.

8-38.   When you multiply, the order of the factors does not matter. That means that
        you will get the same answer when multiplying $3 \cdot 2 \cdot 3$ as you would if you were
        multiplying $2 \cdot 3 \cdot 3$. This is the Commutative Property of Multiplication that
        you learned about in Chapter 2.

   a.   Check that $2 \cdot 10$ is equal to $10 \cdot 2$. Is it also true that $2 \div 10$ is equal to
        $10 \div 2$?

   b.   Write the expression $5^2 \cdot x^4 \cdot 5x$ in factored form. Explain how the
        Commutative Property of Multiplication helps you simplify the expression
        to $5^3 \cdot x^5$.

   c.   Write the expression $3w^3 \cdot 3w^2 \cdot 3w \cdot 3$ in simplified exponent form.

8-39.   Multiplying a number by 10 changes the number in a special
        way. Simplify each expression below without using a
        calculator. As you work, pay attention to how the number
        changes when you multiply it by powers of 10.

   a. $9.23 \cdot 10$ b. $9.23 \cdot 10^2$ c. $9.23 \cdot 10^3$ d. $9.23 \cdot 10^4$

8-40.   Talk with your team about any patterns you see in your answers in
        problem 8-39.

   a.   Based on those patterns, what do you think $9.23 \cdot 10^7$ would be? Why?

   b.   Use the patterns you have found to find the product for each
        expression without using your calculator.

        i. 78.659×10^2 ii. 346.38×10^5

   c.   With your team, write a statement describing in general how you can
        quickly multiply by powers of 10. You may want to include information
        about where the decimal point moves after multiplying the number by a
        power of 10 or why you have to add zeros. Work with your team to write a
        clear explanation for why this pattern works.

8-41.   When astronomers describe distances in space, often the numbers are so large that they are difficult to write. For example, the diameter of the sun is approximately one million, three hundred ninety thousand kilometers, or 1,390,000 km. To make these large numbers easier to write, astronomers and other scientists use **scientific notation**. In scientific notation, the diameter of the sun is:

$$1.39 \times 10^6 \text{ km}$$

a.   Rewrite 10^6 as a single number without an exponent. What happens when you multiply 1.39 by this number?

b.   In scientific notation, the mass of the sun is approximately 1.99×10^{30} kg. What does this number mean? Discuss with your team how to rewrite this number without scientific notation, and then write it.

8-42.   Scientific notation requires that one factor is a power of 10, and the other factor is a number greater than or equal to 1 but less than 10. For example, 2.56×10^5 is correctly written in scientific notation, but 25.6×10^4 is not. Scientific notation also uses the symbol "$\times$" for multiplication instead of "$\cdot$" or parentheses. None of the numbers below is correctly written in scientific notation. Explain why each one does not meet the criteria for scientific notation, and then write it using correct scientific notation.

a. 25.6×10^4 b. $5.46 \cdot 100$ c. 0.93×10^8

8-43.   Write each number below in scientific notation.

a.   370,000,000   b.   48,710,000,000

8-44.   Scientific notation makes large numbers easier to write. It also provides you with quick information about the sizes of the numbers. For example, Pluto and Haumea are both dwarf planets. Pluto has a mass of 1.305×10^{22} kilograms, and Haumea has a mass of 4.006×10^{21} kilograms.

Without rewriting the mass of each planet, can you tell which of these dwarf planets is larger? Explain your reasoning.

8-45.   Without using a calculator, estimate how many times bigger the larger dwarf planet is than the smaller one in problem 8-44.

8-46.   LEARNING LOG

In your Learning Log, explain to someone who missed today's class what scientific notation is and the difference between 3^8 and 3×10^8. Title this entry "Scientific Notation" and label it with today's date.

8-47.   Rewrite each of the expressions below in a simpler form using exponents.

a. $4 \cdot 4 \cdot 5 \cdot 5 \cdot 5$

b. $3 \cdot 3 \cdot 3 \cdot 3 \cdot 3 \cdot y \cdot y$

c. $(6x)(6x)(6x)(6x)$

8-48.   Calculate the following products without using a calculator.

Factors	Product
6.5901×10^2	
0.6893×10^7	
5.86×10^4	
0.092×10^3	

8-49.   Graph the following points on a coordinate grid: $(1,1)$, $(4,1)$, and $(3,4)$.

Connect the points. Then translate the points three units right and three units up. What are the coordinates of the vertices of the new triangle?

8-50. Scientists consider the average growth rate of kelp (a sea plant) to be an indicator of the health of marine plants. They also consider the average weight (mass) of crabs that live in kelp beds to be an indicator of the health of the marine animals. But they want to know if there is an association between the health of sea plants (kelp) and the health of sea animals (crab).

Marine biologists collected data from different parts of the world and created the following relative frequency table. They considered the average growth rate of kelp as the independent variable.

% CRABS		Average Mass of Crabs (kg)			
		< 0.25	0.25 – 0.49	0.50 – 0.75	> 0.75
Average Growth Rate of Kelp (cm/day)	< 5	66%	34%	0%	0%
	≥ 5	12%	49%	35%	4%

Is there an association between the health of sea plants and the health of sea animals?

8-51. Enrollment in math courses at Kennedy High School in Bloomington, Minnesota is shown in the pie chart at right. (If you are unfamiliar with pie charts, refer to the glossary for assistance.) If there are 1000 students enrolled in math courses, approximately how many students are enrolled in Algebra? In Geometry? In Calculus?

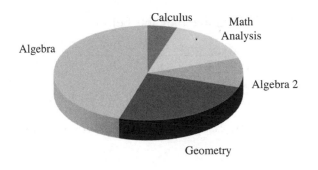

8-52. Determine the compound interest earned on $220 invested at 3.25% compounded annually for 6 years.

8-53. Which number is greater, 3.56×10^4 or 1.9×10^6? Explain how you know.

8-54.   Write the following numbers in scientific notation.

a.   370,000,000

b.   7,600

8-55.   Simplify each expression.

a. 6^5

b. $\left(\frac{2}{3}\right)^3$

c. $(2+3)^4$

d. $2(-\frac{1}{2}+\frac{3}{4})^3$

8-56.   Consider the equation $7 = 3x - 5$.

a.   Stanley wants to start solving the equation by adding 5 to both sides, while Terrence first wants to subtract 7 from both sides. Will both strategies work? Is one strategy more efficient than the other?

b.   Solve $7 = 3x - 5$. Show your steps.

8-57.   Examine the table below.

x	0.5	0	2	4	5
y	−0.5	−2	4	10	13

a.   What is the rule for the table?

b.   Explain the strategy you used to find the rule.

8-58.   Graph the equation $y = -2x^2 - 4x$. Start by making an $x \rightarrow y$ table. Be sure to include negative values for x. Does this graph linear or non-linear?

8.2.2 How can I write it in simpler form?

Exponent Rules

$$3^5 \cdot 3^2 = 3^7$$

In the previous lesson, you expanded expressions written with exponents into factored form and then rewrote them in simpler form. You also looked at ways to rewrite very large numbers in scientific notation to compare them more easily.

In this lesson, you will continue to develop ways to rewrite expressions using exponents. Use the questions below to focus discussion in your study team.

> What part of the expression is being raised to a power?
>
> What are the factors?
>
> How can we rewrite the expression to have fewer terms?

8-59.   Rewrite each expression below in a simpler form.

a. $10^2 \cdot x^3 \cdot 10 \cdot y$ b. $20^3 \cdot 20^8$ c. $x^2 y^2 z^2 \cdot x^3 z^5$

8-60.   Erin wants to rewrite the expression $5^2 x^2 \cdot 5^4 x^3$ in simpler form. She started by expanding the expression like this:

$$5 \cdot 5 + x \cdot x + 5 \cdot 5 \cdot 5 \cdot 5 + x \cdot x \cdot x$$
$$25 + x^2 + 625 + x^3$$

Do you agree with her work so far? Work with your team to complete the problem or, if you do not agree, to write Erin a note explaining how to correct her work and find the correct simplification.

8-61.   When a number is raised to a power, and then raised to a power again, the result follows a consistent pattern. Complete the table below on the Lesson 8.2.2 Resource Page, or copy and complete it on your own paper. Expand each expression into factored form and then rewrite it with new exponents as shown in the example.

Original Form	Factored Form	Simplified Exponent Form
$(5^2)^5$	$(5 \cdot 5)(5 \cdot 5)(5 \cdot 5)(5 \cdot 5)(5 \cdot 5)$	5^{10}
$(2^2)^4$		
$(3^7)^2$		
$(x^3)^5$		
$(x^3 y^2)^2$		

a.   Work with your team to describe the pattern between the exponents in the original form and the exponent(s) in the simplified exponent form.

b.   Visualize $(20^3)^8$ written in factored form. What is multiplied? That is, what is the base? How many times is it multiplied? Use the expression you visualized to help you rewrite the expression in simplified exponent form. Describe in detail how you figured out what exponent to use in the simplified exponent form.

8-62.   In problem 8-59, you simplified the expression $20^3 \cdot 20^8$. Compare the factored form you wrote for that expression to the expression you visualized in part (b) of problem 8-61. How are the two expressions different?

8-63.   Heidi is trying to rewrite the two expressions below.

$$(2x)^3 \qquad 2x^3$$

"Are these two ways of writing the same thing? Or do they mean something different?" Heidi wonders.

a.   Rewrite $(2x)^3$ by expanding and then simplifying. What part is being raised to the third power?

b.   Heidi thinks $2x^3$ is the same as $2 \cdot x^3$. Show that she is correct by expanding the expression.

c.   Are $(2x)^3$ and $2x^3$ equivalent? Explain why or why not.

8-64.   AJ was trying to simplify the exponent expression $\frac{5^7}{5^3}$. He started by writing out the factored form. Once he saw the factors he recognized a Giant One in his work.

   a.   Copy AJ's expression on your paper and write out the factored form. Where did he see a Giant One?

   b.   Work with your study team to use the Giant One to simplify and rewrite AJ's expression. What is the result?

8-65.   Expand each expression below into factored form. Then rewrite it in simplified exponent form.

   a. $\frac{2^4}{2^2}$ b. $\frac{3^4}{3^5}$ c. $\frac{y^7}{y^4}$ d. $\frac{x^3y^2}{xy^2}$

──────── Review & Preview ────────

8-66.   Simplify each expression.

   a. $\frac{3^2 \cdot 5^3 \cdot 8}{3 \cdot 5^3 \cdot 8}$ b. $(3x)^4$ c. $3^3 \cdot 3^5 \cdot (\frac{1}{3})^2$ d. $\frac{7^4 \cdot 9^2}{9^3 \cdot 7^2}$

8-67.   Janet lit a 12-inch candle. She noticed that it was getting an inch shorter every 30 minutes.

   a.   Is the association between the time the candle is lit and the height of the candle positive or negative?

   b.   In how many hours will the candle burn out? Support your answer with a reason.

8-68.   Show the "check" for each of the problems below. Write whether the solution is correct or incorrect.

   a.   For $3x + 2 = x - 2$, does $x = 0$?

   b.   For $3(x - 2) = 30 + x - 2 - x + 2$, does $x = 12$?

8-69.   On graph paper, graph the shape that has coordinates $(-2,-1)$, $(1,2)$, and $(-2,3)$.

a.   Predict the coordinates of the shape after it is translated three units to the right and one unit down. Check your prediction on the graph.

b.   Dilate the original shape by multiplying both the x- and y-coordinates by 2.

c.   Reflect the original shape over the y-axis. What are the new coordinates?

8-70.   Solve the equations below for the indicated variable.

a. $3(2x-1)+2y = 5x$ for y

b. $600x + 200y = 500x$ for x

8-71.   Use $<$, $>$, or $=$ to compare the number pairs below.

a. 0.183 _____ 0.18

b. -13 _____ -17

c. 0.125 _____ $\frac{1}{8}$

d. -6 _____ -4

e. 72% _____ $\frac{35}{30}$

f. -0.25 _____ -0.05

8.2.3 What happens if the exponent is negative?

· ·

$3^5 \cdot 3^2 = 3^7$

Negative Exponents

Earlier in this chapter you learned how to write large numbers in scientific notation. Astronomers use those large numbers to measure great distances in space. Not all scientists work with such a large scale, however. Some scientists use very small numbers to describe what they measure under a microscope. In this lesson, you will continue your work with exponents, and then you will turn your attention to using scientific notation to represent small numbers.

8-72. Two of the problems below are correct, and four contain errors. Expand each original expression to verify that it is correct. If it is not, identify the mistake and simplify to find the correct answer.

a. $x^3 y^2 x^4 \overset{?}{=} x^7 y^2$

b. $2^3 \cdot 2^4 \overset{?}{=} 2^{12}$

c. $\frac{7^2 \cdot 8^3}{7^3 \cdot 8^2} \overset{?}{=} \frac{8}{7}$

d. $3^5 \cdot 3^2 \overset{?}{=} 9^7$

e. $\frac{6^2}{6^5} \overset{?}{=} 6^3$

f. $\frac{z^3}{z^3} \overset{?}{=} 0$

8-73. Rewrite each expression in a simpler form using the patterns you have found for rewriting expressions with exponents. If it is reasonable, write out the factored form to help you.

a. $2^3 \cdot 2^4$

b. $\frac{2^8}{2^5}$

c. $(5x^2)^3$

d. $(4x)^2(5x^2)$

8-74. LEARNING LOG

You have worked with your team to describe ways to rewrite and simplify exponent expressions involving multiplication and division. In your Learning Log, give examples of each kind of expression. Describe in words how to rewrite each one. Include factored and simplified expressions to go with your descriptions. Title this entry "Simplifying Exponent Expressions" and label it with today's date.

8-75. Salvador was studying microscopic pond animals in science class. He read that amoebas were 0.3 millimeters to 0.6 millimeters in length. He saw that euglenas are as small as $8.0 \cdot 10^{-2}$ millimeters, but he did not know how big or small a measurement that was. He decided to try to figure out what a negative exponent could mean.

a. Copy and complete Salvador's calculations at right. Use the pattern of dividing by 10 to fill in the missing values.

b. How is 10^2 related to 10^{-2}?

c. What type of numbers did the negative exponents create? Did negative exponents create negative numbers?

$$10^3 = 1000 \quad \div 10$$
$$10^2 = 100 \quad \div 10$$
$$10^1 = 10 \quad \div 10$$
$$10^0 =$$
$$10^{-1} =$$
$$10^{-2} =$$
$$10^{-3} =$$

8-76. Ngoc was curious about what Salvador was doing and began exploring patterns, too. He completed the calculations at right.

a. Copy and complete his calculations. Be sure to include all of the integer exponents from 5 to −3.

b. Look for patterns in his list. How are the values to the right of the equal sign changing? Is there a constant multiplier between each value?

$$2^5 = 32$$
$$2^4 = 16$$
$$2^3 = 8$$
$$\cdots$$
$$\cdots$$
$$2^{-1} = \tfrac{1}{2}$$
$$2^{-2} =$$
$$2^{-3} =$$

8-77. In problems 8-75 and 8-76, you saw that 10^0 and 2^0 both simplify to the same value. What is it? Do you think that any number to the zero power would have the same answer? Explain.

8-78. Both Ngoc and Salvador are looking for ways to calculate values with negative exponents without extending a pattern. Looking at the expression 5^{-2}, they each started to simplify differently.

Salvador thinks that 5^2 is 25, so 5^{-2} must be $\tfrac{1}{25}$. Ngoc thinks 5^{-2} is $\tfrac{1}{5^2}$. Which student is correct?

8-79.   Salvador's first questions about negative
         exponents came from science class, where he
         had learned that euglenas measured
         8.0×10^{-2} millimeters. Use your
         understanding of negative exponents to
         rewrite 8.0×10^{-2} in standard form.

8-80.   The probability of being struck by lightening in the United States is 0.000032%,
         while the probability of winning the grand prize in a certain lottery is
         6.278×10^{-7} percent. Which event is more likely to happen? Explain your
         reasoning, including how you rewrote the numbers to compare them.

8-81.   The list below contains a star, a river, and a type of bacteria. Which one is
         which? Use your understanding of scientific notation to put the three items
         listed below in order from largest to smallest and identify which is which.

    a.   Yangtze measures 6.3×10^5 meters.

    b.   Staphylococcus measures 6×10^{-7} meters.

    c.   Eta Carinae measures 7.1×10^{17} meters.

8-82.   Which of the numbers below are correctly written in scientific
         notation? For each that is not, rewrite it correctly.

    a. 4.51×10^{-2} b. 0.789×10^5

    c. 31.5×10^2 d. 3.008×10^{-8}

8-83.   Create a fraction from these expressions, and then show how you use a Giant
         One to simplify.

    a. $6^5 \cdot 6^{-3}$ b. $w^5 w^{-2}$ c. $10^{-4} \cdot 10^5$

8-84.   Now it is time to reverse your thinking. If negative exponents can create fractions, then can fractions be written as expressions with negative exponents? Simplify the expressions below. Write your answer in two different forms: as a fraction and as an expression with a negative exponent.

a. $\dfrac{6^3}{6^5}$

b. $\dfrac{m^5}{m^6}$

c. $\dfrac{10^2}{10^5}$

8-85.   Rewrite each expression in a simpler form. Visualize the factored form and the Giant One to help you, or write it out if it is reasonable to do so.

a. $(5x^2)^3$

b. $(4x)^2(5x^2)$

c. $\dfrac{a^2 c^{11}}{a^5 c^3}$

8-86.   Lamar has a list of 600 pages to read to finish his book for his upcoming book report. He sets a goal to read half of the pages left in his book each day.

a.   How many pages will Lamar have to read the first day to meet his goal? How many will he have left to read after 3 days?

b.   How many pages will he need to read on day 8? With your team, write two different expressions to show how you found your answer.

8-87.   **Additional Challenge:** Alice was simplifying the expressions at right when she noticed a pattern. Each exponent under the radical (square root) sign was two times the exponent of the final answer. She wanted to know more about why this was happening.

$$\sqrt{3^4} = \sqrt{81} = 9 = 3^2$$
$$\sqrt{6^2} = \sqrt{36} = 6 = 6^1$$
$$\sqrt{5^4} = \sqrt{625} = 25 = 5^2$$
$$\sqrt{2^6} = \sqrt{64} = 8 = 2^3$$

a.   Confirm Alice's pattern by simplifying the expression $\sqrt{5^6}$ on your calculator. Can you rewrite your answer as 5 raised to a power?

b.   What does the operation "square root" do to an expression? What operation does it "undo"?

c.   Investigate this pattern using the expression $\sqrt{4^6}$.

- Expand the expression.

- Rewrite 4^6 as an expression raised to the second power.

- Use the square root to "undo" the squaring.

- Write your final answer, and check it on your calculator.

d.   Use that thinking to rewrite each expression below.

i. $\sqrt{7^4}$

ii. $\sqrt{9^8}$

iii. $\sqrt{3^{14}}$

METHODS AND MEANINGS

MATH NOTES

Scientific Notation

Scientific notation is a way of writing very large and very small numbers compactly. A number is said to be in scientific notation when it is written as a product of two factors as described below.

- The first factor is less than 10 and greater than or equal to 1.

- The second factor has a base of 10 and an integer exponent.

- The factors are separated by a multiplication sign.

Scientific Notation	Standard Form
5.32×10^6	5,320,000
3.07×10^{-4}	0.000307
2.61×10^{-15}	0.00000000000000261

8-88. Decide which numbers below are correctly written in scientific notation. If they are not, rewrite them.

a. 92.5×10^{-2} b. 6.875×10^2 c. 2.8×10 d. 0.83×100^2

8-89. In the table at right, write each power of 10 as a decimal and as a fraction.

a. Describe how the decimals and fractions change as you progress down the table.

b. How would you tell someone how to write 10^{-12} as a fraction? You do not have to write the actual fraction.

Power of 10	Decimal Form	Fraction Form
10^0		
10^{-1}	0.1	$\frac{1}{10}$
10^{-2}		$\frac{1}{100}$
10^{-3}		
10^{-4}		
10^{-5}		

8-90.   Mary wants to have $8500 to travel to South America when she is 21. She
         currently has $6439 in a savings account earning 4% annual compound interest.
         Mary is 13 now.

    a.   If Mary does not take out or deposit any money, how much money will
         Mary have when she is 15?

    b.   Will Mary have enough money for her trip when she is 21?

    c.   If Mary were to graph this situation, describe what the graph would look
         like.

8-91.   Recall that vertical lines around a number are the symbol for the absolute value
         of a number. Simplify each expression.

    a. $|6|$ b. $|-17|$ c. $-|-4.5|$

    d. $|2-5|$ e. $|2-3\cdot5|$ f. $-2\cdot|-2|$

8-92.   For each equation below, solve for x. Sometimes the easiest strategy is to use
         mental math.

    a. $x - \frac{3}{5} = 1\frac{2}{5}$ b. $5.2 + x = 10.95$

    c. $2x - 3.25 = 7.15$ d. $\frac{x}{16} = \frac{3}{8}$

8-93.   Determine the coordinates of each point of intersection without graphing.

    a. $y = 2x - 3$ b. $y = 2x - 5$
         $y = 4x + 1$ $y = -4x - 2$

8-94.   Write each number in scientific notation.

    a.   5467.8   b.   0.0032   c.   8,007,020

8-95.   Simplify each expression using the rules for exponents.

    a. $\frac{3^5}{3^{10}}$ b. $10x^4(10x)^{-2}$ c. $(\frac{1}{4})^3 \cdot (4)^2$ d. $\frac{(xy)^3}{xy^3}$

8-96.   Simplify each expression.

a. $-\frac{9}{5} \cdot \frac{8}{15}$

b. $\frac{1}{5} + (-\frac{2}{15}) - (-\frac{4}{9})$

c. $-\frac{4}{8} \cdot \frac{3}{7} \cdot (-\frac{2}{5})$

d. $\frac{3}{5} \cdot (-\frac{2}{7}) + (-\frac{5}{7})(\frac{3}{10})$

e. $-8\frac{1}{9} + 3\frac{5}{6}$

f. $2\frac{1}{2} \cdot 4\frac{1}{5}$

8-97.   Athletes in the Middle Plains School District regularly receive personal advising on their nutrition. Coaches wondered if the nutritional advising was having an impact, so they divided athletes into two groups. One group received advice and one group did not. After six months, they collected the following data:

# OF ATHLETES	Received Nutrition Advice	Did Not Receive Nutrition Advice
Regularly Ate a Balanced Breakfast	46	39
Often Did Not Eat a Balanced Breakfast	89	73

a.   Which is the independent variable?

b.   Make a relative frequency table.

c.   Is there an association between receiving the nutritional advice and regularly eating a balanced breakfast?

8-98.   Graph the points $X(-3,5)$, $Y(-2,3)$, and $Z(-1,4)$. Connect them to make a triangle.

a.   Reflect the triangle across the y-axis. What are the new coordinates of point Z?

b.   Translate the original triangle down 6 units and right 3 units. What are the new coordinates of point Y?

c.   Dilate the original triangle by multiplying each coordinate by -1. Describe the new shape you create.

8-99.   The table below shows the amount of money Francis had in his bank account each day since he started his new job.

Days at New Job	Money in Account
0	$27
1	$70
2	$113
3	$156

a.   Write a rule for the amount of money in Francis's account. Let x represent the number of days and y represent the number of dollars in the account.

b.   When will Francis have more than $1000 in his account?

$8.2.4$ How do I compute it?

$$3^5 \cdot 3^2 = 3^7$$

Operations with Scientific Notation

Scientific notation is an application of exponents and the base 10 system. It is very useful when writing very large numbers, like the distance to Alpha Centauri, which is 4.13×10^{16} m, or the radius of the hydrogen atom, which is 5.29×10^{-11} m. But what if you wanted to know how many times larger the distance to Alpha Centauri is than the hydrogen atom? How would you calculate this? What if you wanted to add or subtract two numbers written in scientific notation? In this lesson, you will learn how to do operations with numbers written in scientific notation.

8-100.   A typical dwarf sperm whale, the planet's smallest whale species, weighs about 3×10^2 pounds. A blue whale, the planet's largest whale, might weigh about 4.5×10^5 pounds. Estimate about how many times heavier a blue whale is than a dwarf sperm whale, without using a calculator.

8-101. There are about 1.8×10^{21} molecules in one gram of table sugar ($C_{12}H_{22}O_{11}$). A baker uses 8×10^2 grams in a recipe for cinnamon pastries.

a. How many molecules of sugar does the baker use? Do not use your calculator.

b. When the baker multiplied, her calculator displayed the answer below.

| 1.44E24 |

What do you think her calculator is displaying? Explain.

8-102. Find $(1.75 \times 10^{20})(6.01 \times 10^{14})$ in scientific notation without using a calculator. Then check your answer with your calculator. Write down exactly what your calculator displayed.

8-103. The average distance from the sun to the earth is 1.488×10^{11} meters. If the length of the average paperclip is 3×10^{-2} meters, how many paperclips would need to be connected together to reach the sun?

8-104. Jeremiah wanted to do the following problem. However, he was not sure how to get started, because the numbers were in scientific notation. He knew that if he wrote them out in standard form, without scientific notation, then he could line up the numbers with the same place value and add them together. He does not want to have to do that, though, because he does not want to write all of those zeroes. He is worried that he might just get more confused if he did write them all out. Work with your team to find a way to add the numbers required without first rewriting them in standard form. Here is the problem Jeremiah wanted to solve:

The average distance of each of the first five planets from sun is shown in the table below. Is the distance to Jupiter more or less than the combined distances of the first four planets (Mercury, Venus, Earth, and Mars)?

Planet	Average Distance from the Sun (miles)
Mercury	5.79×10^7
Venus	6.72×10^7
Earth	9.3×10^7
Mars	1.416×10^8
Jupiter	4.836×10^8

8-105. The United States Department of Agriculture reported in *Vegetables and Melons Outlook* in 2007 that the average American consumes about 7.4×10^3 potato chips in a year. Since Idaho had about 1.5×10^6 people in 2007, how many potato chips would Idaho residents have consumed in 2007? Without using a calculator, make an exact computation and record your answer in scientific notation.

8-106. One of the giant pyramids of Egypt is made of about 2.4×10^6 carved blocks of stone. If each block weighs approximately 4.95×10^3 pounds, about how many pounds of block make up the pyramid?

8-107. Simplify.

a. $1.24 \times 10^3 + 2.3 \times 10^4$

b. $\frac{4 \times 10^5}{8 \times 10^7}$

c. $8.5 \times 10^{10} \cdot 7.6 \times 10^{12}$

8-108. **Additional Challenge:** The radius of the earth is about 6×10^8 cm.

a. The volume of a sphere can be estimated by $V = \frac{88}{21} r^3$, where r is the radius of the sphere. Without using a calculator, estimate the earth's volume in scientific notation.

b. Density can be found from $\frac{mass}{volume}$. The earth's mass is about 6×10^{24} kg. Without a calculator, estimate the earth's density. Answer in scientific notation.

METHODS AND **M**EANINGS

MATH NOTES

Laws of Exponents

Expressions that include exponents can be expanded into factored form and then rewritten in simplified exponent form.

Expression	**Factored Form**	**Simplified Exponent Form**
$(5x)^3(2y)(x^2)y$	$5 \cdot x \cdot 5 \cdot x \cdot 5 \cdot x \cdot 2 \cdot y \cdot x \cdot x \cdot y$	$250x^5y^2$

The **Laws of Exponents** summarize several rules for simplifying expressions that have exponents. The rules below are true if $x \neq 0$ and $y \neq 0$.

$$x^a \cdot x^b = x^{(a+b)} \qquad (x^a)^b = x^{ab} \qquad \frac{x^a}{x^b} = x^{(a-b)}$$

$$x^0 = 1 \qquad (x^a y^b)^c = x^{ac} y^{bc} \qquad x^{-a} = \frac{1}{x^a}$$

Review & Preview

8-109. Compute each product or quotient. Convert the final answer to scientific notation if necessary.

a. $(3 \times 10^2)(2 \times 10^3)$

b. $(2.75 \times 10^{-2})(2.5 \times 10^8)$

c. $\frac{8 \times 10^{12}}{4 \times 10^7}$

8-110. Use the laws of exponents to simplify the following expressions.

a. $(x^2)(x^5)$

b. $\frac{y^7}{y^4}$

c. $x^3 \cdot x^4$

8-111.   For the following examples, tell whether there is positive association, negative association, or no association.

   a.   The number of inches of rain per hour and the height of water in a reservoir.

   b.   The amount of food a person eats and how many pets he or she has.

   c.   The height of a tree and the amount of nutrients it gets.

   d.   The number of hours spent hiking in the mountains and the amount of water left in your water bottle.

8-112.   Silvia has a picture from her trip to the Grand Canyon. The photo is 4 inches tall by 6 inches wide.

   a.   She would like to make a larger photo for her wall that is as big as possible. The widest the enlarged photo can be is 48 inches. How tall will the enlarged photo be?

   b.   Silvia also wants a wallet-sized photo to carry around and show her friends. She wants it 1.5 inches tall. How wide will it be?

8-113.   Since the beginning of school, Steven has been saving money to buy a new MP3 player. His bank balance is represented by the graph below.

   a.   According to the graph, about how much money had Steven saved after 2 weeks of school?

   b.   About how much money did Steven probably have after 4 weeks of school? How can you tell?

   c.   If he keeps saving at the same rate, how much will he have saved by Week 7? Explain how you know.

8-114.   The science club is selling homemade cookies to raise money for a field trip. The club members know that 12 dozen cookies uses 3 pounds of flour. Use that information to solve each part below.

   a.   How much flour is needed for 18 dozen cookies?

   b.   How many cookies can be made with 10 pounds of flour?

$8.3.1$ Can I predict the output?

Functions in Graphs and Tables

Throughout this course, you have used rules that relate two variables to make graphs and find information. An example of such a rule is $y = 5x - 3$. Today you will look more closely at how rules that relate two variables help establish a relationship between the variables.

8-115.　Draw a sketch of an example of each graph described below.

　　a.　A graph that neither increases nor decreases.

　　b.　A graph that decreases non-linearly.

　　c.　A graph that increases linearly and then decreases linearly.

　　d.　A graph that is consistently increasing.

8-116.　**ARE WE RELATED?**

Examine the table of input (x) and output (y) values below. Is there a relationship between the input and output values? If so, state the relationship.

x	−3	−2	−1	0	1	2	3
y	−16	−10	−4	2	8	14	20

8-117.   FUNCTION MACHINES

A **function** works like a machine. Numbers
are put into the machine one at a time, and
then the rule performs the operation(s) on each
input to determine each output. For example,
when $x = 3$ is put into a machine with the rule
$y = 5x - 7$, the rule multiplies the input, 3, by
5 and then subtracts 7 to get the output, which
is 8. This input and output can be written as an ordered pair: $(3,8)$. Then it can
be placed on an xy-coordinate graph.

a.   Find the output of the function machine at
       right when the input is $x = 4$.

b.   Likewise, find y when $x = -1$ and $x = 10$.

c.   If the output of this relation is 45, what was
       the input? That is, if $y = 45$, then what is x?
       Is there more than one possible input?

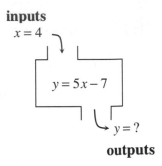

inputs

$x = 4$

$y = 5x - 7$

$y = ?$

outputs

8-118.   Some relationships are special in that they are called **functions**. Below are two
relationships, one of which ($y = x^2 - 2$) is a function and the other,
($x = y^2 - 2$), is not. Look at the graph and table of values below for each
relationship and discuss with your team why you think the relationship in
part (a) is a function and the one in part (b) is not. Use your ideas to create a
definition of a function. Be prepared to share your ideas with the rest of the
class. Use these questions to guide your discussion:

What is similar about the two relationships?

What is different about the two relationships?

What can we predict about the outputs for each relationship for a given input?

$y = x^2 - 2$

x	-3	-2	-1	0	1	2	3
y	7	2	-1	-2	-1	2	7

$x = y^2 - 2$

x	7	2	-1	-2	-1	2	7
y	-3	-2	-1	0	1	2	3

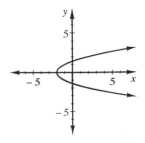

8-119.   Examine each of the relationships below. Compare the inputs and outputs of each relation and decide if the relationship is a function. Explain your reasoning. Use your definition of a function from problem 8-118 to help you justify your conclusion.

a.

x	7	–2	0	4	9	–3	6
y	6	–3	4	2	10	–3	0

b.

x	3	–1	2	0	1	2	9
y	4	–5	9	7	4	–8	2

c.

d.

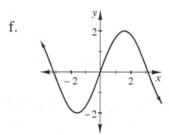

e.

x	y
–8	11
4	3
11	–8
6	3
–8	11

f.

8-120.   **LEARNING LOG**

In your Learning Log, describe what it means for a relationship to be a function. How can you describe the differences between graphs of functions and graphs of non-functions? In your Learning Log, give examples of what a function and a non-function look like in a table and on a graph. Title this entry "Functions and Non-Functions" and include today's date.

8-121.   For each part below, work with your team to create a graph based on the given information. Do each part on a separate set of axes. If necessary, make a table with sufficient points so that the pattern of the graph is clear.

a.

x	0	1	1	4	4
y	0	1	–1	2	–2

b. $y = |x - 2|$

c.   A starting value of 8 and a rate of change of $-\frac{2}{3}$.

d. $xy = 12$

8-122. Use your previous experiences to describe each of the graphs above mathematically and as clearly as possible. Use the questions below to help you get started. Also, as you "read the graph from left to right," tell whether the y-values are increasing, decreasing, or both. Are there any points on the graph where something special happens?

Is it linear or non-linear?

Is it a function or not?

Is the graph discrete or continuous?

How else can I describe the graph?

8-123. Find the relationship between x and y in the table below and write the rule.

x	−2	1	10	4	7		0	5	6
y		1			2401	16		625	

Relationship: $y =$ _____

8-124. Find the corresponding inputs or outputs for the following relationships. If there is no solution, explain why not. Be careful: In some cases, there may be no solution or more than one possible solution.

a. $x = 8$

$y = |x|$

$y = ?$

b. $x = ?$

$y = 3 - |x|$

$y = 2$

c. $k = -6$

$y = \frac{k}{2} + 1$

$y = ?$

d. $x = 3$

$y = -x^2$

$y = ?$

8-125. Compute each product or quotient. Convert the final answer to scientific notation if necessary.

a. $(6 \times 10^2)(4 \times 10^5)$

b. $(1.75 \times 10^{-2})(8 \times 10^{-8})$

c. $\frac{9 \times 10^5}{4 \times 10^7}$

8-126. Simplify and solve each equation below for x. Show your work and check your answer, if possible.

a. $24 = 3x + 3$

b. $2(x - 6) = y - 14$

c. $3(2x - 3) = 4x - 5$

d. $\frac{3}{4} y = 2x - 6$

8-127.   Complete the table.

x	−6	3	6	0			1
y		4		2	−4		

   a.   Find the rule.

   b.   What is the slope?

   c.   Is this an example of linear or non-linear growth? Justify your answer.

8-128.   The two triangles at right are similar shapes.

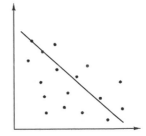

   a.   What is the scale factor between shape A
        and shape B?

   b.   Find the missing sides.

   c.   If you wanted to make shape A smaller instead of bigger, what is a scale
        factor you could use?

8-129.   Anthony has added a trend line to the scatterplot
          at right. Do you agree with where he put the
          line? Explain your reasoning.

8-130.   Find the value of each indicated angle in the following figures. Do not use a
          protractor. Use the properties of straight and vertical angles to help you.

   a.   b.   c.

   d.   e.

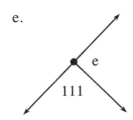

Core Connections, Course 3

8-131. Daniella has $210 in the bank, and her balance is growing at a rate of $3 each month. Lori has $187 in the bank, but her balance is growing at a rate of $4.50 each month. Write a system of equations to find when the girls will have the same amount of money. Be sure to define your variables.

8-132. A candy store's specialty is taffy. Customers can fill a bag with taffy, and the price is based on how much the candy weighs. The store charges $2 for 10 ounces (oz) of taffy.

  a. Copy the table below and fill in the missing values. Add three more entries.

Amount of Taffy (oz)	2	5	10	12	15	20
Price ($)			$2			$4

  b. Graph the values in the table. Let x represent the number of ounces and y represent the price in dollars.

  c. Is this situation proportional? Explain your reasoning.

  d. What is the slope of the line you graphed? What information does the slope tell you?

  e. Write the equation that represents the candy store's pricing.

8-133. Solve each equation below for the given variable. Be sure to check your solution.

  a. $6x - 11 = 3x + 16$

  b. $-2(5 - 3x) + 5 = 9 + 3x$

  c. $\frac{6}{k-2} = 10$

  d. $\frac{4}{3x-1} = \frac{2}{x+3}$

8-134. Compute each product or quotient. Convert the final answer to scientific notation if necessary.

  a. $(2 \times 10^2)(3.2 \times 10^{-5})$

  b. $(4 \times 10^2)(2.5 \times 10^{-3})$

  c. $\frac{2.5 \times 10^5}{5 \times 10^8}$

8-135.	This problem is a checkpoint for transformations. It will be referred to as Checkpoint 8.

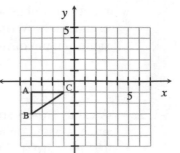

△ABC at right is transformed into △XYZ. Tell the coordinates of the vertices of the new triangle after each of the following transformations.

a.	Translate △ABC 2 units right and 3 units up.

b.	Reflect △ABC across the y-axis.

c.	Rotate △ABC 90° clockwise about the origin.

d.	Dilate △ABC with a scale factor of 2 from the origin.

Check your answers by referring to the Checkpoint 8 materials located at the back of your book.

Ideally, at this point you are comfortable working with these types of problems and can solve them correctly. If you feel that you need more confidence when solving these types of problems, then review the Checkpoint 8 materials and try the practice problems provided. From this point on, you will be expected to do problems like these correctly and with confidence.

Chapter 8 Closure   What have I learned?

Reflection and Synthesis

The activities below offer you a chance to reflect about what you have learned during this chapter. As you work, look for concepts that you feel very comfortable with, ideas that you would like to learn more about, and topics you need more help with.

①   SUMMARIZING MY UNDERSTANDING

This section gives you an opportunity to show what you know about certain math topics or ideas.

THE INTEREST GAME

Today you are going to play a game with your teacher. Your team's goal is to have more money in your account than any other team at the end of the game. You will start with an account balance of $1000. You will record your work and your balances throughout the game on the Chapter 8 Closure Resource Page A. Your team will also need an envelope containing interest rate cards.

To start the game, your teacher will select a card that gives you a time. Record the starting balance and time in the first section on your resource page. Then, as a team, pull a card from the envelope and compute the interest on your account based on the card and the time given to you by your teacher. When you have finished with a card, you will leave it on the desk. Transfer your new account balance to the starting amount in a new section on the resource page. Your teacher will then give you a new time and you will draw another card from your envelope. Your teacher will tell you how many cards to select during the course of the game. While playing the game, ask your teammates the following questions.

- How do we determine compound interest?

- How do we find simple interest?

- How is the interest growing? How can we see this in the interest expression?

Activity continues on next page. →

① Activity continued from previous page.

When playing the Interest Game, you were trying to get the most amount of money in your team account.

a. What was your final amount?

b. Did you do more compound-interest or simple-interest problems?

c. What do you think made the most difference in the amount of money you made, the interest rate or the kind of interest earned (simple or compound)?

② WHAT HAVE I LEARNED?

Doing the problems in this section will help you to evaluate which types of problems you feel comfortable with and which ones you need more help with.

Solve each problem as completely as you can. The table at the end of this closure section provides answers to these problems. It also tells you where you can find additional help and where to find practice problems like them.

CL 8-136. Rewrite each expression in a simpler form. If it is reasonable, write out the factored form to help you.

a. $3^2 \cdot 3^5$ b. $\frac{4^5}{4^3}$ c. $(3x^2)^4$ d. $(3x^3)(7x^5)$

CL 8-137. Daniel has $1200 in the bank. He is earning 3.5% compound interest each month. How much money will he have in the bank in one year?

CL 8-138. Complete the following table.

Scientific Notation	Standard Form
1.9231×10^3	
	0.00356
	243,700,000
8.149×10^{-6}	

CL 8-139.   Solve each equation or system of equations.

    a. $\frac{x+3}{2} = \frac{x-1}{5}$ b. $y = \frac{1}{2}x + 3$

                                                                               $y = \frac{1}{3}x - 4$

CL 8-140.   The triangles at right are similar.

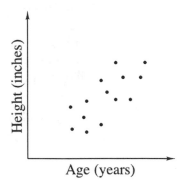

    a.   Find x.

    b.   Find y.

    c.   Find the ratio of the perimeters of the two triangles.

CL 8-141.   At a family reunion, each family member recorded his or her age and height.

    a.   What kind of association does the scatter plot have?

    b.   Copy the scatterplot and draw the trend line.

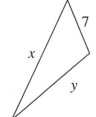

CL 8-142.   At the farmer's market, Laura bought three pounds of heirloom tomatoes. If the tomatoes are priced at $8 per five pounds, what did Laura pay for her tomatoes?

CL 8-143.   Matt moved Triangle A on the graph at right to match up with Triangle B in three moves. Follow the steps Matt wrote below. What was his final move?

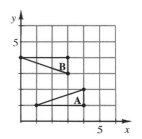

    1.   *Slide the triangle up 3 units.*

    2.   *Reflect the triangle across the line $y = 4$.*

    3.   *?*

CL 8-144.   For each of the problems above, do the following:

- Draw a bar or number line that represents 0 to 10.

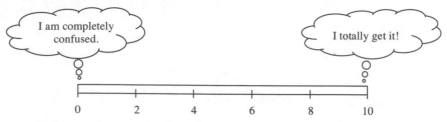

- Color or shade in a portion of the bar that represents your level of understanding and comfort with completing that problem on your own.

If any of your bars are less than a 5, choose *one* of those problems and do one of the following tasks:

- Write two questions that you would like to ask about that problem.
- Brainstorm two things that you DO know about that type of problem.

If all of your bars are a 5 or above, choose one of those problems and do one of these tasks:

- Write two questions you might ask or hints you might give to a student who was stuck on the problem.
- Make a new problem that is similar and more challenging than that problem and solve it.

③   WHAT TOOLS CAN I USE?

You have several tools and references available to help support your learning – your teacher, your study team, your math book, and your Toolkit, to name only a few. At the end of each chapter you will have an opportunity to review your Toolkit for completeness as well as to revise or update it to better reflect your current understanding of big ideas.

The main elements of your Toolkit should be your Learning Log, Math Notes, and the vocabulary used in this chapter. Math words that are new to this chapter appear in bold in the text. Refer to the lists provided below and follow your teacher's instructions to revise your Toolkit, which will help make it a useful reference for you as you complete this chapter and as you work in future chapters.

Learning Log Entries
- Lesson 8.1.3 – Simple and Compound Interest
- Lesson 8.2.1 – Scientific Notation
- Lesson 8.2.3 – Simplifying Exponent Expressions
- Lesson 8.3.1 – Functions

- Lesson 8.1.1 – Simple Interest
- Lesson 8.1.2 – Exponents
- Lesson 8.1.3 – Compound Interest
- Lesson 8.2.3 – Scientific Notation
- Lesson 8.2.4 – Laws of Exponents
- Lesson 8.3.1 – Functions

Mathematical Vocabulary

The following is a list of vocabulary found in this chapter. Some of the words you have been seen in previous chapters. The words in bold are the words new to this chapter. Make sure that you are familiar with the terms below and know what they mean. For the words you do not know, refer to the glossary or index. You might also add these words to your Toolkit so that you can reference them in the future.

base	Commutative Property of Multiplication	
compound interest	**exponent**	**exponential function**
exponential growth	factoring	**function**
interest	linear equation	**linear growth**
linear function	period	principal
relationship	**scientific notation**	simple interest

Answers and Support for Closure Problems
What Have I Learned?

Note: MN = Math Note, LL = Learning Log

Problem	Solution	Need Help?	More Practice
CL 8-136.	a. 3^7 b. 4^2 c. $81x^8$ d. $21x^8$	Lessons 8.2.1, 8.2.2, and 8.2.3 MN: 8.1.2 and 8.2.4 LL: 8.2.3	Problems 8-37, 8-38, 8-47, 8-55, 8-59, 8-65, 8-60, 8-72, 8-73, and 8-85
CL 8-137.	$1813.28	Lesson 8.1.2 MN: 8.1.3	Problems 8-13, 8-14, 8-27, 8-30, and 8-35

Problem	Solution		Need Help?	More Practice
CL 8-138.	Scientific Notation	Standard Form	Lessons 8.2.1, 8.2.2, and 8.2.3 MN: 8.2.3 LL: 8.2.1	Problems 8-48, 8-54, 8-84, and 8-88
	1.9231×10^3	1923.1		
	3.56×10^{-3}	0.00356		
	2.437×10^8	243,700,000		
	8.149×10^{-6}	0.000008149		
CL 8-139.	a. $x = -\frac{17}{3}$ b. $y = -18$, $x = -42$		Lessons 2.1.8, 2.1.9, 5.2.2, and 5.2.3 MN: 2.1.8, 2.1.9, 5.2.2, and 5.2.3 LL: 2.1.9	Problems 8-126, 8-131, and 8-133
CL 8-140.	a. 15.75 b. 12.25 c. $\frac{35}{20} = \frac{7}{4}$		Lesson 6.2.2 MN: 6.2.2 and 6.2.6	Problems 8-12, 8-16, and 8-128
CL 8-141.	a. positive association b.		Lessons 7.1.3 and 7.3.2 MN: 7.1.3 and 7.3.2 LL: 7.1.3 and 7.3.2	Problems 8-21, 8-67, 8-111, and 8-129
CL 8-142.	$4.80		Lessons 1.2.1 and 1.2.2 MN: 1.2.2 and 1.2.2 LL: 1.2.1	Problems 8-50, 8-114, and 8-132
CL 8-143.	Slide the triangle left 1 unit.		Lessons 6.1.1 and 6.1.4 MN: 6.1.3 LL: 6.1.3	Problems 8-34, 8-69, 8-98, and 8-135

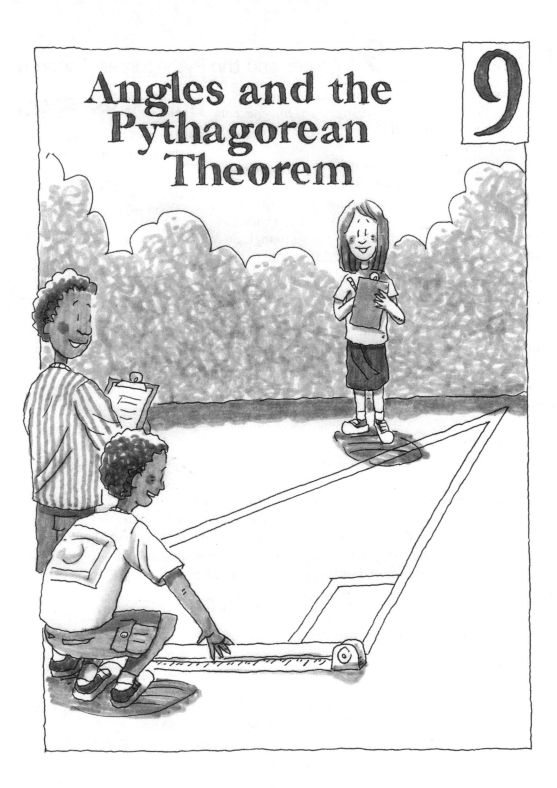

Angles and the Pythagorean Theorem

9

CHAPTER 9 Angles and the Pythagorean Theorem

This chapter focuses on several important geometry concepts. You will begin to investigate several concepts in this chapter, but you will learn a lot more about them in future courses.

Section 9.1 focuses on angle relationships. The angle relationships you will explore are the ones found with parallel lines and the angles inside and outside of triangles. You will also learn how you can use what you know about angles to decide if a pair of triangles is similar, without even knowing the side lengths!

In Section 9.2, you will focus on the relationships between side lengths in individual triangles. You will learn how to decide if three different lengths will be able to form a triangle and what kind of triangle will be formed. You will use the unique relationship between the side lengths of right triangles to solve problems.

Guiding Questions

Think about these questions throughout this chapter:

How are they related?

Can I make a triangle?

What if it is a right triangle?

What do I know about this triangle?

You will also learn some more about numbers. In particular, you will learn the mathematical operation called "square root" and explore how it relates to squaring a number. You will learn how to convert both terminating and repeating decimals to fractions. Finally, you will look at some special numbers called "irrationals."

In this chapter, you will learn how to:

➤ Find the measurements of missing angles made by a line that intersects parallel lines.

➤ Find unknown angles inside and outside of triangles.

➤ Determine if two triangles are similar by looking at their angles.

➤ Find missing side lengths of right triangles using the Pythagorean Theorem.

➤ Find the square root of a number and identify irrational numbers.

➤ Convert terminating and repeating decimals to fractions.

Chapter Outline

Section 9.1 You will look at angles formed when a third line intersects a set of parallel lines, identifying the relationships between certain pairs of angles. You will also learn about the special relationships between the angles inside and outside a triangle and how to tell if two triangles are similar without knowing anything about their side lengths.

Section 9.2 You will learn how to determine if any three lengths will form a triangle, and, if they do, whether that triangle will be acute, obtuse, or right. You will find missing sides of right triangles using the Pythagorean Theorem. You will also learn about the square root operation and irrational numbers.

9.1.1 How are the angles related?

Parallel Line Angle Pair Relationships

In a previous course you probably learned the vocabulary and considered the relationships created by two intersecting lines. Now you will look at the vocabulary and relationships created by a line that intersects two parallel lines.

9-1. The box below has some reminders about notation. Read the information, and then use it to complete the following problems.

	Arrowheads at the end of lines indicate that they extend indefinitely. Marks on pairs of lines or segments like **>** and **>>** indicate that the lines (or segments) are **parallel**.
	The small box at the point of intersection of two lines or segments indicates that the lines (or segments) are **perpendicular** (that is, form right angles).

In Figure 1 below, line *s* is parallel to line *t* , and line *r* intersects (cuts) line *s* and line *t*. In Figure 2, lines *x* and *y* are *not* parallel, and line *w* intersects lines *x* and *y*. Lines *r* and *w* are called **transversals** because they cut across (intersect) 2 lines. Transversals can also intersect several lines, each at different points.

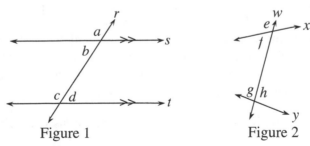

Figure 1   Figure 2

a. Take a sheet of plain paper (tracing paper is best, but binder paper will work) and place it over ∠*a*. Using a ruler as a guide, make a precise copy of the angle. Slide the copy of ∠*a* to ∠*c* and compare the sizes of the two angles. What do you observe?

b. Trace a copy of ∠*b* and place it over ∠*d*. What do you observe?

c. Trace a copy of ∠*e* and place it over ∠*g*. What do you observe?

Problem continues on next page. —

9-1.   *Problem continued from previous page.*

   d.   Trace a copy of ∠*f* and place it over ∠*h*. What do you observe?

   e.   Both figures show two lines that are intersected by a transversal. Summarize your findings by describing the relationship between pairs of angles and parallel lines cut by a transversal. That is, when the angles are congruent, what must be true? And vice versa: If the lines are parallel, then what must be true?

9-2.   Your teacher will provide you with a Lesson 9.1.1 Resource Page. On it, you will find the figures below. Keep it in an easily accessible place, as you will use it in several problems.

   Each figure below shows a pair of <u>parallel</u> lines, *p* and *q*, which are intersected (cut) by a third line, *m*. Line *m*, often called a transversal, forms several angles at each point of intersection with *p* and *q*. If you need help with some of the vocabulary from a previous course, see the Math Notes box in this lesson.

Figure 1   Figure 2   Figure 3

   a.   Use what you know about straight angles to calculate the measures of these angles: *b*, *d*, *f*, *k*, *r*, and *s*. When everyone in your team has completed the calculations and agrees with the results, check with your team to be sure that everyone agrees that the results are correct.

   b.   Keep in mind that lines *p* and *q* must be parallel as you complete the directions below.

   •   In Figure 1, compare the measures of angles *a* and *d*, and then compare the measures of angles *b* and *e*.

   •   In Figure 2, compare the measures of angles *f* and *j*, and then compare the measures of angles *g* and *k*.

   •   In Figure 3, make similar comparisons for angles *n* and *s*, and then for angles *r* and *t*.

Problem continues on next page. →

Core Connections, Course 3

9-2.   *Problem continued from previous page.*

> Angles on the same side of two lines and on the same side
> of a third line (the transversal) that intersects the two lines
> are called **corresponding angles**. In the figure at right,
> angles 1 and 2 are corresponding angles, as are angles 3
> and 4. Other examples of corresponding angles are on
> your resource page: angles *a* and *d* in Figure 1, angles *g*
> and *k* in Figure 2, and angles *r* and *t* in Figure 3.

c. A **conjecture** is an inference or judgment based on incomplete evidence.
Use the definition above and your observations in part (b) to complete the
following conjecture.

Conjecture: If two parallel lines are cut by a transversal, then pairs of
corresponding angles are ___ .

9-3.   Now focus on a different set of angles on the Lesson 9.1.1 Resource Page.

a. Use what you know about straight angles and/or vertical angles and your
results from the previous problem to find the measures of angles *c*
(Figure 1), *h* (Figure 2), and *w* (Figure 3).

b. Compare the measures of the following three pairs of angles.

• Figure 1: $m\angle c$ and $m\angle d$

• Figure 2: $m\angle h$ and $m\angle j$

• Figure 3: $m\angle w$ and $m\angle s$

How is each pair of angles related?

c. Read the following definition, and then use it along with your observation
in part (a) to complete the conjecture that follows.

> Angles between a pair of lines and on opposite sides
> of a transversal are called **alternate interior angles**.
> In the figure at right, angles 1 and 2 and angles *x* and
> *y* are examples of *pairs* of alternate interior angles.
> Other examples of alternate interior angles are on
> your resource page: angles *c* and *d* in Figure 1,
> angles *h* and *j* in Figure 2, and angles *w* and *s* in
> Figure 3.

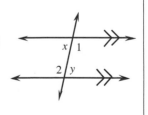

Conjecture: If parallel lines are cut by a transversal, then alternate interior
angles are _____ .

9-4.   Use Figures 1 through 3 on the Lesson 9.1.1 Resource Page from problems 9-2 and 9-3.

   a.   Examine the pairs of angles b and d, g and j, and r and s on the resource page. If you add the measures of each *pair*, what do you observe?

   b.   Write a conjecture about two angles on the *same side* of a transversal and are *between* two parallel lines. Note: These are called **same side interior angles**.

        Conjecture: The sum of the measures of two interior angles on the same side of a transversal is _____.

        Use your conjecture and the figure below right to answer parts (c) and (d).

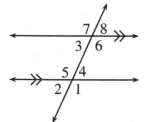

   c.   If $m\angle 2 = 67°$, what is $m\angle 5$?

   d.   If $m\angle 4 = 4x + 23°$ and $m\angle 6 = 3x + 17°$, find $m\angle 4$. Explain your steps.

9-5.   Classify each of the following pairs of angles as corresponding, alternate interior, same side interior, straight, or "none of these."

   a.   b.   c.

   d.   e.   f.

   g.   h.   i.

                    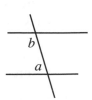

   j.   What condition is necessary to be able to say that the pairs of corresponding angles or alternate interior angles above are equal?

Core Connections, Course 3

9-6.   Use your conjectures about parallel lines and the angles formed by a transversal to find the measures of the labeled angles. These figures are also on the Lesson 9.1.1 Resource Page. Show the step-by-step procedure you use *and* name each angle conjecture you use (e.g., corresponding, alternate interior, vertical, or straight) to justify your calculation.

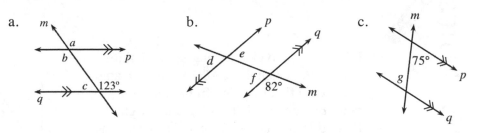

a.   b.   c.

9-7.   LEARNING LOG

What are the angle relationships that you have encountered so far? Answer this question in your Learning Log. Use your geometry vocabulary and include diagrams to show the relationships. Title this entry "Angle Relationships" and label it with today's date.

METHODS AND MEANINGS

MATH NOTES

Angle Vocabulary

It is common to identify angles using three letters. For example, ∠*ABC* means the angle you would find by going from point *A* to point *B* to point *C* in the diagram at right. Point *B* is the **vertex** of the angle (where the endpoints of the two sides meet), and $\overrightarrow{BA}$ and $\overrightarrow{BC}$ are the rays that define it. A **ray** is a part of a line that has an endpoint (starting point) and extends infinitely in one direction.

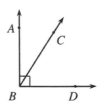

If two angles have measures that add up to 90°, they are called **complementary angles**. For example, in the diagram above, ∠*ABC* and ∠*CBD* are complementary because together they form a right angle.

If two angles have measures that add up to 180°, they are called **supplementary angles**. For example, in the diagram at right, ∠*EFG* and ∠*GFH* are supplementary because together they form a **straight angle** (that is, together they form a line).

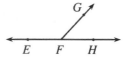

Two angles do not have to share a vertex to be complementary or supplementary. The first pair of angles at right are supplementary; the second pair of angles are complementary.

Supplementary

Complementary

Adjacent angles are angles that have a common vertex, share a common side, and have no interior points in common. So angles ∠*c* and ∠*d* in the diagram at right are adjacent angles, as are ∠*c* and ∠*f*, ∠*f* and ∠*g*, and ∠*g* and ∠*d*.

Vertical angles are the two opposite (that is, non-adjacent) angles formed by two intersecting lines, such as angles ∠*c* and ∠*g* in the diagram above right. By itself, ∠*c* is not a vertical angle, nor is ∠*g*, although ∠*c* and ∠*g* together are a pair of vertical angles. Vertical angles always have equal measure.

9-8.   Use the conjectures and definitions in this lesson
         to solve parts (a) and (b). Each part is a separate
         problem.

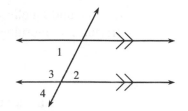

a.   If $m\angle 1 = 63°$, find $m\angle 2$ and $m\angle 3$ by
     calculation.

b.   If $m\angle 1 = 74°$ and $m\angle 4 = 3x - 18°$, write an
     equation and find x.

c.   If $m\angle 2 = 3x - 9°$ and $m\angle 1 = x + 25°$, write an equation to find x.
     Then find $m\angle 2$.

9-9.   If $m\angle 5 = 53°$ and $m\angle 7 = 125°$, find the
         measures of each numbered angle. Then explain
         how you found each angle, citing definitions and
         conjectures that support your steps.

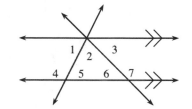

9-10.   Graph the following data as a scatterplot.

Height (Inches)	Test Scores (Percent)
24	3
56	86
72	98
49	50
18	0
36	12
70	90
66	81
61	75
34	25
59	80
57	77
64	88

a.   Does the graph show either a positive or
     a negative association?

b.   Does there appear to be an association between
     height and spelling ability?

c.   Does greater height cause better spelling ability?

d.   What other factors could create the association
     you see?

9-11.   Josue called his father to say that he was almost
         home. He had traveled 61.5 miles, which was $\frac{3}{4}$ of
         the way home. Write and solve an equation to
         calculate the total distance he will travel to get home.

9-12.   Ryan and Janelle are each driving from a different location to meet. When they
         each stopped for lunch at 12 noon, they called each other on their cell phones.
         Ryan had traveled 245 miles in $3\frac{1}{2}$ hours. Janelle had driven 260 miles in
         4 hours.

         If Ryan and Janelle were originally 910 miles apart when they had started
         driving that morning, at what time will they meet?

9-13.   Determine whether the graphs below are functions or not functions. Explain
         your reasoning.

a.

b.

c.

d.

e.

f.

Core Connections, Course 3

9.1.2 How can I find a missing angle?

Finding Unknown Angles in Triangles

In today's lesson, you will be challenged again to use what you *do* know to determine information that you did *not* previously know, in order to solve problems with variables. You will do an investigation to learn a new geometric relationship for triangles.

9-14.   Quigley was excited about what he had learned about angles. He went home, grabbed his older brother's math book, and tried to find some problems that he could do with angles. He came across the following problem that he wanted to solve.

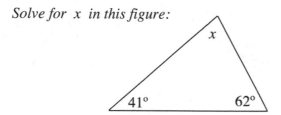

Solve for x in this figure:

a.   Using what you have learned about angles, can you find the measure of the angle? Why or why not?

b.   Estimate the measure of the angle.

9-15.   TANGLED TRIANGLES

Your teacher will give your team a copy of the Lesson 9.1.2 Resource Page. Cut out the three copies of the triangle.

Your Task: Determine the measure of the missing angle *without* using a protractor. As you work with your team, the following questions might help guide your discussion.

What do we know about angles?

Can we combine the unknown angle with any other angles to create a new angle that we do know?

9-16. Be prepared to contribute what your team has discovered to a whole-class discussion. Your teacher will use a technology tool to show what each team has discovered for their triangle. Keep track of what each team has found to see if you can find a relationship that would allow you to find a missing angle in *any* triangle.

9-17. Now use what you have discovered about the angles in a triangle to find the answer to the problem that Quigley was trying to solve in problem 9-14. How close was your estimate?

9-18. Use what you have learned about triangles and angles to write an equation that represents each situation. Then find each of the missing angle(s) in the triangles below.

a.

b.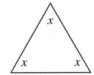

9-19. **Additional Challenge:** Use what you know about triangles and angle relationships to find the missing angles in the triangles below.

a.

b.

c.

d.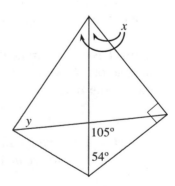

9-20.   LEARNING LOG

Today you explored a fundamental concept about a
triangle and the sum of its angles. In your Learning Log,
state this relationship in your own words and include at
least one example that shows how to use this idea. Title
this entry "Angles in a Triangle" and label it with today's date.

ＭETHODS AND ＭEANINGS

MATH NOTES

Parallel Lines and Angle Pairs

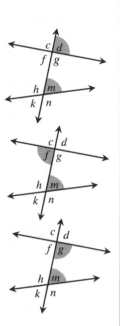

Corresponding angles lie in the same
position but at different points of intersection of the
transversal. For example, in the diagram at right,
$\angle m$ and $\angle d$ form a pair of corresponding angles,
since both of them are to the right of the transversal
and above the intersecting line. Corresponding
angles are congruent when the lines intersected by
the transversal are parallel.

$\angle f$ and $\angle m$ are **alternate interior angles** because
one is to the left of the transversal, one is to the
right, and both are between (inside) the pair of lines.
Alternate interior angles are congruent when the
lines intersected by the transversal are parallel.

$\angle g$ and $\angle m$ are **same side interior angles** because
both are on the same side of the transversal and both
are between the pair of lines. Same side interior
angles are supplementary when the lines intersected
by the transversal are parallel.

9-21.   Find the measure of the missing angle in each triangle below and then classify the triangle as acute, right, or obtuse.

a.

b.

9-22.   Find the measures of the angles requested and explain how you found them. Each part is a separate problem.

a.   If $m\angle 4 = 61°$, find $m\angle 6$.

b.   If $m\angle 1 = 48°$, find $m\angle 8$.

c.   If $m\angle 2 = 137°$, find $m\angle 8$.

9-23.   Graph the rule $y = 2x - 6$. Create a table if it will help.

9-24.   On graph paper, graph the data in the table at right. Is there an association?

Age of Car (years)	Avg. Miles per Gallon
7	28
2	36
5	29
1	42
4	32
10	16
2	39
3	35
8	18

9-25.   Tina's rectangular living room floor measures 15 feet by 18 feet.

a.   How many square feet of carpet will Tina need to cover the entire floor?

b.   The carpet Tina likes is sold by the square yard. How many square yards will she need?

9-26.   Solve for y in terms of x. That is, rewrite each equation so that it starts with "$y = $".

a. $6x + 5y = 20$

b. $4x - 8y = 16$

9.1.3 What if the angle is on the outside?

Exterior Angles in Triangles

So far in this section, you have investigated angle relationships in situations with parallel lines and within triangles. In this lesson, you will continue to look at angle relationships. This time, you will investigate the angle relationships on the inside and outside of a triangle.

9-27.   Use the diagram at right to name each of the indicated angles below using three letters. Reread the Math Notes box in Lesson 9.1.1 if you need to remember how to do this.

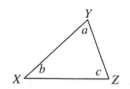

   a. $\angle a$ b. $\angle b$ c. $\angle c$

9-28.   Read the information below. Then follow the directions that follow.

Exterior angles are formed by extending a side of the triangle. The two angles across the triangle from the exterior angle are called **remote interior angles**. In each figure located below part (a), $\angle A$ and $\angle B$ are remote interior angles with respect to exterior angle $\angle BCD$.

These are exterior angles: These are NOT exterior angles:

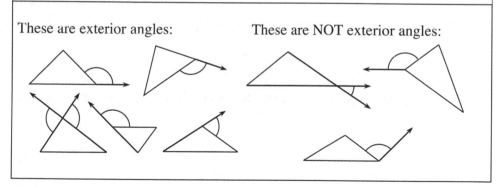

---

   a. On the Lesson 9.1.3 Resource Page provided by your teacher, calculate the missing angle measures in each figure and record them in the table. When you have completed the resource page, look for a pattern in the relationship between the measure of $\angle BCD$ (the exterior angle) and the sum of the measures of $\angle A$ and $\angle B$ (the remote interior angles). (Note that $m\angle BCD$ means the *measure* of $\angle BCD$. Similarly, $m\angle A$ means the measure of $\angle A$.)

Problem continues on next page. →

9-28.   *Problem continued from previous page.*

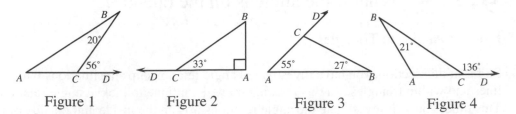

Figure 1   Figure 2   Figure 3   Figure 4

Figure Number	$m\angle A$	$m\angle B$	$m\angle ACB$	$m\angle BCD$	$m\angle A + m\angle B$
1					
2					
3					
4					

b.   Compare your results for $m\angle BCD$ (the exterior angle) and the sum of $m\angle A$ and $m\angle B$ (the remote interior angles) for each figure. Discuss your observations with your team.

c.   Write a conjecture about the relationship of an exterior angle to the two remote interior angles.

9-29.   Calculate the measures of the angles requested. Each part is a separate problem.

a.   If $m\angle 1 = 53°$ and $m\angle 2 = 71°$, find $m\angle 4$.

b.   If $m\angle 2 = 78°$ and $m\angle 4 = 127°$, find $m\angle 1$.

9-30.   Use your conjecture from part (c) of problem 9-28 to solve for x in each figure below.

a.

b.

c.

9-31.   **Additional Challenge:** Solve for x in the figure at right.

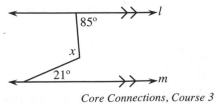

9-32.   LEARNING LOG

Look back at the entry that you created in Lesson 9.1.1
("Angle Relationships"). Add to that entry the angle
relationships that you learned in this lesson. Use
appropriate geometry vocabulary and include diagrams.

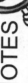

METHODS AND MEANINGS

MATH NOTES

Angle Sum Theorem for Triangles

The measures of the angles in a triangle
add up to 180°. For example, in $\triangle ABC$ at right,
$m\angle A + m\angle B + m\angle C = 180°$.

You can verify this statement by
carefully drawing a triangle with a
ruler, tearing off two of the angles
($\angle A$ and $\angle B$), and placing them side
by side with the third angle ($\angle C$) on
a straight line. The sum of the three
angles is the same as the straight
angle (line), that is, 180°.

9-33.   Based on the given information, determine which pairs of lines, if any, are
parallel. If none are necessarily parallel, write "none."

a. $m\angle 2 = m\angle 7$

b. $m\angle 3 = m\angle 11$

c. $m\angle 1 = m\angle 12$

d. $m\angle 13 = m\angle 12$

e. $\angle 6$ and $\angle 7$ are supplementary.

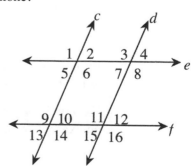

9-34.   In each angle problem below, solve for the variable(s). Write the names of the definition(s) and relationship(s) that justify the steps in your solution.

a.   b.   c.

9-35.   Simplify each expression.

a. $\frac{5}{4} \div \frac{7}{16}$ b. $-\frac{10}{13} \cdot \frac{5}{11}$ c. $\frac{9}{11} \div (-\frac{20}{21})$ d. $-\frac{8}{3} \div (-\frac{5}{18})$

9-36.   Simplify and solve each equation below for x. Show your work and check your answer.

a. $24 = 3x + 3$ b. $2(x - 6) = x - 14$

c. $3(2x - 3) = 4x - 5$ d. $\frac{3}{4} x = 2x - 5$

9-37.   Joaquin has agreed to lend his younger brother $45 so that he can buy a new tank for his pet lizard.

a.   Joaquin is charging his brother 2% simple interest per month. If his brother pays him back in 6 months, how much will Joaquin get back?

b.   If Joaquin's brother instead borrowed the money from a bank at 2% compound interest per month, how much would he have to pay the bank at the end of 6 months?

9-38.   Martha is saving money to buy a new laptop computer that costs $1800. She received $200 for her birthday and has a job where she makes $150 each week.

a.   Make a table and a graph for this situation.

b.   Explain how you can use the table or graph to predict how many weeks it will take Martha to earn enough money to pay for the new computer.

c.   Explain how you can tell from both the table and the graph whether this is an example of linear or non-linear growth.

Core Connections, Course 3

9.1.4 Can angles show similarity?

AA Triangle Similarity

In Chapter 6 you learned that you can create similar figures by using dilations. Today you will investigate what happens to the angles in a figure when you enlarge or reduce the figure to create a similar figure.

9-39.   ANGLES IN SIMILAR FIGURES

   a.   Using a sheet of graph paper and a straightedge, graph the quadrilateral
        $M(0, 3), N(4, 0), P(2, -2), Q(-2, 1)$.

   b.   Enlarge the quadrilateral by a scale factor of 2.

   c.   What do you notice about side MN and side $M'N'$? Explain.

   d.   What can you say about $\angle M$ and $\angle M'$? Explain your reasoning.
        Hint: Extend sides MN and QM.

   e.   Remember that a conjecture is an inference or judgment based on
        incomplete evidence. Based on your work in this problem so far, make a
        conjecture about the angles in similar figures.

   f.   Test your conjecture in part (e) using a figure of your own design and a
        different scale factor. Each team member should create a different figure.
        Compare your work with your teammates' work. Does your conjecture
        seem to work always, sometimes, or never?

9-40.   Imagine that two pairs of corresponding angles in two triangles are of equal
         measure. What could you then conclude about the third set of angles? Justify
         your answer and draw a diagram.

9-41.   Use your conjecture from part (e) of problem 9-39 along with your work from
         problem 9-40 to explain how you can use the angles in a pair of triangles to
         determine if they are similar. Be sure to include how many angles you need and
         what needs to be true about them.

9-42.   The relationship in the previous problem is called **Angle-Angle Similarity** and is written AA~. The symbol ~ means "similarity" or "is similar to." In the figure at right, is $\triangle ABC \sim \triangle EDC$ (that is, is $\triangle ABC$ similar to $\triangle EDC$)? Explain your reasoning.

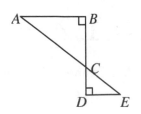

9-43.   Eleanor and John were working on a geometry problem together. They knew that in the figure below, line m is parallel to side BC. They wanted to find the side lengths of each triangle. First they decided that they needed to show that $\triangle AED \sim \triangle ABC$.

Eleanor said, *"This is easy. We have parallel lines, so the triangles are similar by AA~."*

"Hold on a minute!" John replied, *"Which angles are equal?"*

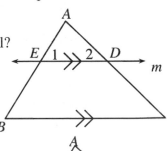

a.   Using the diagram at right, name the pairs of equal angles Eleanor sees. Why are they equal?

b.   Are the triangles ($\triangle AED$ and $\triangle ABC$) similar? Explain.

c.   Now that John sees how the triangles are similar, he suggests redrawing them separately as shown at right. *"Look,"* he says, *"Now we just write a proportion."* He suggests the following equation:

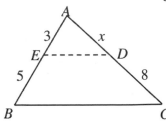

$$\frac{3}{3+5} = \frac{x}{x+8}$$

Explain how John came up with this equation.

d.   Solve the proportion equation in part (c) for x and check you answer.

9-44.   LEARNING LOG

What is Angle-Angle Similarity? What does it tell you about a pair of triangles? In your Learning Log, explain the relationship and how you can use it. Be sure to include a diagram. Title this entry "Angle-Angle Similarity" and include today's date.

METHODS AND MEANINGS

Exterior Angle Theorem for Triangles

An **exterior angle** of a triangle is an angle outside of the triangle created by extending one of the sides of the triangle. In the diagram at right, $\angle 4$ is an exterior angle. The **Exterior Angle Theorem for Triangles** states that the measure of the exterior angle of a triangle is equal to the sum of the **remote interior angles**. In the diagram, $\angle 1$ and $\angle 2$ are the remote interior angles to $\angle 4$. Note that some texts call these angles "opposite interior angles." In symbols:

$$m\angle 4 = m\angle 1 + m\angle 2$$

Review & Preview

9-45. $\triangle ABC$ is similar to $\triangle DEF$.

a.   Find the scale factor from $\triangle ABC$ to $\triangle DEF$.

b.   Find x.

c.   Find y.

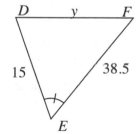

9-46.   Sketch an example of each type of graph described below.

a.   linear and decreasing

b.   non-linear and increasing

9-47.   Louis recorded how many times he could jump rope without stopping. Here is his data:

50   15   102   64   29   55   100   97   48   81   61

Find the median, first quartile, and third quartile of his data.

9-48. Solve the system of equations at right by each of the ways described in parts (a) and (b) below. Then compare your answers in part (c).

a. Graph the system on graph paper. Then write its solution (the point of intersection) in (x, y) form.

b. Now solve the system using the Equal Values Method.

c. Did your solution in part (b) match your result from part (a)? If not, check your work carefully and look for any mistakes in your algebraic process or on your graph.

9-49. Use what you know about the angles in a triangle to find x in each diagram below. Show all work. Then classify each triangle as acute, right, or obtuse.

a.

b.

9-50. This problem is a checkpoint for scatterplots and association. It will be referred to as Checkpoint 9.

Jason is interested in buying a used Panda hybrid car because he heard of its incredible gas mileage. Jason collected data from listings on the Internet.

Age of Car (years)	Listed Cost (in 1000s)
5	20
3	26
4	24
2	29
8	11
9	8
3	25
10	6

a. Jason would like to know the typical cost of advertised Pandas. What kind of a graphical display should he use?

b. What type of graph should be used to display the relationship between age and cost?

c. Make a scatterplot of the data.

d. Fully describe the association.

e. Draw a line of best fit for the data. Find the equation of the line of best fit.

f. Use the equation to predict the expected cost of a 6-year-old car.

g. Interpret the slope and y-intercept in context.

Check your answers by referring to the Checkpoint 9 materials located at the back of your book.

Ideally, at this point you are comfortable working with these types of problems and can solve them correctly. If you feel that you need more confidence when solving these types of problems, then review the Checkpoint 9 materials and try the practice problems provided. From this point on, you will be expected to do problems like these correctly and with confidence.

9.2.1 What kind of triangle can I make?

Side Lengths and Triangles

Triangles are made of three sides. But can any three lengths make a triangle? Is it possible to predict what kind of triangle – obtuse, acute, or right – three side lengths will make? Today, you will investigate these questions with your team.

9-51.   IS IT A TRIANGLE?

When do three lengths form a triangle? Are there special patterns in lengths that always make obtuse triangles? Or are there combinations of lengths that make right or acute triangles? To investigate these questions, you and your study team will build triangles and look for patterns that will allow you to predict what kind of triangle three lengths will make.

Discussion Points

How can we organize our data?

What other combinations can we make?

What do we expect will happen?

Your Task: Your teacher will provide you with three resource pages for this activity. Carefully cut out each square on the Lesson 9.2.1A Resource Page, shown at right. Using different combinations of three squares, decide if a triangle can be made by connecting the corners of the squares. If you can make a triangle, what kind of triangle is it? (The angle on the Lesson 9.2.1B Resource Page can help you determine if an angle is a right (90°) angle.) Record the side lengths and areas for each combination of squares you try on the Lesson 9.2.1C (or D) Resource Page. Complete the other columns of the chart.

9-52.   Look at your data for the combinations that did *not* form triangles.

- What do you notice about how the three side lengths compare to each other?

- How are the sets of three side lengths that did not form triangles different from the sets of side lengths that *did* form triangles? Be as specific as you can.

When your team has reached a conclusion, copy and complete the two statements below in your Learning Log. Title your entry "Triangle Inequality" and include examples and today's date.

Three side lengths WILL NOT make a triangle if...

Three side lengths WILL make a triangle if...

9-53.   Look at the data that you collected for the acute, obtuse, and right triangles. What patterns do you see between the sum of the areas of the two smaller squares and the area of the larger square that formed the triangles in each row? Copy and complete the sentence starters below in your Learning Log to summarize the patterns that you see. Title the entry "Triangle Side-Length Patterns" and include some examples along with the date.

If three squares have sides that make an acute triangle, *then the sum of the areas of the two small squares...*

If three squares have sides that make an obtuse triangle, *then the sum of the areas of the two small squares...*

If three squares have sides that make a right triangle, *then the sum of the areas of the two small squares...*

9-54.   Use the patterns you found to predict whether each set of lengths below will form a triangle. If a set will form a triangle, state whether the triangle will be acute, obtuse, or right. Justify your conclusion.

a.   5 cm, 6 cm, and 7 cm

b.   2 cm, 11 cm, 15 cm

c.   10 cm, 15 cm, 20 cm

d.   10 cm, 24 cm, 26 cm

e.   1 cm, 3 cm, 9 cm

f.   2 cm, 10 cm, 11 cm

9-55.   **Additional Challenge:** Lewis wants to build an obtuse triangle. He has already decided to use a square with an area of 81 square units and a square with an area of 25 square units.

a.   What area of square could he use to form the third side of his triangle? Explain your reasoning.

b.   If he makes an acute triangle instead, what size square should he use? Explain your reasoning.

ETHODS AND MEANINGS

AA Similarity for Triangles

For two triangles to be similar, corresponding angles must have equal measure.

However, it is sufficient to know that two pairs of corresponding angles have equal measures, because then the third pair of angles must have equal measure.

This is known as the **Angle-Angle Triangle Similarity Conjecture**, which can be abbreviated as "AA Similarity" or "AA ~."

AA ~: If two pairs of corresponding angles have equal measure, then the triangles are similar.

Review & Preview

9-56.   Consider the triangles at right:

a.   Are the two triangles at right similar? How do you know?

b.   Find the value of x. Show your strategy.

c.   What is the scale factor ($\frac{\text{big}}{\text{small}}$)?

d.   Find the area of each triangle.

9-57.   Jenna is working with three squares. Their areas are 16 cm², 9 cm², and 36 cm². She thinks they will make an obtuse triangle. Do you agree? Explain your reasoning.

9-58.   Copy and complete the following table.

x	5		4		−2	3
y	−17	−5		−2	4	−11

a.   What is the rule?

b.   What is the slope?

9-59.   Write an equation to represent the situation below, and then answer the question.

Ella is trying to determine the side lengths of a triangle. She knows that the longest side is three times longer than the shortest side. The medium side is ten more than twice the shortest side. If the perimeter is 142 cm, how long is each side?

9-60.   Cisco was looking at a table of values for the rule $y = x^2$. She said, "*This table contains* $(0,0)$, *so I think it shows a proportional relationship.*" Is Cisco correct? Why or why not?

9-61.   Solve these equations for x. Check your answers.

a. $2(x + 4.5) = 32$ b. $6 + 2.5x = 21$ c. $\frac{x}{9} = \frac{5}{16}$

9-62.   What kind of triangle will the edges of the squares at right form? What will the side lengths be?

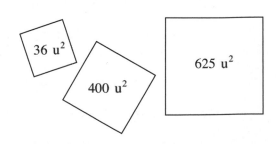

9-63.   Determine by inspection whether the lines in each system below intersect, coincide, or are parallel. Do not actually solve the systems. Justify your reasons.

a. $y = 2x + 3$
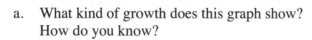
$y = \frac{1}{2}x - 2$

b. $2x + 3y = 6$
$2x + 3y = 9$

c. $y = \frac{1}{3}x + 2$

$y = \frac{1}{3}x - 2$

d. $x - 2y = 4$
$-2x + 4y = -8$

9-64.   Use the graph below to answer the following questions.

a.   What kind of growth does this graph show? How do you know?

b.   What is this graph describing? Write an appropriate title for the graph.

c.   How far from home is the person when the graph starts?

d.   How fast is the person traveling? Explain how you can use the graph to determine the rate of travel.

e.   Write an equation to represent the line on the graph.

9-65.   Eric set up this ratio for two similar triangles:

$$\frac{x}{12} = \frac{5}{9}$$

He solved the problem and found $x \approx 6.67$. What was his mistake?

9-66.   If one atom of carbon weighs 1.99×10^{-22} g and one atom of hydrogen weighs 1.67×10^{-27} g, which element weighs more? Explain your choice.

9-67.   Andrea wants to have $9500 to travel to France when she is 22. She currently has $5976 in a savings account earning 5% annual compound interest. Andrea is 14 now.

a.   If she does not take out or deposit any money, how much money will Andrea have when she is 18?

b.   Will Andrea have enough money for her trip when she is 22?

9.2.2 What is special about a right triangle?

Pythagorean Theorem

In Lesson 9.2.1, you saw that for three lengths to form a triangle, they must be related to each other in a special way. Today, you will investigate a special relationship between the side lengths of right triangles. This relationship will allow you to find the length of a missing side.

9-68.   Use your patterns from Lesson 9.2.1 to decide if the squares listed below will form a right triangle.

a.   Squares with side lengths 6, 8, and 10 meters

b.   Squares with areas 64 in², 100 in², 144 in²

c.   Two squares with side length 5 feet and a square with area 50 square feet

d.   Explain how you know whether three squares will join at their corners to form a right triangle.

9-69.   THE PYTHAGOREAN RELATIONSHIP

Based on your work so far, if you know the area of three squares, you can tell if they will connect at their corners to form a right triangle. But what if you know that a triangle has a right angle? Will the lengths of the sides be related in this way? Work with your team to look more closely at side lengths of some right triangles.

a.   On centimeter graph paper, form a right angle by drawing one 5-cm length and one 12-cm length as shown at right. If you do not have centimeter graph paper, then use any graph paper to draw and measure these lengths with a ruler. After drawing the two lengths, create a right triangle by connecting the ends of the two lengths with a third side.

b.   With a ruler, measure the longest side of the triangle in centimeters and label this length. If you do not have a centimeter ruler or you are using another kind of graph paper, create your triangle using 5 and 7 grid units. Then use an edge of the page and the grid lines as your ruler.

Problem continues on next page. →

9-69.   *Problem continued from previous page.*

c.   Visualize a square connected to each side of the right triangle in part (b). On your paper, sketch a picture like the one at right. What is the area of each square? Is the area of the square that is connected to the longest side equal to the sum of the areas of the other two squares?

d.   Check this pattern with a new example.

   •   Draw a new right angle on the centimeter paper like you did in part (a). This time, use 9-cm and 12-cm lengths.

   •   Connect the endpoints to create a triangle, and measure the third side.

   •   Create a sketch for this triangle like the one you created in part (c), and find the areas of the squares.

   Is the area of the square that is connected to the longest side equal to the sum of the other two areas?

e.   The two shortest sides of a right triangle are called the **legs**, and the longest side is called the **hypotenuse**.

   You previously wrote a statement about the relationship between the areas of squares drawn on the sides of a right triangle. Now use words to describe the relationship between the *lengths* of the legs and the *length* of the hypotenuse.

9-70.   The relationship you described in part (e) of problem 9-69 is called the **Pythagorean Theorem**. It states that in a right triangle, the length of one leg squared plus the length of the other leg squared is equal to the length of the hypotenuse squared. It can be written as an equation like this:

$$(\text{leg A})^2 + (\text{leg B})^2 = (\text{hypotenuse})^2$$

Use the Pythagorean Theorem to write an equation for each diagram below. Then find each missing area.

a.

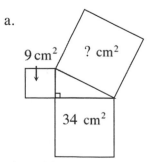

$9\,\text{cm}^2$? cm^2

$34\ \text{cm}^2$

b.

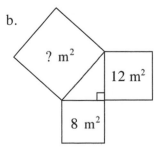

? m^2 $12\ \text{m}^2$

$8\ \text{m}^2$

c.

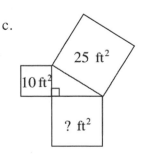

$25\ \text{ft}^2$ $10\,\text{ft}^2$

? ft^2

9-71.   In Lesson 9.2.1 you found a relationship between the squares of the sides of triangle and the type of triangle (acute, obtuse, or right). You discovered that if the sum of the squares of the two shortest sides in a triangle equals the square of the length of the longest side, then the triangle is a right triangle. Use this idea to determine whether the lengths listed below form a right triangle. Explain your reasoning.

a.   15 feet, 36 feet, and 39 feet   b.   20 inches, 21 inches, and 29 inches

c.   8 yards, 9 yards, and 12 yards   d.   4 meters, 7 meters, and 8 meters

9-72.   Find the area of the square in each picture below.

a.

b.

c.

d.
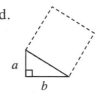

9-73.   How long is the missing side of each triangle in parts (b) and (c) of problem 9-72? Be prepared to explain your reasoning.

418   *Core Connections, Course 3*

Ⓜ️ETHODS AND MEANINGS

Triangle Inequality and Side-Length Patterns

The **Triangle Inequality** establishes the required relationships for three lengths to form a triangle. You can also use these lengths to determine the type of triangle they form — acute, obtuse, or right — by comparing the squares of the lengths of the sides as described below.

For any three lengths to form a triangle, the sum of the lengths of any two sides must be greater than the length of the third side.

For example, the lengths 3 cm, 10 cm, and 11 cm will form a triangle, because:

$$3 + 10 > 11$$
$$3 + 11 > 10$$
$$10 + 11 > 3$$

The lengths 5 m, 7 m, and 15 m will not form a triangle, because $5 + 7 = 12$, and $12 \not> 15$.

Acute triangle: The sum of the squares of the lengths of the two shorter sides is greater than the square of the length of the longest side.

$$x^2 + y^2 > z^2$$

Obtuse triangle: The sum of the squares of the lengths of the two shorter sides is less than the square of the length of the longest side.

$$p^2 + q^2 < r^2$$

Right triangle: The sum of the squares of the lengths of the two shorter sides is equal to the square of the length of the longest side.

$$a^2 + b^2 = c^2$$

9-74.   If you have 24 square tiles, how many different rectangles can you make? Each rectangle must use all of the tiles and have no holes or gaps. Sketch each rectangle on graph paper and label its length and width. Can you make a square with 24 tiles?

9-75.   Lydia has four straws of different lengths, and she is trying to form a right triangle. The lengths are 8, 9, 15, and 17 units. Which three lengths should she use? Justify your answer.

9-76.   The Wild West Frontier Park now offers an unlimited day pass. For $29.00, visitors can go on as many rides as they want. The original plan charged visitors $8.75 to enter the park, plus $2.25 for each ride. Write an equation to determine the number of rides that would make the total cost equal for the two plans. Solve the equation.

9-77.   a.   Write the rule for the table at right.

b.   What is the slope?

c.   What is the y-intercept?

x	4	$\frac{1}{2}$	-2		-1	7
y	-11		1	-3	-1	

9-78.   Solve for x. Each part is a separate problem.

a.   If $m\angle 1 = 3x - 18°$ and $m\angle 5 = 2x + 12°$, find x.

b.   If $m\angle 3 = 4x - 27°$ and $m\angle 6 = x + 39°$, find x.

c.   If $m\angle 4 = 49°$ and $m\angle 6 = 5x + 41°$, find x.

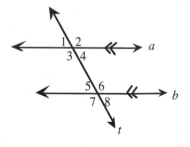

9-79.   Calculate the value of x.

a.

b.

9.2.3 How can I find the side length?

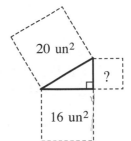

Understanding Square Root

You have developed a way to decide if a triangle is a right triangle by looking at the squares of the side lengths of the triangle. If you already know a triangle is a right triangle, how can the Pythagorean Theorem help you determine the length of a leg or the hypotenuse? Today you and your team will develop new ways to find missing lengths of right triangles.

9-80. Nikita wants to use the area of the squares in the figure at right to find the lengths of the sides of a right triangle.

a. Find the missing area.

b. What are the lengths of the legs of the right triangle in Nikita's diagram? How do you know?

c. About how long is the hypotenuse? Are you able to find the length exactly? Explain your reasoning.

9-81. The numbers 36, 64, 4, 16, 100, 144, 121, and 225 are all examples of **perfect squares**.

a. If each of these numbers represents the number of square units in a square, what is the side length of each square?

b. Why do you think these numbers are called perfect squares?

9-82. To find the side length of a square with a particular area, you use an operation called the **square root**. The square root symbol looks like this: $\sqrt{}$. It is also called a **radical sign**.

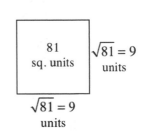

To find the side length of a square with an area of 81 square units, for example, you would write $\sqrt{81}$ and would read it as "the square root of 81." Since $9 \cdot 9 = 81$, then $\sqrt{81} = 9$.

Copy each square root expression below. Rewrite each square root as an equivalent expression without the radical sign. Explain your method for finding the square root of these numbers.

a. $\sqrt{49}$ b. $\sqrt{121}$ c. $\sqrt{9}$ d. $\sqrt{169}$

9-83.   In problem 9-74, you tried to make a perfect square with 24 tiles and could not.

a.   Why was it not possible?

b.   Estimate the length of a side of a square with an area of 24 square units. What two whole numbers is the length between?

c.   Is $\sqrt{24}$ closer to one of the whole numbers or to the other? If you did not already do so, estimate to the nearest tenth.

d.   Multiply your estimate by itself. How close to 24 is your answer? If you revised your estimate, how would you change it?

9-84.   Between which two whole numbers is each of the following square roots? To which whole number do you think it is closer? Estimate the value of the square root to the nearest tenth (0.1). You may find it helpful to create a list of the whole numbers from 1 to 17 and their squares to use with this kind of problem.

a. $\sqrt{40}$ b. $\sqrt{95}$ c. $\sqrt{3}$

d. $\sqrt{59}$ e. $\sqrt{200}$ f. $\sqrt{154}$

g.   Describe your method for estimating the approximate value of a square root when the number is not a perfect square. Check each estimate for parts (a) through (f) on a calculator.

9-85.   ESTIMATING WITH A GRAPH

In Chapters 6, 7, and 8, you examined the graphs of various relationships. What would the relationship between the side length of a square and the area of a square look like on a graph?

a.   On the Lesson 9.2.3 Resource Page, complete the table for the side lengths and areas. Graph the points. Does it make sense to connect them? If so, connect them with a smooth curve.

b.   Describe the relationship between the side length of a square and the area of the square. How is it the same or different than other relationships you have graphed?

Problem continues on next page. →

9-85.   *Problem continued from previous page.*

c.   How can you use the graph to estimate the side length for a square with an area of 24 square units? Does this estimate match your estimate in problem 9-83?

d.   Use your graph to estimate these square roots:

   i. $\sqrt{10}$ *ii.* $\sqrt{15}$ *iii.* $\sqrt{5}$ *iv.* $\sqrt{33}$

9-86.   **Additional Challenge:** Nikita wonders, *"What can we say about the square root of a negative number?"* Discuss this question with your team. For example, can you find $\sqrt{-16}$? Write an explanation of your thinking. Be ready to share your ideas with the class.

9-87.   LEARNING LOG

What is a square root? How can you estimate a square root? In your Learning Log, write directions for a fifth grader to follow. Explain what a square root is and how to estimate a square root to the nearest tenth. Include examples of perfect squares and non-perfect squares. Title this entry "Square Roots" and label it with today's date.

METHODS AND **M**EANINGS

Right Triangles and the Pythagorean Theorem

A right triangle is a triangle in which the two shorter sides form a right (90°) angle. The shorter sides are called **legs**. The third and longest side, called the **hypotenuse**, is opposite the right angle.

The **Pythagorean Theorem** states that for any right triangle, the sum of the squares of the lengths of the legs is equal to the square of the length of the hypotenuse.

$$(\text{leg 1})^2 + (\text{leg 2})^2 = (\text{hypotenuse})^2$$

Example:

3 in.

4 in.

$$3^2 + 4^2 = x^2$$
$$9 + 16 = x^2$$
$$25 = x^2$$
$$5 = x$$

The **converse of the Pythagorean Theorem** states that if the sum of the squares of the lengths of the two shorter sides of a triangle equals the square of the length of the longest side, then the triangle is a right triangle. For example:

Do the lengths 6, 9, and 11 form a right triangle?

$$6^2 + 9^2 \overset{?}{=} 11^2$$

$$36 + 81 \overset{?}{=} 121$$

$$117 \neq 121$$

No, these lengths do not form a right triangle.

Do the lengths 9, 40, and 41 form a right triangle?

$$9^2 + 40^2 \overset{?}{=} 41^2$$

$$81 + 1600 \overset{?}{=} 1681$$

$$1681 = 1681$$

Yes, these lengths form a right triangle.

9-88.   Find the missing length or area.

a. x

   x | 225 cm²

b.

   11 cm

   11 cm

c. 5 m | 100 m²

   w

d. y

   y | 150 ft²

9-89.   Determine the positive value that makes each equation true. If the answer is not a whole number, write it as a square root, and then approximate it as a decimal rounded to the nearest tenth.

a.   If $x^2 = 36$, $x = ?$

b.   If $x^2 = 65$, $x = ?$

c.   If $x^2 = 84$, $x = ?$

d.   If $x^2 = 13$, $x = ?$

9-90.   Use the rule $y = -2x + 5$ to answer the questions below.

a.   What is the slope of the line?

b.   Where does the line cross the y-axis?

9-91.   Copy and complete each of the Diamond Problems below. The pattern used in the Diamond Problems is shown at right.

a.

b.

c.

d.

9-92.   Identify which of the relationships shown below is not a function. Explain your reasoning.

a.

x	3	8	1	9	−1	0
y	12	4	0	4	−3	−8

b.

x	5	2	−1	0	−15	2
y	2	0	−11	8	−25	1

9-93.   Kenneth claims that $(2, 0)$ is the point of intersection of the lines $y = -2x + 4$ and $y = x - 2$. Is he correct? How do you know?

9-94.   Daniel needed to paint his patio, so he made a scale drawing of it. He knows that the width of the patio is 10 feet, but the scale drawing is in inches.

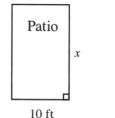

a. Find the length of the patio in feet.

b. Find the area of the patio so Daniel knows how much area he needs to paint.

c. One can of paint covers 125 square feet. How many cans of paint will Daniel need to buy?

9-95.   Juan found that 20 new pencils weigh 12 ounces. How much will 50 new pencils weigh? Show your reasoning.

9-96.   For each diagram below, solve for x. Explain what method you used for each problem.

a.

$6x$
$4x + 10°$

b.
$5x + 13°$ $3x + 7°$

c.

$3x + 5°$
$2x + 18°$ $2x + 17°$

d.

x
$30°$

9-97.   Find the surface area and volume of the prism at right.

9-98.   Find the area of each circle below.

a.   radius = 8 cm   b.

9-99.   Write each number in scientific notation.

a.   49.63   b.   0.0000005   c.   3,120,000,000

9.2.4 What kind of number is it?

Real Numbers

Any number that can be written as the ratio of two integers $\frac{a}{b}$ with $b \neq 0$ is called a **rational number**. A rational number can be matched to exactly one point on a number line. There are many other points on the number line, however, for which there is not a corresponding rational number. These numbers are called **irrational numbers**. Numbers such as π, $\sqrt{2}$, and $-\sqrt{5}$ are irrational numbers. The rational numbers and the irrational numbers make up all of the numbers on the number line and together are called the **real numbers**.

In this lesson you will learn how to identify a number as rational or irrational. You will also write decimals as fractions to show that they are rational. Then you will compare these kinds of numbers and place them on the number line.

9-100.   In previous courses, you worked with decimals that repeated and terminated. All of these are called **rational numbers** because they can be written as a ratio, like $\frac{2}{3}$ and $\frac{5}{1} = 5$. Because $\sqrt{9} = 3$, $\sqrt{9}$ is also a rational number.

However, there are some numbers that do not repeat or terminate when they are written as decimals, such as $\sqrt{2}$. Such numbers are called **irrational numbers**. An irrational number cannot be written as a ratio of any two integers. In other words, an irrational number cannot be written as a fraction.

$\sqrt{2} = 1.41421356237...$

Use your calculator to find the square root of the following numbers. Decide whether the decimals are rational (having decimals that terminate or repeat) or irrational.

a. $\sqrt{6.25}$ b. $\sqrt{100}$ c. $\sqrt{7}$

9-101. Do you think that you can decide by looking at it whether a number is rational or irrational? You will explore this idea in parts (a) through (d) below.

a. Without doing any calculations, which of the numbers below do you think are rational numbers? Which do you think are irrational numbers? Discuss this with your team and make predictions.

$$-\frac{5}{9} \qquad\qquad \sqrt{7} \qquad\qquad \frac{21}{4} \qquad\qquad -\sqrt{15}$$

$$\pi^2 \qquad\qquad -\sqrt{76} \qquad\qquad \frac{730}{99} \qquad\qquad -6.4 \times 10^{-2}$$

b. Now use your calculator and write the equivalent decimal for each of the numbers in the list. Were your predictions correct?

c. What do you notice about the decimal forms of rational numbers compared to irrational numbers?

d. Is $\sqrt{42.25}$ rational or irrational? Explain your answer.

9-102. Every rational number can be written as a fraction, that is, as a ratio of two integers. Since 0.78 is described in words as "seventy-eight hundredths," it is not a surprise that the equivalent fraction is $\frac{78}{100}$. Use what you know about place value to rewrite each terminating decimal as a fraction. Check your answers with a calculator.

a. 0.19

b. 0.391

c. 0.001

d. 0.019

e. 0.3

f. 0.524

9-103. Jessica knows that $0.\overline{57}$ is a rational number, so she should be able to write it as a fraction. She wonders how to rewrite it, though. She started to rewrite it as $\frac{57}{100}$, but she is not sure if that correct. Is $\frac{57}{100}$ equal to $0.\overline{57}$? Be ready to justify your answer.

9-104. To help Jessica with her problem, find the decimal equivalents for the fractions below.

a. $\frac{19}{99}$ b. $\frac{391}{999}$ c. $\frac{3}{9}$

d. $\frac{1}{999}$ e. $\frac{524}{999}$ f. $\frac{19}{999}$

g. What patterns do you see between the fractions and their equivalent decimals? What connections do these fractions have with those you found in problem 9-102? Be ready to share your observations with the class.

h. Use your pattern to predict the fraction equivalent for $0.\overline{24}$. Then test your guess with a calculator.

i. Use your pattern to predict the decimal equivalent for $\frac{65}{99}$. Check your answer with your calculator.

9-105. REWRITING REPEATING DECIMALS AS FRACTIONS

Jessica wants to figure out why the pattern from problem 9-104 works. She noticed that she could eliminate the repeating digits by subtracting, as she wrote at right. This gave her an idea. *"What if I multiply by something before I subtract, so that I'm left with more than zero?"* she wondered. She wrote:

$$0.\overline{57} = 0.575757....$$
$$-0.\overline{57} = -0.575757....$$
$$0 = 0$$

$$10(0.\overline{57}) = 5.75757...$$
$$- (0.\overline{57}) = -0.575757...$$

"The repeating decimals don't make zero in this problem. But if I multiply by 100 instead, I think it will work!" She tried again:

$$100(0.\overline{57}) = 57.575757...$$
$$- (0.\overline{57}) = - 0.575757....$$
$$99(0.\overline{57}) = 57.0$$

a. Discuss Jessica's work with your team. Why did she multiply by 100? How did she get 99 sets of $0.\overline{57}$? What happened to the repeating decimals when she subtracted?

b. *"I know that 99 sets of $0.\overline{57}$ are equal to 57 from my equation,"* Jessica said. *"So to find what just one set of $0.\overline{57}$ is equal to, I will need to divide 57 into 99 equal parts."* Represent Jessica's idea as a fraction.

c. Use Jessica's strategy to rewrite $0.\overline{98}$ as a fraction. Be prepared to explain your reasoning.

Core Connections, Course 3

9-106.   Show that the following repeating decimals are rational numbers by rewriting them as fractions.

  a. $0.\overline{42}$ b. $0.\overline{312}$ c. $0.1\overline{6}$ d. $0.\overline{8}$

9-107.   Indicate the approximate location of each of the following real numbers on a number line. What can make this task easier? Try to do it without using a calculator.

$$\tfrac{2}{3}, -0.75, \sqrt{8}, -\tfrac{9}{5}, \tfrac{\pi}{3}, 2\tfrac{1}{4}$$

9-108.   Without using a calculator, order the numbers below from least to greatest.

$$\sqrt{102}, 10, 3\pi, \sqrt{99}, 1.1 \times 10^{1}, 9.099$$

9-109.   Copy and complete the following sentences.

  a.   The set of all numbers on the number line are called the _____.

  b.   A number that has an equivalent terminating or repeating decimal is called a(n) _____.

  c.   A number that has an equivalent decimal that is non-repeating is called a(n) _____.

  d.   Any number that can be written as a fraction of integers is a(n) _____.

MₑₜHODS AND MₑₐNINGS

The Real-Number System

The **real numbers** include all of the **rational numbers** and **irrational numbers**.

Rational numbers are numbers that can be written as a fraction in the form $\frac{p}{q}$, where p and q are integers and $q \neq 0$. Rational numbers written in decimal form either terminate or repeat. The number 7 is a rational number, because it can be written as $\frac{7}{1}$. The number -0.687 is rational, because it can be written as $-\frac{687}{1000}$. Even $\sqrt{25}$ is rational, because it can be written as $\frac{5}{1}$. Other examples of rational numbers include $-12, 0, 3, \frac{1}{8}, \frac{5}{9}, 0.25$, and $\sqrt{81}$.

Irrational numbers are numbers that cannot be written as fractions. Decimals that do not terminate or repeat are irrational numbers. For example, $\sqrt{3}$ is an irrational number. It cannot be written as a fraction, and when it is written as a decimal, it neither terminates nor repeats ($\sqrt{3} \approx 1.73205080756...$). Other irrational numbers include $\sqrt{2}$, $\sqrt{7}$, and π.

9-110. Graph each of the pairs of points listed below and draw a line segment between them. Use the graph to help you find the length of each line segment. State whether each length is irrational or rational.

   a. $(-3,0)$ and $(0,-3)$ b. $(2,3)$ and $(-1,2)$ c. $(3,2)$ and $(3,-3)$

9-111. Howie and Steve are making cookies for themselves and some friends. The recipe they are using will make 48 cookies, but they only want to make 16 cookies. They have no trouble reducing the amounts of flour and sugar, but the original recipe calls for $1\frac{3}{4}$ cups of butter. Help Howie and Steve determine how much butter they need.

9-112.   Find the perimeter and area of the figure at right.
          Copy the figure on your paper, and show your work
          for each of the steps that you use.

9-113.   Write the following numbers in scientific notation.

          a.   370,000,000   b.   0.0000000000076

9-114.   Simplify each of the following expressions.

          a. $4x^3y \cdot 3xy^2$ b. $6a^5b^2 \cdot 3ab^2$ c. $m^2n \cdot 9mn$

          d. $\dfrac{3^5 \cdot 8 \cdot 5^3}{3^2 \cdot 2^3 \cdot 5^3 \cdot 3^3}$ e. $\dfrac{m^4 \cdot n}{n^3}$ f. $\dfrac{9a^4b^2}{15b}$

9-115.   Simplify each numerical expression.

          a. $|5-6+1|$ b. $-2|-16|$ c. $|6-2|+|-8-1|$

9-116.   Identify the following numbers as rational or irrational. If the number is
          rational, show that it can be written as a fraction.

          a. $\sqrt{36}$ b. $0.\overline{62}$ c. $\sqrt{92}$

9-117.   Solve each system.

          a. $y = 2x+1$ b. $y = \frac{1}{3}x+4$
               $y = -3x-4$ $y = \frac{1}{2}x-2$

9-118.   For the rule $y = 6+(-3)x$:

          a.   What is the y-intercept?   b.   What is the slope?

9-119.   Make a table and graph the rule $y = \sqrt{x-2}$ that includes x-values from -1 to 10. Graph the rule on graph paper.

9-120.   Dawn drove 420 miles in 6 hours on a rural interstate highway. If she maintains the same speed, how far can she go in 7.5 hours?

9-121.   The attendance at the county fair was lowest on Thursday, the opening day. On Friday, 5500 more people attended than attended Thursday. Saturday doubled Thursday's attendance, and Sunday had 3000 more people than Saturday. The total attendance was 36,700. Write and solve an equation to find how many people attended the fair each day.

9.2.5 How can I find missing parts?

Applications of the Pythagorean Theorem

In this section, you have studied different properties of triangles. You have used the Pythagorean Theorem to describe the special relationship between the sides of a right triangle. In this lesson, you will use these ideas to solve a variety of different problems.

9-122. Ann is measuring some fabric pieces for a quilt. Use the Pythagorean Theorem and your calculator to help her find each of the missing lengths below. Decide whether each answer is rational or irrational. If it is rational, explain whether the decimal repeats or terminates.

a.

32 in.

24 in.

b.

10 m

20 m

c.

7.6 cm   9.5 cm

9-123. Coach Kelly's third-period P.E. class is playing baseball. The distance between each base on the baseball diamond is 90 feet. Lisa, at third base, throws the ball to Dano, at first base. How far did she throw the ball? State whether your answer is rational or irrational.

9-124. As the city planner of Right City, you are responsible to report information to help the Board of Supervisors make decisions about the budgets for the fire and police departments. The board has asked for a report with answers to the following questions. Each grid unit in the figure at right represents 1 mile.

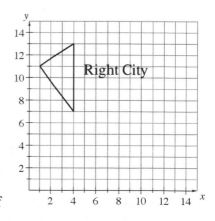

a. For fire safety, bushes will be cleared along the perimeter of the city. What is the length of the perimeter? Include all of your calculations in your report.

b. Some people say that Right City got its name from its shape. Is the shape of the city a right triangle? Show how you can tell.

9-125.   Clem and Clyde have a farm with three different crops: a square field of corn, a rectangular field of artichokes, and a right-triangle grove of walnut trees (as shown at right). A fence totally surrounds the farm. Find the total area of Clem and Clyde's land in square miles and tell them how much fencing they need to enclose the outside of their farm.

1 mi

1.2 mi

1.2 mi   1.6 mi

9-126.   Scott and Mark are rock climbing. Scott is at the top of a 75-foot cliff, when he throws a 96-foot rope down to Mark, who is on the ground below. If the rope is stretched tightly from Mark's feet to Scott's feet, how far from the base of the cliff (directly below Scott) is Mark standing? Draw a diagram and label it. Then find the missing length. Is the length irrational?

9-127.   Nicole has three long logs. She wants to place them in a triangle around a campfire to allow people to sit around the fire. The logs have lengths 19, 11, and 21 feet.

a.   Can she form a triangle with these lengths? If so, what type of triangle (acute, obtuse, or right) will the logs form? Justify your answers.

b.   Nicole realized she wrote the numbers down incorrectly. Her logs are actually 9, 11, and 21 feet. Will she still be able to surround her campfire with a triangular seating area? If so, will the shape be a right triangle? Justify.

9-128.   LEARNING LOG

The Pythagorean Theorem describes the special relationship that exists between the side lengths of a right triangle. In your Learning Log, describe how the Pythagorean Theorem can be used to find a missing side length on a right triangle. Make up examples in which either the hypotenuse length is missing or a leg length is missing. Be sure to include pictures and describe how you would find each missing length. Title this entry "Pythagorean Theorem" and label it with today's date.

METHODS AND MEANINGS

MATH NOTES

Squaring and Square Root

When a number or variable is multiplied by itself, it is said to be **squared**. Squaring a number is like finding the area of the square with that number or variable as its side length. For example:

$6 \cdot 6 = 6^2 = 36$ and $\boxed{36 \text{ cm}^2}$ 6 cm $\qquad a \cdot a = a^2$ and $\boxed{a^2}$ a

6 cm $\qquad\qquad\qquad\qquad\qquad$ a

The **square root** of a number or variable is the positive factor that, when multiplied by itself, results in the given number. Use a **radical sign**, $\sqrt{}$, to show this operation. If you know the area of a square, then the square root of the numerical value of the area is the side length of that square.

For example, $\sqrt{49}$ is read as, "the square root of 49," and means, "Find the positive number that multiplied by itself equals 49." $\sqrt{49} = 7$, since $7 \cdot 7 = 49$.

By definition, -7 is not the square root of 49 even though $(-7) \cdot (-7) = 49$, since only consider positive numbers are considered to be square roots. No real square region could have a negative side length.

9-129.   On a coordinate grid, draw a triangle with vertices at $(2,6)$, $(2,2)$, and $(5,6)$.

   a.   Find the lengths of each side of the triangle. What is the perimeter?

   b.   What type of triangle is formed by these points? Justify your answer.

9-130.   Ann lives on the shoreline of a large lake. A market is located 24 km south and 32 km west of her home on the other side of the lake. If she takes a boat across the lake directly toward the market, how far is her home from the market?

9-131.   Change each number below from a decimal to an equivalent fraction. For help with the repeating decimals, review the Math Notes box from Lesson 9.2.4.

   a. 0.7 b. $0.\overline{7}$ c. 0.15 d. $0.\overline{15}$

9-132.   Simplify each of the following expressions.

   a. $3\frac{1}{5}\cdot\frac{7}{4}$ b. $5^3\cdot(-\frac{4}{5})$ c. $2^4\cdot\frac{5}{8}$

   d. $-\frac{1}{2}\cdot3^2$ e. $-\frac{5}{6}+(\frac{1}{2})^2$ f. $(-\frac{4}{5})^2-\frac{3}{50}$

   g. $(\frac{3}{10})^2-(-\frac{2}{5})^2$ h. $8^2(-\frac{7}{8})-\frac{1}{2}$

9-133.   Simplify each expression.

   a. $(3x)^4 x^3$ b. $\frac{2^4\cdot3}{2^3\cdot3^2}$ c. $4^{-3}\cdot4^2$

9-134.   Identify the type of growth in each table below as linear or non-linear.

   a.

x	−2	−1	0	1	2	3
y	−8	−1	0	1	8	27

   b.

x	−2	−1	0	1	2	3
y	4	6	8	10	12	14

   c.

x	−2	−1	0	1	2	3
y	$\frac{1}{4}$	$\frac{1}{2}$	1	2	4	8

9.2.6   How can I find lengths in three dimensions?

. . . .

Pythagorean Theorem in Three Dimensions

You have been studying right triangles from a two-dimensional viewpoint. However, often triangles occur in three-dimensional settings. In this lesson, you will build a model, use it to visualize the location of right triangles in a three-dimensional situation, and then make calculations to find the triangle lengths.

9-135.   The roof on the Flat Family's house is one large flat rectangle. It is parallel to the ground. The TV antenna is mounted in the center of the roof. Guy wires are attached to the antenna five feet below its highest point, and they are attached to the roof at each corner and at the midpoint of each edge. These wires support the antenna in the wind.

Each guy wire is the hypotenuse of a right triangle. Mr. Flat needs to know how long each wire needs to be to keep the antenna upright. He also needs to find the total amount of wire needed.

a.   Build a model of the Flat Family Roof. The model will serve as a reference while your team finds the lengths of the sides of the right triangles in a three-dimensional setting.

   1.   For the roof, use a rectangular piece of cardboard. Draw the diagonals of the rectangle to locate the center.

   2.   Tape the string guy wires to the antenna (straw). Do not forget to leave a gap that represents the five feet between the strings and the top of the antenna. How many guy wires are there?

   3.   Attach the antenna to the center of the roof. Use tape, tie knots, or make slits to anchor your antenna and guy wires to the roof.

b.   Locate as many vertical right triangles as you can on your model. How many right triangles did you find?

c.   Identify which right triangles are the same size and which are different sizes. How many different-sized right triangles did you find? How many of each size are there?

d.   Sketch each of the different-sized right triangles on a different color of paper. Cut out the triangle. Tape the triangle in position on your model.

9-136.   The Flat Family's roof is 60 feet long and 32 feet wide. The TV antenna is 30 feet tall. The wires are attached five feet below the top of the antenna.

   a.   How long must each guy wire be? Show all of your steps to get your solution.

   b.   Mr. Flat needs to buy the wire at his local hardware store. He decides to buy an additional 10% more than the amount that you calculated so that he can attach the wires on each end. How much total wire should he buy? Show all of your work so that Mr. Flat can understand it, and round your answer reasonably.

9-137.   A child's shoe box measures 4" by 6" by 3". What is the longest pencil you could fit into this box? An empty box may help you visualize the various ways you could fit the pencil in the box. If possible, draw a diagram to show the pencil's position. Show your steps.

9-138.   **Additional Challenge:** A fly was sitting on the ground in the back left corner of your classroom. He flew to the ceiling in the opposite corner of the room. How far did he fly if he went in a straight line? Draw a diagram of your classroom, complete with the correct measurements. Write equations. Show your steps.

9-139.   The hypotenuse and one leg of a right triangle are 65 and 60 meters. What is the length of the third side?

9-140.   Find the missing length on this right triangle.

7 mm

30 mm

9-141.   Solve these equations for x.

   a. $(x+3.5)2=16$ b. $23+5x=7+2.5x$ c. $3x+4.4=-(6.6+x)$

Core Connections, Course 3

9-142.   Simplify each expression.

   a. $\frac{3^5}{3^{10}}$ b. $10x^4(10x)^{-2}$ c. $(\frac{1}{4})^3 \cdot (4)^2$ d. $\frac{(xy)^3}{xy^3}$

9-143.   Complete the table.

   a.   Find the rule.

x	−5	1	3	0	8	−2	−1
y	7			2		4	

   b.   What is the slope?

9-144.   **Additional Challenge:** Use the diagram and your answer to problem 9-138 above. If your classroom measured 30 ft by 30 ft by 10 ft, what distance would the fly travel?

9.2.7 Does it always work?

Pythagorean Theorem Proofs

You have seen that you can find the missing side of a right triangle using the Pythagorean Theorem. To show that it is always true, no matter how long the sides are, it must be proven. There are over 100 different ways to prove this important relationship. Today you will look at two ways to prove the Pythagorean Theorem. As you may remember, the Pythagorean Theorem states that in a right triangle with sides a and b, and hypotenuse c, $a^2 + b^2 = c^2$.

9-145.   PYTHAGOREAN THEOREM PROOF

Obtain the Lesson 9.2.7A Resource Page from your teacher. Start by cutting out four copies of the right triangle with legs labeled a, b, and hypotenuse labeled c units.

a. First, arrange the triangles to look like the diagram at right. Draw this diagram on your paper. Explain why the area of the unshaded region is c^2.

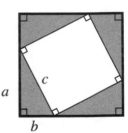

b. Will moving the triangles within the bold outer square change the total unshaded square?

c. Move the shaded triangles to match the diagram at right. In this arrangement, tell why the total area that is unshaded is $a^2 + b^2$.

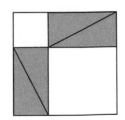

d. Write an equation that relates the unshaded region in part (a) to the unshaded region in part (b).

9-146. Here is another proof of the Pythagorean Theorem for you to try. Obtain the Lesson 9.2.7B Resource Page from your teacher.

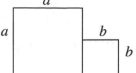

a. Start with two squares as shown at right. What is the total area?

b. Use a ruler or another piece of paper to place a mark of length *b* on the bottom left side of the larger square. Then draw the dotted lines as shown in the diagram at right to create two right triangles. How do you know that the legs of both triangles are legs *a* and *b*? Label each hypotenuse *c*.

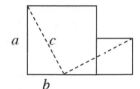

c. Cut out the shaded triangles shown in the diagram at right. Then work with your team to determine how to arrange the shaded triangles and the unshaded portion of the original figure to create a square. What is the area of the square? How do you know?

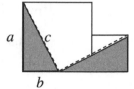

d. How does what you have done in this problem prove the Pythagorean Theorem?

9-147. The **converse** of a theorem reverses the evidence and the conclusion. The Pythagorean Theorem states that in a right triangle with legs of *a* and *b*, and hypotenuse *c*, that $a^2 + b^2 = c^2$.

a. State the converse of the Pythagorean Theorem.

b. Look back at your work from problem 9-51. What can you conclude about a triangle if $a^2 + b^2 = c^2$?

c. Why is this not a *proof* of the converse of the Pythagorean Theorem?

9-148. Graph the points $A(-2,2)$ and $B(1,-2)$. Then find the distance between them by creating a right triangle (like a slope triangle) and computing the length of the hypotenuse.

9-149. Use a graph to find the distance between the points $C\ (-4,-1)$ and $D\ (4,1)$.

9-150. Jack has a tree in his backyard that he wants to cut down to ground level. He needs to know how tall the tree is, because when he cuts it, it will fall toward his fence. Jack measured the tree's shadow, and it measured 20 feet long. At the same time, Jack's shadow was 12 feet long. Jack is 5 feet tall.

a. How tall is the tree?

b. Will the tree hit the fence if the fence is 9 feet away?

9-151. Examine the diagrams below. What is the geometric relationship between the labeled angles? What is the relationship of their measures? After you determine the relationship of their measures, use the relationship to write an equation and solve for x.

a.

$3x + 5°$

$5x - 57°$

b.

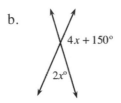

$4x + 150°$

$2x°$

9-152. On graph paper, graph the system of equations at right. Then state the solution to the system. If there is not a solution, explain why not.

$y = -\frac{2}{5}x + 1$

$y = -\frac{2}{5}x - 2$

9-153. A principal made the histogram at right to analyze how many years teachers had been teaching at her school.

Years of Teaching

a. How many teachers work at her school?

b. If the principal randomly chose one teacher to represent the school at a conference, what is the probability that the teacher would have been teaching at the school for more than 10 years? Write the probability in two different ways.

c. What is the probability that a teacher on the staff has been there for fewer than 5 years?

9-154. Simplify each expression.

a. $\frac{12}{5} \div \frac{7}{10}$

b. $\frac{9}{4} \div \left(-\frac{1}{3}\right)$

c. $-\frac{3}{5} \div \left(-\frac{1}{6}\right)$

Chapter 9 Closure   What have I learned?

Reflection and Synthesis

The activities below offer you a chance to reflect about
what you have learned during this chapter. As you work,
look for concepts that you feel comfortable with, ideas
that you would like to learn more about, and topics with
which you need more help.

①   SUMMARIZING MY UNDERSTANDING

This section gives you an opportunity to show what you know about properties
of triangles and applying the Pythagorean Theorem, two of the main ideas of
this chapter.

Triangular Treasure Hunt

Jasmine and Mason are spending the summer with their Uncle Simon. He lives
in an old castle that has many interesting doors, not all of which are rectangles.
One day, while looking through the books in the castle library, Jasmine found
an unusual piece of paper in a book. *"Look, Mason! This looks like some kind
of a treasure map,"* she exclaimed. Mason looked at the paper and read, *"A
valuable secret is hidden inside. But beware – danger lurks behind the other
doors. Only those who can follow the clues will succeed in the search."* He
also saw that it had a series of clues and pictures of triangular doors. Read the
clues below and, with your team, help Jasmine and Mason find the secret door
and the treasure.

- My sides are not congruent.
- My angles are not congruent.
- I am similar to another door.
- One of my sides is $\sqrt{41}$ units long.

a.   Look at the doors on the Chapter 9 Closure Resource Page.

b.   Using what you have learned in this chapter, decide which door is the secret
door. Justify your answer.

c.   List the triangles that were *not* the secret door and justify why each did not
fit the clues.

② WHAT HAVE I LEARNED?

Doing the problems in this section will help
you to evaluate which types of problems you
feel comfortable with and which ones you
need more help with.

Solve each problem as completely as you can.
The table at the end of this closure section provides answers to these
problems. It also tells you where you can find additional help and where to
find practice problems like them.

CL 9-155.   Solve for x.

a.   b.

CL 9-156.   Solve for x.

a.   b.

CL 9-157.   Determine the length of side x. Give the answer
in radical form and as a decimal.

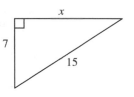

CL 9-158.   Simplify the following exponential expressions. Give answers without
negative exponents.

    a. $4^{-3} \cdot 4^{7}$ b. $(5x^{4})^{3}$

    c. $\dfrac{3^{7}}{3^{4}}$ d. $(4x^{5})(3x^{-8})$

CL 9-159.	Visualize a line that goes through the two points on the graph at right.

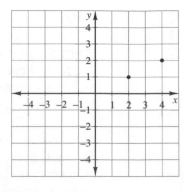

a.	What is the slope of the line?

b.	What is the rule for the line?

CL 9-160.	Casey was building a rectangular pen for his pigs. He has 62 feet of fencing. The length of his pen is 9 feet longer than the width. Write and solve an equation to find the dimensions of the pen.

CL 9-161.	Clay and his friend Lacey are making cookies for the school dance. Clay started early and has already made 3 dozen cookies. He can make an additional 2 dozen cookies an hour. Lacey has not started making cookies yet, but she has a bigger oven and can make 4 dozen cookies an hour. If Lacey starts baking her cookies right away, how long will it take for her to have made as many cookies as Clay? How many cookies will they each have made?

CL 9-162.	Sarah loves to order paperback mystery books. Some of her recent orders are shown in the table below.

# of Books	1	3	1	4	2	5
Total Cost	10.25	18.00	10.25	21.75	14.00	26.25

a.	Draw a scatterplot with this information.

b.	Fully describe the association.

c.	Determine the equation of the line of best fit.

d.	Based on the equation, estimate the total cost of an order of 10 books.

CL 9-163. For each of the problems above, do the following:

- Draw a bar or number line that represents 0 to 10.

- Color or shade in a portion of the bar that represents your level of understanding and comfort with completing that problem on your own.

If any of your bars are less than a 5, choose *one* of those problems and do one of the following tasks:

- Write two questions that you would like to ask about that problem.
- Brainstorm two things that you DO know about that type of problem.

If all of your bars are a 5 or above, choose one of those problems and do one of these tasks:

- Write two questions you might ask or hints you might give to a student who was stuck on the problem.
- Make a new problem that is similar and more challenging than that problem and solve it.

WHAT TOOLS CAN I USE?

You have created or have available to you several tools and references that help support your learning – your teacher, your study team, your math book and your Toolkit to name a few. At the end of each chapter you will have an opportunity to review your Toolkit for completeness as well as to revise or update your Toolkit to better reflect your current understanding of big ideas.

Listed below are the main elements of your Toolkit, Learning Log Entries, Methods and Meanings Boxes, and vocabulary used in this chapter. The words that appear in bold are new to this chapter. Use these lists and follow your teacher's instructions to ensure that your Toolkit is a useful tool as well as a complete reference for you as you complete this chapter and prepare to begin the next one.

Learning Log Entries

- Lesson 9.1.1 – Angle Relationships
- Lesson 9.1.2 – Angles in a Triangle
- Lesson 9.1.4 – Angle-Angle Similarity
- Lesson 9.2.1 – Triangle Inequality
- Lesson 9.2.1 – Triangle Side-Length Patterns
- Lesson 9.2.3 – Square Roots
- Lesson 9.2.5 – Pythagorean Theorem

Math Notes

- Lesson 9.1.1 – Angle Vocabulary
- Lesson 9.1.2 – Parallel Lines and Angle Pairs
- Lesson 9.1.3 – Angle Sum Theorem for Triangles
- Lesson 9.1.4 – Exterior Angle Theorem for Triangles
- Lesson 9.2.1 – AA Similarity for Triangles
- Lesson 9.2.2 – Triangle Inequality and Side-Length Patterns
- Lesson 9.2.3 – Right Triangles and the Pythagorean Theorem
- Lesson 9.2.4 – The Real Number System
- Lesson 9.2.5 – Squaring and Square Root

Mathematical Vocabulary

The following is a list of vocabulary found in this chapter. Some of the words have been seen in previous chapters. The words in bold are the words new to this chapter. Make sure that you are familiar with the terms below and know what they mean. For the words you do not know, refer to the glossary or index. You might also add these words to your Toolkit so that you can reference them in the future.

AA~ (Angle-Angle Similarity)	acute angle
adjacent angles	**alternate interior angles**
complementary angles	**corresponding angles**
exterior angle	**hypotenuse**
leg (of a right triangle)	obtuse angle
parallel	**perfect square**
perpendicular	**Pythagorean Theorem**
radical sign	**remote interior angle**
right angle	**square (of a number)**
square root	supplementary angles
straight angle	**transversal**
vertex	vertical angles

Answers and Support for Closure Problems
What Have I Learned?

Note: MN = Math Note, LL = Learning Log

Problem	Solution	Need Help?	More Practice
CL 9-155.	a. 5 b. 35	Lessons 9.1.2 and 9.1.3 MN: 9.1.2, 9.1.3, and 9.1.4 LL: 9.1.1, 9.1.2, and 9.1.4	Problems 9-14, 9-18, 9-22, 9-28, 9-29, 9-30, 9-33, 9-34, 9-49, 9-78, 9-79, 9-82, 9-151, and 9-154
CL 9-156.	a. 25 b. 81	Lessons 9.1.2 and 9.1.3 MN: 9.1.2, 9.1.3, and 9.1.4 LL: 9.1.1, 9.1.2, and 9.1.4	Problem CL 9-155
CL 9-157.	$\sqrt{176} \approx 13.27$	Lessons 9.2.2, 9.2.3, and 9.2.5 MN: 9.2.3 and 9.2.5 LL: 9.2.3 and 9.2.5	Problems 9-70, 9-122, 9-139, and 9-140
CL 9-158.	a. 4^4 b. $125x^{12}$ c. 3^3 d. $\frac{12}{x^3}$	Lesson 8.2.1 MN: 8.1.2 and 8.2.4 LL: 8.2.3	Problem CL 8-136
CL 9-159.	a. The slope is $\frac{1}{2}$. b. $y = \frac{1}{2}x$	Lesson 7.2.4 LL: 7.3.1	Problems CL 7-122 and 9-90

Problem	Solution	Need Help?	More Practice
CL 9-160.	$2x + 2(x+9) = 62$ OR $4x + 18 = 62$ The dimensions of the pen are 11 feet by 20 feet.	MN: 1.1.3	Problem 9-59
CL 9-161.	In $1\frac{1}{2}$ hours, they will each have made 72 cookies.	Lessons 5.2.2 and 5.2.3 MN: 5.2.2, 5.2.3, and 5.2.4	Problems 9-48, 9-76, and 9-152
CL 9-162.	a. See graph at right. b. Strong positive association c. $y = 4x + 6$ d. $46.00	Lesson 7.1.3 and 7.3.2 MN: 7.1.3 and 7.3.2 LL: 7.1.3 and 7.3.2	Problems 9-10, 9-24, and 9-150

Surface Area and Volume

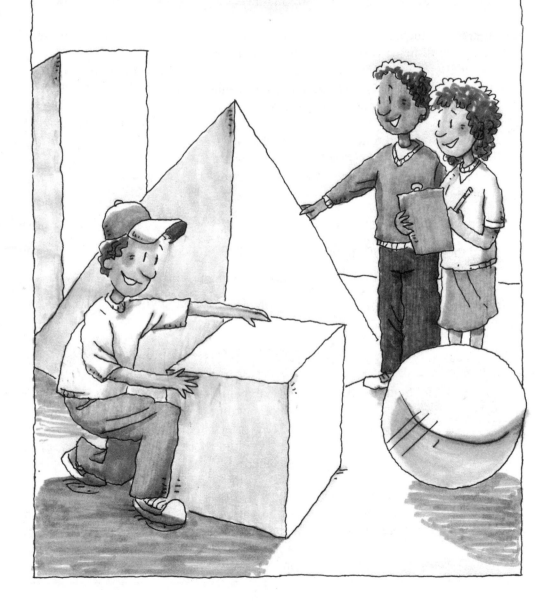

CHAPTER 10 Surface Area and Volume

The geometry you explored in Chapter 9 focused on triangles and angles. In this chapter, you will continue to explore geometry concepts but now you will focus on surface areas and volumes.

In Section 10.1, you will explore how to find the side length of a cube when you already know the volume. You will measure the surface area and volume of a cylinder, a three-dimensional solid that has a circle as the base. Finally, you will look at the surface areas and volumes of shapes that cannot be sliced into equal layers, such as pyramids, cones, and spheres.

In the course closure and reflection (Section 10.2), you will work with your team to solve challenging problems that allow you to reflect about your learning throughout the course.

Guiding Questions

Think about these questions throughout this chapter:

How much will it hold?

Am I measuring in one, two, or three dimensions?

How are they related?

In this chapter, you will learn how to:

> Find the cube root of a number.

> Find the surface areas of cylinders and pyramids.

> Find the volumes of non-rectangular shapes, including cylinders, pyramids, cones, and spheres.

Chapter Outline

Section 10.1   You will begin by learning how to find the cube root of a number. Then you will learn how to find the surface areas of cylinders and pyramids and the volumes of cylinders, pyramids, cones, and spheres.

Course Closure and Reflection (Section 10.2)   You will work with your team to solve challenging problems using your learning from the entire course. You will reflect about your learning and how you have been thinking as you have solved problems this year.

10.1.1   How long is the side?

Cube Roots

You have previously calculated the volumes and surface areas of cubes (and, more generally, prisms) using the lengths of the sides. But what if you wanted to reverse this process? In this lesson, you will learn how to determine the length of the side of a cube when you already know the volume. You will learn about a new operation, which is similar to the square-root operation, that will help you do this.

10-1.   Using the cube at right as a model, work with your team to create two problem situations that would require knowing the surface area of the cube. Then make another two problem situations that would require knowing the volume of the cube.

3 feet

10-2.   Find the surface area and the volume of the cube in problem 10-1. Show your steps.

10-3.   A different cube has a side of length 5. Write two expressions that would represent how to find the volume of the cube. One expression should use exponents.

10-4.   Now reverse the process. If you know the volume, how long is the side? Given the volumes of different cubes below, work with your team to find the length of a side of each cube.

a. 8 un^3 b. 125 m^3 c. 1000 ft^3 d. 40 in.^3

10-5.   In problem 10-4, did you find the solution by guessing and checking, or did you find a special key on your calculator that helped?

10-6.   If $s =$ the length of a side of a cube, then s^3 or "s cubed" represents the volume of the cube. If the volume of the cube is 64 cubic units, write an equation (using s) stating that volume is 64 cubic units.

10-7.   In Chapter 9, you solved equations with squares, such as $x^2 = 16$, by using the square-root operation, $\sqrt{}$. To solve equations with cubes, such as $x^3 = 64$, you need an operation that undoes cubing. You need the operation called **cube root**. It uses the symbol $\sqrt[3]{}$. Find the cube-root key on your calculator. Different calculators perform this operation in different ways, so figure out how to do this on your calculator and then find $\sqrt[3]{64}$ to get the solution to $x^3 = 64$.

10-8.   If you have not already done so, use the $\sqrt[3]{}$ key on your calculator to check your answers for problem 10-4.

10-9.   Just like with perfect squares and square roots, cube roots of perfect cubes are positive integers. Some of them are listed below.

$$\sqrt[3]{0} = 0, \quad \sqrt[3]{1} = 1, \quad \sqrt[3]{8} = 2, \quad \sqrt[3]{27} = 3, \quad \sqrt[3]{64} = 4, \quad \sqrt[3]{125} = 5, \quad \sqrt[3]{216} = 6$$

Cube roots of non-perfect cubes like $\sqrt[3]{40} = 3.419951...$ are irrational numbers. Without a calculator, you can *approximate* the cube root to be between consecutive integers, as you did with square roots. Look at the example below.

$$\sqrt[3]{27} < \sqrt[3]{40} < \sqrt[3]{64}$$
$$3 < \sqrt[3]{40} < 4$$

Approximate each of the following cube roots between consecutive integers. Write each answer in the same way as the above example.

a. $\sqrt[3]{10}$ b. $\sqrt[3]{100}$ c. $\sqrt[3]{52}$ d. $-\sqrt[3]{150}$

10-10.   The office building where Ryan works is made up of two cube-shaped pieces. At lunchtime, Ryan and his other office workers walk around the edge of the building for exercise. If the volume of the larger part is $65,000$ m^3 and the volume of the smaller part is 4000 m^3, what is the distance around the edge of the building?

10-11.   LEARNING LOG

How do you find the length of the side of a cube if you know its volume? What is this operation called? In your Learning Log create examples that demonstrate what you know about cube roots and how to find them. Title this entry "Cube Root" and label it with today's date.

10-12. Find the cube root of the following numbers. Use your calculator as needed and round any decimal answers to the nearest hundredth. Identify each answer as a rational or irrational number.

   a.   1728   b.   54   c.   0.125

10-13. Given that the volume of a certain cube is 125 cubic inches, find the dimensions given below.

   a.   Find the length of one side of the cube.

   b.   Find the surface area of the cube.

10-14. Find the area and perimeter of the shape at right. Show your steps.

   10 m   21.25 m   7.6 m

10-15. Change each number below from a decimal to an equivalent fraction. For help with repeating decimals, review the Math Notes box from Lesson 9.2.4.

   a.   0.72   b. $0.\overline{72}$ c.   0.175   d. $0.1\overline{75}$

10-16. Johanna is planting tomatoes in the school garden this year. Tomato plants come in packs of 6. She needs 80 plants in the garden and already has 28. How many packs of plants will she need?

10-17. Solve the following equations for the given variable.

   a. $3x+(-4)=2y+9$ for y b. $12=\frac{6}{7}x$ for x

   c. $\frac{38}{6}=\frac{x}{18}$ for x d. $\frac{9}{x}=\frac{85}{10y}$ for y

10.1.2 What if the base is not a polygon?

· ·

Surface Area and Volume of a Cylinder

Soup cans and rolls of paper towels are examples of **cylinders**. Cylinders are like prisms in many ways. However, a prism has a polygon as its base, while a cylinder has a circle as its base. In this lesson, you will compare the surface areas and volumes of prisms and cylinders.

10-18. COMPARING THE GYM BAGS

The CPM Sports Company is planning a new product line of gym bags. The outside of the bag (without the ends) will be made with a rectangular piece of cloth that is 40 inches by 52 inches. The company is trying to decide whether the end pieces will be squares or circles. CPM designers want to compare the surface area and volume of each bag and consider the advantages and disadvantages of each shape. Your team will help provide data for the designers' decision.

Use a standard piece of paper that measures 8.5 inches on one edge and 11 inches on the other to create a model of each gym bag. To model the square-based prism:

- Fold the paper in half so that the 8.5-inch edges match up, and then unfold.

- Fold each 8.5-inch edge in to the center crease, and then unfold.

- Tape the 8.5-inch edges together to form the **lateral faces** (the faces that are not the bases) of a square-based prism. The open squares at either end are the bases.

Use a new piece of paper to model the cylinder:

- Roll the paper so that one 8.5-inch edge matches up with the other.

- Tape the edges together to form the lateral face of a cylinder. The open circles formed at each end are the bases.

Problem continues on next page. →

10-18. *Problem continued from previous page.*

Your Task: Using the models for reference, find the surface area and volume of each gym bag. How much fabric will it take to make each bag? How much will each bag hold? Remember that the shorter length on the paper (8.5 inches) models the 40-inch dimension of the cloth, and the longer length (11 inches) models the 52-inch dimension of the cloth. The model you have created is *not* to scale.

Discussion Points

What dimensions will we need to find?

How can we organize our work?

What shape is each surface?

How are prisms and cylinders alike? How are they different?

Further Guidance

10-19. Focus first on the square-based prism. Sketch the prism on your paper, and then use the dimensions given for the cloth to answer the questions below.

a. What is the perimeter of the square base? How long is each side of the square base?

b. What is the surface area of the prism?

c. Calculate the volume of the prism.

10-20. Sketch the cylinder on your paper.

a. On your sketch, label all of the lengths that you know. What shape is the lateral face of the cylinder? This is the face formed by the original piece of paper. Find the area of the lateral face and the area of each base. If you do not have enough information to find the area, list the measurements that you need.

b. Melissa is looking at the base of the cylinder and realizes that the only measurement she knows is the circumference of the circle. She thinks she can use the circumference to find out other measurements. What is the circumference of this circle? What other lengths can Melissa find using this measurement?

c. Find the area of each base of the cylinder and then calculate the total surface area.

10-21.   To find the volume of the cylinder, Melissa started by comparing it to a prism. *"To find the volume of a prism, I slice it into equal layers. I wonder if the same method will work for a cylinder?"* she asks. Work with your team to answer Melissa's question. How could a cylinder be sliced into layers? What shape would each layer be? Find the volume of the cylinder.

*Further Guidance
section ends here.*

10-22.   How does the amount of fabric required to make the cylindrical bag compare to the amount of fabric required to make the square-based-prism bag? How much will each bag hold? Based on this information, which bag style do you think the CPM sports company should make? Explain your reasoning.

10-23.   Find the surface area and volume of the cylinder at right. Show your work clearly.

diameter = 10 cm

12 cm

10-24.   **Additional Challenge:** Louise calculated the volume of the prism at right to be 702 m^3. She is trying to find the surface area, but she needs help.

12 m

9 m   13 m

a.   Sketch the shape on your paper and label any lengths that you know. How can you find the lengths of the unlabeled edges?

b.   What are the length and width of each rectangle?

c.   What is the total surface area of the shape?

10-25.   LEARNING LOG

With your team, look carefully at how you found the surface area of the cylindrical bag. What measurements did you use to find the area of the base of a cylinder? What measurements did you use to find the lateral area? What measurement is important for both calculations? After your team has discussed these questions, record your ideas in your Learning Log. Title this entry "Surface Area and Volume of a Cylinder" and label it with today's date.

METHODS AND MEANINGS

MATH NOTES

Volume of a Cylinder

The volume of a cylinder can be calculated in exactly the same way as the volume of a prism. First divide the cylinder into layers that are each one unit high. Then, to calculate the total volume, multiply the volume of one layer by the number of layers it takes to fill the shape.

The volume of a cylinder can also be calculated by multiplying the area of the base (B) by the height (h).

Volume = (area of base)(height)

$$V = Bh = (r^2\pi)(h)$$

For example, for the cylinder at right:

Area of the base: $B = (12)^2\pi = 144\pi$ cm^2

Volume: $V = 144\pi(15) = 2160\pi \approx 6785.84$ cm^3

12 cm

15 cm

Review & Preview

10-26.   Find the area of the base of each cylinder below, and then calculate the volume of each cylinder. Show your steps.

a.

$r = 5$ cm

10 cm

b.

$r = 3.4$ cm

9 cm

10-27.   What is the volume of a hexagonal-based prism with a height of 12 in. and a base area of 62 in.^{2}? Would the volume be different if the base were a pentagon with an area of 62 in.^{2}? Explain.

10-28.   Find the length of the side labeled x in each of the right triangles pictured below. Identify each answer as a rational or irrational number.

a.

b.

c.

10-29.   Simplify each expression.

a. $\dfrac{5^3}{5^9}$

b. $\dfrac{(ab)^4}{ab^3}$

c. $8x^{-3}(8x)^2$

d. $(\tfrac{1}{6})^5 \cdot (6)^3$

10-30.   Simplify each expression.

a. $\left|-5+-1\right|$

b. $\left|-2 \cdot 4\right|$

c. $3\left|-8\right|$

d. $-3 \cdot \left|8\right|$

e. $5-\left|-5+10\right|$

f. $\left|6-10\right|$

10-31.   Tim wants to invest some money that his grandmother gave him. He has $2000 and can put it in an account with simple interest or an account with compound interest.

a.   The simple interest account has an interest rate of 10%. With this interest rate, what is the total amount in the bank after 5 years?

b.   The compound interest account is also for 5 years (compounded yearly), but it has an interest rate of 8%. Find the total amount that he would have in this account.

c.   Which account is a better investment?

10.1.3 What if the layers are not the same?

Volumes of Cones and Pyramids

Cones and pyramids are three-dimensional objects that have only one base, and that come to a point opposite their base. A **cone** has a circular base. A **pyramid** has a base that is a polygon and lateral faces that are triangles. Today you will be investigating how to use what you know about cylinders and prisms to find the volume of a cone and a pyramid. Questions to keep in mind as you work are:

What is the shape of the base?

How does the shape compare to a cylinder or a prism?

10-32.   HOW MUCH SHOULD IT COST?

You have a choice of purchasing a small or a large serving of popcorn at the movies. A small popcorn comes in a cone and costs $1.50, and a large popcorn comes in a cylinder that costs $3.50. Both containers have the same height and have bases with the same circular area. Based on their prices, discuss with your team which container of popcorn you think is a better deal. Be prepared to share your reasons with the class.

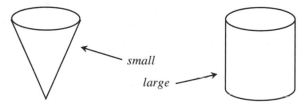

10-33.   Your teacher will lead you through a demonstration about the volume of a cone.

a.   How are the radius and height of each cone related to the radius and height of each corresponding cylinder?

b.   Sketch each cone and cylinder on your paper, and estimate which cone will have a greater volume.

c.   How many cones full of rice were needed to fill each corresponding cylinder?

d.   Based on the demonstration, describe how the volume of a cone compares to the volume of a cylinder when their heights and base areas are equal.

10-34.   Based on the relationship you found in problem
          10-33, determine what a fair price would be for the
          cylinder of popcorn in problem 10-32 if the cone of
          popcorn costs $1.50. At the advertised prices,
          which popcorn is the better deal?

10-35.   A different movie theater sells popcorn in the containers shown below. This
          time, the small container is a pyramid priced at $2.50. The large container is a
          prism with the same height and base as the pyramid, and it is priced at $5.50.
          At this theater, which popcorn do you think is a better deal? Be prepared to
          give reasons for your prediction.

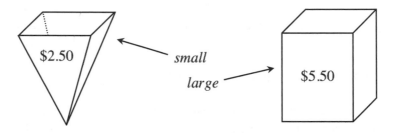

10-36.   Your teacher will now lead you through another demonstration to help you
          decide if you need to adjust your thinking about the relationship between the
          volume of a pyramid and a prism that have the same base and the same height.
          After you have seen the demonstration with the pyramid and the prism,
          determine which container of popcorn is a better deal. Justify your answer.

10-37.   Ann and Dan were trying to find the volume of the
          cone at right. Ann thinks that the cone is 8 inches
          tall, and Dan thinks that the cone is 10 inches tall.
          Write them a note explaining who is correct.

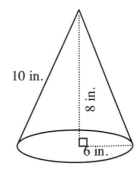

10-38.   Ann, Dan, and Jan calculated the volumes of some shapes and got different answers. Look at their work shown below and make a sketch of the shape that each set of calculations might represent. Why do Dan's and Jan's calculations have the same result even though they look different?

Dan's work: $V = \frac{(4^2\pi)(9)}{3} = 150.8$ cm^3

Ann's work: $V = (4^2\pi)(9) = 452.4$ cm^3

Jan's work: $V = \frac{1}{3}(4^2\pi)(9) = 150.8$ cm^3

10-39.   Find the volume of the pyramid at right. The hexagonal base has an area of 128 cm^2.

$h = 15$ cm

10-40.   LEARNING LOG

If you know the volume of any prism, how can you find the volume of a pyramid that has the same base area and height as the prism? If you know the volume of any cylinder, how can you find the volume of a cone that has the same base area and height as the cylinder? Answer these questions in your Learning Log. Label this entry with today's date, and title it "Volumes of Cones and Pyramids."

Ⓜ️ETHODS AND MEANINGS

Surface Area of a Cylinder

A **cylinder** has two congruent, circular bases. The **lateral surface** of the cylinder, when opened flat, forms a rectangle with a height equal to the height of the cylinder and a width equal to the circumference of the cylinder's base.

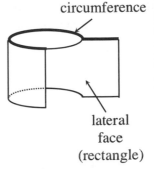

The surface area of a cylinder is the sum of the two base areas and the lateral surface area. The formula for the surface area is:

$$S.A. = 2r^2\pi + \pi dh$$
$$= 2r^2\pi + 2\pi rh$$

where r = radius, d = diameter, and h = height of the cylinder.

For example, to find the surface area of the cylinder below:

Area of the two circular bases:
$$2(28 \text{ cm})^2 \pi = 1568\pi \text{ cm}^2$$

Area of the lateral face:
$$\pi(56)(25) = 1400\pi \text{ cm}^2$$

Total surface area $= 1568\pi \text{ cm}^2 + 1400\pi \text{ cm}^2 = 2968\pi \text{ cm}^2$
$$\approx 9324.25 \text{ cm}^2$$

10-41.   Find the volume of the cone shown in problem 10-37.

10-42.   The pyramid at right has a volume of 312 cubic feet. If the prism next to it has the same base area and height, what is its volume? Explain how you know.

10-43.   Which table or tables below show a proportional relationship? Justify your answers.

a.

x	5	7	9	−8	0	11	15
y	9	13	17	−17	−19	21	29

b.

x	7	14	91	9	−12	−36	81
y	$2\frac{1}{3}$	$4\frac{2}{3}$	$30\frac{1}{3}$	3	−4	−12	27

c.

x	−3	−10	0	10	5	4	$\frac{1}{2}$	$-\frac{3}{2}$
y	−27	−1000	0	1000	125	48	$\frac{1}{8}$	$-\frac{27}{4}$

10-44.   Find the volume of the prism at right. All angles are right angles.

10-45.   Graph the points $(-2,4)$, $(2,1)$, and $(-2,-2)$ and connect the points to create a triangle.

a.   What is the perimeter of the triangle?

b.   Translate the triangle up 2 and right 3. What are the new coordinates?

c.   What is the perimeter of the triangle after its translation in part (b)?

10-46.   a.   Make a table for the rule $y = \sqrt{x}$ that includes x-values from −1 to 10. What happened?

b.   Graph the rule on graph paper.

c.   What kind of growth does the rule show? How do you know?

d.   Is this relationship a function? How do you know?

10.1.4 What if it is a three-dimensional circle?

Volume of a Sphere

So far in this chapter you have been finding the volume of three-dimensional solids with circular bases, but what if the object is a three-dimensional circle? A **sphere** is a three-dimensional object shaped like a ball. Every point on the outside of a sphere is the same distance from its center. Today you will use what you have learned about the volume of a cylinder to find the volume of a sphere.

10-47.   Myron's family is putting a pool in their backyard. He is so excited that he wants to figure out how long it will take to fill the pool! He found the blueprints for the pool and recreated the sketches at right, but he is not quite sure how to use them to find the volume of the pool.

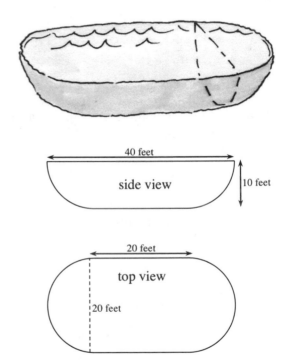

What three-dimensional figures does Myron need to be able to find the volume of before he can determine the volume of the pool?

10-48.   Your teacher will lead you through a demonstration about the volume of a sphere.

   a.   How are the diameter of the half sphere related to the diameter and height of the cylinder?

   b.   How many half spheres full of rice were needed to fill the cylinder to the height of the sphere's diameter?

   c.   Based on the demonstration, describe how the volume of a full sphere compares to the volume of a cylinder when their heights and diameters are equal.

10-49.   VOLUME OF A SPHERE

What is the formula for the volume of a sphere?
How can you use what your class figured out
about the relationship between the cylinder and
the bowl in problem 10-48 to generalize a
formula for the volume of a sphere?

a.   If 3 bowls of water completely filled a cylinder in which the diameter was
the same as the height, how many spheres is this? Write your answer as a
fraction.

b.   Write an equation relating the volume of a sphere and the volume of a
cylinder.

c.   If the height and diameter of the cylinder are equal, write an equation for
the height of the cylinder using the radius.

d.   Use substitution and your equation from part (b) to write an equation for
the volume of a sphere. Simplify your answer.

10-50.   Use what you have learned in the previous problems to help Myron calculate
the volume of the pool in problem 10-47.

10-51.   If there is 0.1337 of a cubic foot in 1 gallon, how many gallons of water will it
take to fill Myron's swimming pool completely?

10-52.   Since Myron wants to know how long it will take to fill the pool, he needs to
know how fast water flows out of the hose. He gets an empty gallon jug, turns
the water up as high as possible, and finds that it takes 6 seconds to fill the jug.
At this rate, how long will it take to fill the entire pool?

10-53.   If a sphere has a volume of 36π ft^3, what is the radius? Work with your team
to write and solve an equation to find the radius of the sphere.

10-54.   LEARNING LOG

How can you calculate the volume of a sphere? What
information do you need to know? Answer these questions
as an entry in your Learning Log. Include an example that
demonstrates how to find the volume of a sphere. Title the
entry "Volume of a Sphere" and label it with today's date.

METHODS AND **M**EANINGS

Volume of a Pyramid and a Cone

In general, the **volume of a pyramid** is one-third of the volume of the prism with the same base area and height. Thus:

$$V = \tfrac{1}{3}(\text{base area})(\text{height})$$

height

base area

The **volume of a cone** is one-third of the volume of the cylinder with the same radius and height. Therefore, the volume of a cone can be found using the formula shown below, where r is the radius of the base and h is the height of the cone.

$$V = \tfrac{1}{3}(\text{base area})(\text{height}) = \tfrac{1}{3}\pi r^2 h$$

h

$2r$

Review & Preview

10-55.   Calculate the volume of each sphere described below.

a.   radius = 5 cm

b.   diameter = 3 feet

10-56.   If the volume of a sphere is 113.04 ft^3, write and solve and equation to find the radius.

10-57.   Find the volume of each shape below.

a.   Rectangle-based prism

9 m

7 m

20 m

b.   Rectangle-based pyramid

18 cm

12 cm

22 cm

472

10-58.   a.   Make a table for the rule $y = 2x^3$ that includes x-values from –3 to 3.

          b.   Graph the rule on graph paper.

          c.   What kind of growth does the rule have? Is the rule a function? Explain your answers.

10-59.   Sarah and three of her friends left her house for a long bike ride on the river bike path. They rode for three hours at 10 miles per hour and then rested for an hour while they ate their lunches. After lunch, they raced each other back to Sarah's house at 15 miles per hour.

          a.   Draw a graph that could represent this situation. Place "Time (hours)" on the horizontal axis and "Distance (miles from Sarah's house)" on the vertical axis.

          b.   Describe each part of the graph using the following words: linear, nonlinear, decreasing, increasing, and constant.

10-60.   Sherice can fill lemonade cups at a rate of four cups per minute.

          a.   How many cups can she fill in 6 minutes?

          b.   How many cups can she fill in 10 minutes?

          c.   If Sherice fills c cups in t minutes, write an equation that relates c and t.

10-61.   Calculate the value of x.

          a.   b.

                        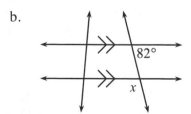

10.1.5   How much will it hold?

Applications of Volume

In this section, you have learned how to find the surface area and the volume of several kinds of solids – cylinders, cones, pyramids, and spheres. These skills can be very useful when solving real-world problems such as the one that you will encounter in this lesson. Use all of what you have learned and work together with your team to accomplish a challenging task!

10-62.   Sam Mallory, the owner of Mallory's Ice Cream Shop, wants to be able to advertise that his cones hold the most ice cream. His cones are made out of circular waffles with a set diameter. His employees cut a wedge-shaped piece from the circle and then fold it into a cone shape. He needs help determining how they can do this to create a cone with the largest volume. You have been hired to help solve this problem.

As you work through the steps below, neatly record your work. When you are finished, you will make a presentation of your findings for the owner.

Your Task: Using the materials provided by your teacher, create cones of various sizes and calculate their volumes. Determine the angle of the removed **sector** (a wedge-shaped piece of the circle) that results in the largest volume. Follow the steps below for creating a cone.

Before you get started, decide on the angle of the sector that each pair in your team will use to create a cone. Repeat the process below using different angles until you think that you have solved the task and found the largest volume possible.

1. Locate the center of the circle by folding it in half in two different directions. The intersection of the folds is the center of the circle. Place a dot at the center.

2. Use a ruler to draw a radius of the circle.

3. Use a protractor to measure the angle of the sector that you chose to be removed. Then use the ruler to draw the second radius for that angle.

4. Cut out the sector and then tape the edges of the sector together to create a cone.

5. Use a ruler to make the measurements of the cone that you need and calculate its volume. Record your work.

10-63.   Your team needs to present your findings to the owner of the ice-cream shop.
           Create a stand-alone poster displaying your results and advice for the owner.
           Be sure to include enough information that someone unfamiliar with the
           problem will understand your work and how you came to your conclusion.
           Also be sure to make your poster neat and presentable.

10-64.   **Additional Challenge:** Now that the ice-cream-shop owner knows how to
           create cones with the largest volume, he wants to know how many cones he can
           make with each tub of ice cream.

           He has measured a cylindrical tub and informed you
           that it has a diameter of 9.5 inches and a height of
           10.5 inches. Each waffle cone is created from a
           circular waffle with a diameter of 5 inches. Then it
           is packed full and has a half spherical scoop on the
           top, as shown in the diagram at right.

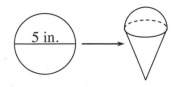

           How many cones can the owner create with each tub of ice cream?

10-65.   Find the volume of a sphere with a radius of 620,000 miles. Write your answer
          using scientific notation.

10-66.   Find the volume of the cone.

10-67.   Graph the points $(0,2)$, $(6,2)$, $(7,4)$, and $(1,4)$ and connect the points in order
          to create a parallelogram. What is the perimeter of the parallelogram? Is the
          perimeter a rational or irrational number? How do you know?

10-68.   Simplify each of the following expressions.

          a. $(5x^3)^2$ b. $\frac{14a^3b^2}{21a^4b^3}$ c. $2m^3n^2 \cdot 3mn^4$

10-69.   First decide if the triangles below are similar. Then, if they are similar, use the
          information in each diagram to solve for x.

          a.   b.   Careful!

10-70.   The label of the Aloha Pineapple Juice can is
          7 inches high and has an area of 140 square
          inches. What is the diameter of the can?

10-71.   Sketch an example of a graph that meets the description below.

          a.   non-linear and decreasing   b.   linear and increasing

Chapter 10 Closure   What have I learned?

Reflection and Synthesis

The activities below offer you a chance to reflect
about what you have learned during this chapter.
As you work, look for concepts that you feel very
comfortable with, ideas that you would like to learn
more about, and topics you need more help with.

①   WHAT HAVE I LEARNED?

Doing the problems in this section will help you to evaluate which types of
problems you feel comfortable with and which ones you need more help
with.

Solve each problem as completely as you can. The table at the end of this
closure section provides answers to these problems. It also tells you where
you can find additional help and where to find practice problems like them.

CL 10-72.   Find the surface area and volume of each solid below.

a.   All angles are right angles.   b.   Right prism with base area = 48 cm²

CL 10-73.   Find the surface area and volume of the cylinder
at right. Show your work clearly.

CL 10-74.   Find the volume of a pyramid that has a
square base with sides of eight inches and
a height of 12 inches.

CL 10-75.   Ella's cat has climbed up onto the roof of her house and cannot get down!
The roof of the house is 24 feet above the ground. The fire department has
set up a 28-foot ladder to climb to rescue the cat. The base of the ladder is
resting on the ground, and the top of the ladder extends 2 feet beyond the
edge of the roof. How far away from the base of the house is the base of the
ladder? You may want to draw a diagram to help you solve the problem.

CL 10-76.   Simplify the product or quotient. Be sure your final answer is in scientific
notation.

a. $(3.25 \times 10^5)(4 \times 10^3)$ b. $\frac{4 \times 10^3}{2 \times 10^{-2}}$

CL 10-77.   If a cube has a volume of 50 cm³, what is the length of a side?

CL 10-78.   Given the equation of the line $6x - 2y = 10$, complete each of the following
problems.

a.   Solve the equation for y.

b.   State the slope of the line.

c.   Graph the line.

CL 10-79.   Two brothers, Martin and Horace, are in their backyard. Horace is taking
down a wall on one side of the yard while Martin is building a wall on the
other side. Martin starts from scratch and lays 2 bricks every minute.
Meanwhile, Horace takes down 3 bricks each minute from his wall. It takes
Horace 55 minutes to finish tearing down his wall.

a.   How many bricks were originally in the wall that Horace started tearing
down?

b.   Represent this situation with an equation or system of equations. Be
sure to define your variable(s).

c.   When did the two walls have the same number of bricks?

Core Connections, Course 3

CL 10-80. For each of the problems above, do the following:

- Draw a bar or number line that represents 0 to 10.

- Color or shade in a portion of the bar that represents your level of understanding and comfort with completing that problem on your own.

If any of your bars are less than a 5, choose *one* of those problems and do one of the following tasks:

- Write two questions that you would like to ask about that problem.
- Brainstorm two things that you DO know about that type of problem.

If all of your bars are a 5 or above, choose one of those problems and do one of these tasks:

- Write two questions you might ask or hints you might give to a student who was stuck on the problem.
- Make a new problem that is similar and more challenging than that problem and solve it.

You have several tools and references available to help support your learning – your teacher, your study team, your math book, and your Toolkit, to name only a few. At the end of each chapter you will have an opportunity to review your Toolkit for completeness as well as to revise or update it to better reflect your current understanding of big ideas.

The main elements of your Toolkit should be your Learning Logs, Math Notes, and the vocabulary used in this chapter. Math words that are new to this chapter appear in bold in the text. Refer to the lists provided below and follow your teacher's instructions to revise your Toolkit, which will help make it a useful reference for you as you complete this chapter and prepare to begin the next one.

Learning Log Entries

- Lesson 10.1.1 – Cube Roots
- Lesson 10.1.2 – Surface Area and Volume of a Cylinder
- Lesson 10.1.3 – Volumes of Cones and Pyramids
- Lesson 10.1.4 – Volume of a Sphere

Math Notes

- Lesson 10.1.2 – Volume of a Cylinder
- Lesson 10.1.3 – Surface Area of a Cylinder
- Lesson 10.1.4 – Volume of a Pyramid and a Cone
- Lesson 10.1.5 – Volume of a Sphere

Mathematical Vocabulary

The following is a list of vocabulary found in this chapter. Some of the words you have been seen in previous chapters. The words in bold are the words new to this chapter. Make sure that you are familiar with the terms below and know what they mean. For the words you do not know, refer to the glossary or index. You might also add these words to your Toolkit so that you can reference them in the future.

base (of a prism)	circumference	**cone**
cube (of a number)	**cube root**	**cylinder**
diameter	height	**lateral face**
perfect cube	prism	**pyramid**
radius	**sphere**	square (a number)
square root	surface area	volume

Answers and Support for Closure Problems
What Have I Learned?

Note: MN = Math Note, LL = Learning Log

Problem	Solution	Need Help?	More Practice
CL 10-72.	a. SA = 1512 ft^2, V = 2744 ft^3 b. SA = 572 cm^2, V = 672 cm^3	Lesson 10.1.1	Problems 10-2, 10-27, 10-42, 10-44, and 10-57
CL 10-73.	SA: $128\pi \approx 402.12$ cm^2 V: $192\pi \approx 603.19$ cm^3	Lesson 10.1.2 MN: 10.1.2 and 10.1.3 LL: 10.1.2	Problems 10-18, 10-20, 10-23, and 10-26
CL 10-74.	Volume = 256 in.^{3}	Lesson 10.1.3 MN: 10.1.4 LL: 10.1.3	Problems 10-42 and 10-57
CL 10-75.	The base of the ladder will be approximately 10 feet from the base of the house.	Lessons 9.2.2, 9.2.3, and 9.2.5 MN: 9.2.3 and 9.2.5 LL: 9.2.3 and 9.2.5	Problems 10-14, 10-28, and 10-67
CL 10-76.	a. 1.3×10^9 b. 2×10^5	Lessons 8.2.1, 8.2.3, and 8.2.4 MN: 8.2.3 and 8.2.4 LL: 8.2.1	Problems 8-125, 9-113, 9-114, and 10-65
CL 10-77.	$\sqrt[3]{50} \approx 3.68$ cm	Lesson 10.1.1	Problems 10-4, 10-6, 10-12, and 10-13
CL 10-78.	a. $y = 3x - 5$ b. 3 c. See graph.	Lessons 4.1.4, 5.1.1, and 7.2.1 MN: 5.1.1 and 7.2.3	Problem 9-23, 9-26, 9-58, and 9-77
CL 10-79.	a. $55(3) = 165$ b. Let x = minutes, y = # bricks $y = 2x$ $y = 165 - 3x$ c. In 33 minutes, each wall will have 66 bricks.	Lessons 5.2.2 and 5.2.3 MN: 5.2.2, 5.2.3, and 5.2.4	Problems 8-131, 9-48, and 9-152

When most people think of measurement, they think of using a ruler or tape measure to find a length. However, during this course you found the measures of objects using other types of information, a process called **indirect measurement**. Today's activity will provide you with opportunities to connect several ways you know for finding measures. As you work with your team, ask the following questions.

How can we visualize it?

What information do we need?

Which strategy should we use?

10-81.   The beautiful young princess of Polygonia is very sad. A mean ogre has locked her into a tower of a castle. She could escape through the window, but it is 50 feet above the ground, a long distance to jump! A moat full of alligators surrounds the tower. Naturally, Prince Charming wants to rescue her.

The prince has some rope. His plan is to use an arrow to shoot one end of the rope up to her window. The princess can then slide down the rope to the other side of the moat, and off they will ride into the sunset.

Help the prince save the princess by answering the questions below.

a.   The prince knows that the closer he is to the tower, the less rope he will need. However, he is not sure how wide the moat is around the castle.

In a book about the castle, the prince found a diagram of the tower and moat. Using his ruler, he found that the window in the diagram is 7.5 inches above the moat, while the farthest edge of the moat is 1.5 inches from the base of the tower. How close to the tower can the prince get? Draw diagrams and show your work.

b.   Before he shoots the arrow, the prince wants to make sure he has enough rope. If he needs an extra 2 feet of rope for tying it to the window frame and holding it on the ground, how long does his rope need to be? Explain.

Problem continues on next page. →

Core Connections, Course 3

10-81.   *Problem continued from previous page.*

    c.   The princess thinks she might fall off the rope if the slope is steeper than $\frac{5}{4}$. The prince plans to attach the rope to the ground at the edge of the moat, and the princess will attach the rope to the window frame 50 feet above the ground.

        i.   According to the prince's plan, what would the slope of the rope be? Would it be too steep? Justify your answer.

        ii. Should the princess worry about the prince's plan? How steep would the prince's rope be? Find the angle the rope would make with the ground.
Use a protractor to measure the angle.

    d.   If one end of the rope is attached to the window frame and the prince holds his end of the rope 2 feet above the ground, where would the prince need to stand so that the slope of the rope is only $\frac{5}{4}$? If he has a rope that is 62 feet long, will his rope be long enough? Justify your conclusion. Draw a picture and label it with all your measurements.

    e.   What if the prince holds his end of the rope 5 feet above the ground? Can he stand in some location so that the rope is not steeper than $\frac{5}{4}$? (The rope is still 62 feet long.) Justify your conclusion.

10-82.   MAKING CONNECTIONS

When you solved this problem, you needed to use what you learned about several different math ideas.

    a.   Discuss how you solved the problem with your team.

        • Use colors to mark parts of your solution that used particular math ideas. (For example, did you compare portions? Did you solve equations?)

        • Label each math idea with words in the margin of your paper.

    b.   Contribute your ideas to a class discussion. Did any other teams identify math ideas that you used but did not notice? If so, add them to your notes. Then write each math idea on an index card.

    c.   How are these different math ideas connected in this problem? Work with your team and follow your teacher's instructions to make a concept map. Work with your team to find ways to show or explain each of the connections you find.

10-83.   BECOMING MATHEMATICALLY PROFICIENT

During this course, you have been asked lots of different kinds of questions. The purpose of many of the questions is to help you think in new ways.

This book focuses on helping you use some very specific Mathematical Practices. The Mathematical Practices are different ways to approach a mathematics problem, pull it apart, and work on it. They include ways you communicate mathematics to your teammates and teacher. They are what make you a mathematician, not just a number cruncher!

Two of the Mathematical Practices you may have used in this lesson, for example, are **construct viable arguments and critique the reasoning of others** and **use appropriate tools**. Below, you will learn more about what these mean.

a.   With your team, read and discuss the descriptions below.

Construct viable arguments and critique the reasoning of others:

> An important practice of mathematics is to **construct viable arguments and critique the reasoning of others**. In this course, you regularly shared information, opinions, and expertise with your study team. You took turns talking, listening, contributing, arguing, asking for help, checking for understanding, and keeping each other focused.
>
> During this process, you learned to use higher-order thinking. "Critical thinking" is another way to describe "higher-order thinking." It can be difficult to learn, but it is extremely valuable. Learning how to think critically helped you understand concepts more deeply. It allowed you to apply newfound ideas in all sorts of problems, not just the specific concept you happened to be working on.
>
> You and your study teams used higher-order, critical-thinking skills any time you provided clarification, built on each other's ideas, analyzed a problem by breaking it into smaller parts, came to agreement during a discussion, and productively criticized each other's ideas.
>
> Justifying and critiquing was a part of your daily classwork, not an occasional assignment. For each problem, you were expected to communicate your mathematical findings in writing, in oral presentations, or in poster presentations in a clear and convincing manner.

Problem continues on next page. →

Core Connections, Course 3

10-83.   *Problem continued from previous page.*

Use appropriate tools strategically:

> Throughout this course, you had to **use appropriate tools strategically**. In a typical lesson, you had many different tools available to you. Examples of tools include rulers, scissors, diagrams, graph paper, blocks, tiles, and calculators. However, you were not usually told which specific tools to use to solve any particular problem.
>
> Sometimes, different teams decided to use different tools to solve the same problem. Thus, you often shared your solution strategies with the whole class. Frequently, this included a discussion about which tools were most efficient and productive to solve a given problem.
>
> As you continued to do more and more sophisticated mathematics throughout the course, you were introduced to other tools, such as computer applications.

b.   How did you **use appropriate tools strategically** when you solved problem 10-81? Be ready to explain your ideas.

c.   How did you **construct viable arguments and critique the reasoning of others** while doing problem 10-81? How is **critiquing the reasoning of others** important in problems such as this one?

d.   Work with your team to brainstorm other problems in this course in which you **used appropriate tools strategically** and **constructed viable arguments and critiqued the reasoning of others**. Be ready to share your ideas with the class.

10.2.2 How can I figure it out?

Finding Unknowns

Have you ever read a problem and been convinced that you did not have enough information to solve it? Sometimes the relationships just seem too complicated. You may even think it is a trick problem with no logical answer. However, if you persevere, remember all the tools and strategies you have worked with, and try to represent the situation in multiple ways, you may surprise yourself. In this lesson, you will use what you have learned to solve some problems that may at first seem impossible. While you work, keep these questions in mind:

How can we represent it?

What is the best strategy or model for this problem?

Is this like any other problem we have seen?

10-84. NIFTY NECKLACES

Amber and Melissa were making bead necklaces with one-centimeter wooden beads and longer green glass beads when they stopped to admire each other's work. Amber's necklace had only 11 total beads. She had designed a pattern that alternated 5 green beads with 6 wooden beads, as shown below. Melissa's necklace used 4 green beads and 11 wooden beads in the pattern shown below.

Amber's Necklace   Melissa's Necklace

When they compared their progress, they were surprised to find that the necklaces were exactly the same length!

With your team, figure out the length of each green bead and the total length of each necklace. Be prepared to share your strategies with the class.

10-85. The necklaces are so popular that Amber and Melissa have decided to go into the jewelry business. They have located a supply house that will sell them beads in any color and any length. Help Amber and Melissa fill the orders below by figuring out the necessary bead lengths.

a. Cassie wants a necklace 58 cm long that has 12 of the 1-cm wooden beads arranged with some red beads. Red beads are available in lengths of 3 cm or 4 cm. Find at least two different ways in which Amber and Melissa could fill Cassie's order.

b. Justin wants to order a necklace with the same pattern as Melissa's (one green alternating with three wooden beads, with one wooden bead on each end), but he wants it to be 61 centimeters long. Can his order be filled? If so, sketch a diagram and find out how many beads of each are needed. If not, explain how he could adjust his order.

c. **Additional Challenge:** Leonora wants two necklaces that use the 1-cm wood beads and some other bead of any color or any length. She has created the following designs. The longer necklace will use 24 of the 1-cm wooden beads and just one other bead in the center. The shorter one will use 4 of the other beads, each pair separated by just one of the 1-cm wooden beads. She wants one necklace to be exactly 5 cm shorter than the other. What length of bead should be used for this order?

10-86. MAKING CONNECTIONS

When you solved the previous bead problems, you needed to use your knowledge about several different mathematical ideas.

a. With your team, do the following:

- Use colors to mark parts of your solution that used particular mathematical ideas. (For example, did you measure lengths? Did you draw quadrilaterals?)

- Label each mathematical idea with words in the margin of your paper.

b. Contribute your ideas to a class discussion. Did any other teams identify mathematical ideas that you used but had not noticed? If so, add these to your notes. Then write each mathematical idea on an index card.

c. How are these different mathematical ideas connected in this problem? Work with your team and follow your teacher's instructions to make a concept map. You will need to find ways to show or explain each of the connections you find.

10-87.   BECOMING MATHEMATICALLY
         PROFICIENT

During this course, you have been asked lots of
different kinds of questions. The purpose of
many of the questions is to help you think in
new ways.

This book focuses on helping you use some
very specific Mathematical Practices. The
Mathematical Practices are different ways to
approach a mathematics problem, pull it apart,
and work on it. They include ways you
communicate mathematics to your teammates
and teacher. They are what make you a
mathematician, not just a number cruncher!

Two of the Mathematical Practices you may
have used in this lesson, for example, are **make
sense of problems and persevere in solving
them** and **look for and make use of structure**.
Below, you will learn more about what these mean.

a.   With your team, read and discuss the descriptions below.

     Make sense of problems and persevere in solving them:

          Making sense of problems and persevering in solving them means
          that you can solve realistic problems that are full of different kinds of
          mathematics. These types of problems are not routine, simple, or
          typical. Instead, they combine lots of math ideas and real-life
          situations.

          In this course, you made sense of such problems and persevered in
          solving them on a daily basis. You carried out investigations that were
          not simply "word problems." By making sense of a problem, rather
          than being told how to solve it step-by-step, you developed a deeper
          understanding of mathematics. You also learned how to carry out
          mathematical procedures fluently and efficiently.

          In addition to learning and using problem-solving strategies, you had to
          stick with challenging problems, trying different strategies and using
          all of the resources available to you.

Core Connections, Course 3

Look for and make use of structure:

> **Looking for and making use of structure** has been an important part of this course. Since you are working to develop a deep, conceptual understanding of mathematics, you often use this practice to bring closure to an investigation. There are many concepts that you have learned by looking at the underlying structure of a math idea and thinking about how it connects to other ideas you have already learned.

> One example of when you looked at the underlying structure of a math idea is when you learned to simplify with the "Giant One." The "Giant One" was a structure to use in arithmetic with fractions, where the numerator and denominator are the same, giving you a value of 1.

> By being involved in the actual development of math concepts, you gain a deeper understanding of mathematics than you would if you were simply told what they are and how to do related problems.

b. How did you **make sense of problems and persevere in solving them** when you solved problem 10-84? Be ready to explain your ideas.

c. How did you **look for and make use of structure** while doing problem 10-84? How can **looking for and making use of structure** help you do problems like this one?

d. Work with your team to brainstorm other problems in this course in which you **made sense of problems and persevered in solving them** and **looked for and made use of structure**. Be ready to share your ideas with the class.

10.2.3 How is it changing?

Analyzing Data to Identify a Trend

Have you ever tried to figure out whether you could earn enough money to be able to buy something that you want? In this lesson, you will consider the relationship between the time you work and your pay rate as you work with your team to analyze data and make predictions.

10-88. Devon hopes to get a summer job at an amusement park. His goal is to earn enough money during the summer to buy a laptop for $875. He is not sure what pay rate he will be offered, so he asked his friends who work at the same amusement park for information from their last paycheck. The information he gathered is in the table at right.

	Time (hours)	Pay (dollars)
Frieda	21	$200.00
Ben	25	$305.00
Emory	36	$252.00
Si Yun	50	$480.00
Jillian	55	$600.00
Malik	64	$512.00
Dazjon	72	$600.00
Grace	80	$700.00

a. On graph paper, set up a graph, carefully decide how to scale the axes, and graph Devon's data.

b. Find the hourly rate for each of Devon's friends.

c. What is the highest rate per hour one of Devon's friends is earning? What is the lowest rate per hour? Explain how you found your answer.

d. Draw a trend line that represents this data. Use your trend line to help Devon predict how much he will earn. Why does it make sense that the trend line should pass through the origin?

Problem continues on next page. →

Core Connections, Course 3

10-88.   *Problem continued from previous page.*

   e.   Devon hopes to work 4 hours each day. If he works Friday through Sunday for 10 weeks, how many hours would he work?

   f.   Based on your trend line, how much money can Devon expect to be paid per hour? Show how you found your answer.

   g.   Devon knows that he will need to pay 7.5% tax for his laptop. Will he make enough money? Explain how you know.

10-89.   MAKING CONNECTIONS

   When you solved this problem, you needed to use what you learned about several different math ideas.

   a.   Discuss how you solved the problem with your team.

   •   Use colors to mark parts of your solution that used particular math ideas. (For example, did you calculate volume? Did you use transformations?)

   •   Label each math idea with words in the margin of your paper.

   b.   Contribute your ideas to a class discussion. Did any other teams identify math ideas that you used but did not notice? If so, add them to your notes. Then write each math idea on an index card.

   c.   How are these different math ideas connected in this problem? Work with your team and follow your teacher's instructions to make a concept map. Work with your team to find ways to show or explain each of the connections you find.

10-90. BECOMING MATHEMATICALLY PROFICIENT

During this course, you have been asked lots of different kinds of questions. The purpose of many of the questions is to help you think in new ways.

This book focuses on helping you use some very specific Mathematical Practices. The Mathematical Practices are different ways to approach a mathematics problem, pull it apart, and work on it. They include ways you communicate mathematics to your teammates and teacher. They are what make you a mathematician, not just a number cruncher!

Two of the Mathematical Practices you may have used in this lesson, for example, are **model with mathematics** and **look for and express regularity in repeated reasoning.** Below, you will learn more about what these mean.

a. With your team, read and discuss the descriptions below.

Model with mathematics:

When you **model with mathematics**, you are not wearing fancy clothes on a runway in New York! Mathematical modeling is what you do when you work with situations that involve multiple representations. For example, in this course, you frequently modeled different relationships and patterns using tables, graphs, equations, and words or diagrams.

In creating these models, you often first make assumptions, then make predictions, and finally check to see if your predictions make sense in the context of the problem.

In situations involving the variability of data, you learned that although a model may not be perfect, it can still be very useful for describing data and making predictions. You also found that a calculator or computer can help you model situations more efficiently than doing the work by hand.

Look for and express regularity in repeated reasoning:

> **Look for and express regularity in repeated reasoning** means that when you are faced with an investigation of a new mathematical concept, you sometimes look for a simpler or related problem. This strategy can help expand your ability to solve increasingly complex problems.
>
> For example, you **looked for and expressed regularity in repeated reasoning** when you expanded the reasoning for multiplication to develop the rules for exponents.

b. How did **looking for and making use of structure** help you solve problem 10-88? Be ready to explain your ideas.

c. Sometimes you **look for and express regularity in repeated reasoning** to help explain mathematics and to explain your thinking. How did **looking for regularity in repeated reasoning** help you in problem 10-88?

d. Work with your team to brainstorm other problems in this course in which you **looked for and expressed regularity in repeated reasoning** and **looked for and made use of structure**. Be ready to share your ideas with the class.

Core Connections, Course 3
Checkpoint Materials

Notes to Students (and their Teachers)

Students master different skills at different speeds. No two students learn exactly the same way at the same time. At some point you will be expected to perform certain skills accurately. Most of these Checkpoint problems incorporate skills that you should have developed in previous grades. If you have not mastered these skills yet it does not mean that you will not be successful in this class. However, you may need to do some work outside of class to get caught up on them.

Starting in Chapter 1 and finishing in Chapter 9, there are 9 problems designed as Checkpoint problems. Each one is marked with an icon like the one above. After you do each of the Checkpoint problems, check your answers by referring to this section. If your answers are incorrect, you may need some extra practice to develop that skill. The practice sets are keyed to each of the Checkpoint problems in the textbook. Each has the topic clearly labeled, followed by the answers to the corresponding Checkpoint problem and then some completed examples. Next, the complete solution to the Checkpoint problem from the text is given, and there are more problems for you to practice with answers included.

Remember, looking is not the same as doing! You will never become good at any sport by just watching it, and in the same way, reading through the worked examples and understanding the steps is not the same as being able to do the problems yourself. How many of the extra practice problems do you need to try? That is really up to you. Remember that your goal is to be able to do similar problems on your own confidently and accurately. This is your responsibility. You should not expect your teacher to spend time in class going over the solutions to the Checkpoint problem sets. If you are not confident after reading the examples and trying the problems, you should get help outside of class time or talk to your teacher about working with a tutor.

Checkpoint Topics

1. Operations with Signed Fractions and Decimals
2. Evaluating Expressions and Using Order of Operations
3. Unit Rates and Proportions
4. Area and Perimeter of Circles and Composite Figures
5. Solving Equations
6. Multiple Representations of Linear Equations
7. Solving Equations with Fractions ("Fraction Busters")
8. Transformations
9. Scatterplots and Association

Checkpoint 1

Problem 1-61

Operations with Signed Fractions and Decimals

Answers to problem 1-61: a: $-\frac{17}{24}$, b: 4.1, c: $1\frac{2}{5}$, d: $-1\frac{1}{3}$, e: $3\frac{7}{12}$, f: 2.24

Use the same processes with signed fractions and decimals as are done with integers (positive and negative whole numbers.)

Example 1: Compute $\frac{1}{3}+\left(-\frac{9}{20}\right)$

Solution: When adding a positive number and a negative number, subtract the values and the number further from zero determines the sign.

$$\frac{1}{3}+-\frac{9}{20}=\frac{1}{3}\cdot\frac{20}{20}+-\frac{9}{20}\cdot\frac{3}{3}=\frac{20}{60}+-\frac{27}{60}=-\frac{7}{60}$$

Example 2: Compute $-1.25-(-3.9)$

Solution: Change any subtraction problem to "addition of the opposite" and then follow the addition process.

$$-1.25-\left(-3.9\right)\Rightarrow-1.25+3.9=-1.25+3.90=2.65$$

Example 3: Compute $-1\frac{1}{4}\div7\frac{1}{2}$

Solution: With multiplication or division, if the signs are the same, then the answer is positive. If the signs are different, then the answer is negative.

$$-1\frac{1}{4}\div7\frac{1}{2}=-\frac{5}{4}\div\frac{15}{2}=-\frac{5}{4}\cdot\frac{2}{15}=-\frac{\cancel{5}\cdot\cancel{2}}{\cancel{2}\cdot2\cdot3\cdot\cancel{5}}=-\frac{1}{6}$$

Now we can go back and solve the original problems.

a. Both numbers are negative so add the values and the sign is negative.

$$-\frac{1}{3}+-\frac{3}{8}=-\frac{1}{3}\cdot\frac{8}{8}+-\frac{3}{8}\cdot\frac{3}{3}=-\frac{8}{24}+-\frac{9}{24}=-\frac{17}{24}$$

b. Change the subtraction to addition of the opposite.

$$2.6-(-1.5)=2.6+1.5=4.1$$

c. The signs are the same so the product is positive. Multiply as usual.

$$-4\frac{1}{5}\cdot-\frac{1}{3}=-\frac{21}{5}\cdot-\frac{1}{3}=\frac{7\cdot\cancel{3}\cdot1}{5\cdot\cancel{3}}=\frac{7}{5}=1\frac{2}{5}$$

d. The signs are different so the quotient is negative. Divide as usual.

$$\frac{2}{3}\div-\frac{1}{2}=\frac{2}{3}\cdot-\frac{2}{1}=-\frac{2\cdot2}{3\cdot1}=-\frac{4}{3}=-1\frac{1}{3}$$

e. When adding a positive number with a negative number, subtract the values and the number further from zero determines the sign.

$$-1\tfrac{3}{4}+5\tfrac{1}{3}=-\tfrac{7}{4}+\tfrac{16}{3}=-\tfrac{7}{4}\cdot\tfrac{3}{3}+\tfrac{16}{3}\cdot\tfrac{4}{4}=-\tfrac{21}{12}+\tfrac{64}{12}=\tfrac{43}{12}=3\tfrac{7}{12}$$

f. The signs are the same so the quotient is positive. Divide as usual.

$$-2.8\div-1.25=1.25\overline{)2.8}=125\overline{)280}=125\overline{)280.00}^{\,2.24}$$

Here are some more to try. Compute the value of each of the following problems with fractions and decimals.

1. $-\tfrac{2}{3}+\tfrac{1}{2}$

2. $\tfrac{3}{4}-\left(-\tfrac{5}{12}\right)$

3. $-\tfrac{5}{7}+\tfrac{2}{3}$

4. $-1\tfrac{6}{7}+\left(-\tfrac{3}{4}\right)$

5. $-1.75+3.3$

6. $(-2.5)\cdot(-3.3)$

7. $-2\tfrac{7}{12}\div-\tfrac{1}{6}$

8. $3\tfrac{1}{2}+\left(-4\tfrac{3}{8}\right)$

9. $-1\tfrac{1}{4}-\left(-3\tfrac{1}{6}\right)$

10. $\left(2\tfrac{5}{9}\right)\cdot\left(-\tfrac{3}{7}\right)$

11. $4.2\div-0.15$

12. $-32-(-4.7)$

13. $-\tfrac{7}{9}\cdot2\tfrac{3}{4}$

14. $-\tfrac{3}{5}\div-1\tfrac{1}{10}$

15. $-5\tfrac{1}{2}\div-\tfrac{3}{4}$

16. $10\tfrac{5}{8}+\left(-2\tfrac{1}{2}\right)$

17. $5\tfrac{1}{5}+\left(-2\tfrac{2}{15}\right)$

18. $12\tfrac{3}{4}-\left(-1\tfrac{5}{8}\right)$

19. $(0.3)\cdot(-0.032)$

20. $-8.4\div-2.5$

21. $5\tfrac{1}{12}-\left(-2\tfrac{6}{7}\right)$

22. $-6\tfrac{1}{7}\cdot-\tfrac{4}{5}$

23. $-2\tfrac{3}{8}\div3\tfrac{1}{4}$

24. $-4\tfrac{3}{10}-1\tfrac{1}{5}$

25. $-3.4+(-32.65)$

26. $-7.5-14.93$

27. $-2\tfrac{7}{9}\cdot3\tfrac{1}{7}$

28. $-4\tfrac{1}{5}\div-\tfrac{3}{10}$

29. $-4\tfrac{3}{4}-\left(-\tfrac{5}{7}\right)$

30. $\tfrac{2}{3}\div-1\tfrac{4}{9}$

31. $\left(3\tfrac{1}{3}\right)\cdot\left(-\tfrac{2}{5}\right)$

32. $-2\tfrac{1}{4}\cdot\tfrac{2}{3}$

Answers

1. $-\frac{1}{6}$

2. $1\frac{1}{6}$

3. $-\frac{1}{21}$

4. $-2\frac{17}{28}$

5. 1.55

6. 8.25

7. $15\frac{1}{2}$

8. $-\frac{7}{8}$

9. $1\frac{11}{12}$

10. $-1\frac{2}{21}$

11. -28

12. -27.3

13. $-2\frac{5}{36}$

14. $\frac{6}{11}$

15. $7\frac{1}{3}$

16. $8\frac{1}{8}$

17. $3\frac{1}{15}$

18. $14\frac{3}{8}$

19. -0.0096

20. 3.36

21. $7\frac{79}{84}$

22. $4\frac{32}{35}$

23. $-\frac{19}{26}$

24. $-5\frac{1}{2}$

25. -36.05

26. -22.43

27. $-8\frac{46}{63}$

28. 14

29. $-4\frac{1}{28}$

30. $-\frac{6}{13}$

31. $-1\frac{1}{3}$

32. $-1\frac{1}{2}$

Checkpoint 2

Problem 2-89

Evaluating Expressions and Using Order of Operations

Answers to problem 2-89: a: –8, b: 1, c: –2, d: 17, e: –45, f: 125

In general, simplify an expression by using the Order of Operations:

- Evaluate each exponential (for example, $5^2 = 5 \cdot 5 = 25$).
- Multiply and divide each term from left to right.
- Combine like terms by adding and subtracting from left to right.

But simplify *the expressions in parentheses* or any other expressions of grouped numbers first. Numbers above or below a "fraction bar" are considered grouped. A good way to remember is to circle the terms like in the following example. Remember that terms are separated by + and – signs.

Example 1: Evaluate $2x^2 - 3x + 2$ for $x = -5$ Solution: $2(-5)^2 - 3(-5) + 2$

$$2(25) - 3(-5) + 2$$
$$50 - (-15) + 2$$
$$50 + 15 + 2 = 67$$

Example 2: Evaluate $5\left(\frac{x+2y}{x-y}\right)$ for $x = -3$, $y = 2$ Solution: $5\left(\frac{-3+2 \cdot 2}{-3-2}\right)$

$$5\left(\frac{-3+4}{-3-2}\right)$$
$$5\left(\frac{1}{-5}\right) = -1$$

Now we can go back and solve the original problems.

a. $2x + 3y + z$

$2(-2) + 3(-3) + 5$

$-4 + -9 + 5 = -8$

b. $x - y$

$(-2) - (-3)$

$-2 + 3 = 1$

c. $2\left(\frac{x+y}{z}\right)$

$2\left(\frac{-2+-3}{5}\right)$

$2\left(\frac{-5}{5}\right) = 2(-1) = -2$

d. $3x^2 - 2x + 1$

$3(-2)^2 - 2(-2) + 1$

$3(4) - 2(-2) + 1$

$12 - (-4) + 1 = 17$

e. $3y(x + x^2 - y)$

$3(-3)(-2 + (-2)^2 - (-3))$

$3(-3)\left(-2 + 4 - (-3)\right)$

$3(-3)(5) = -45$

f. $\frac{-z^2(1-2x)}{y-x}$

$\frac{-(5)^2(1-2(-2))}{(-3)-(-2)}$

$\frac{-25(1-(-4))}{(-3)-(-2)} = \frac{-25(5)}{-1} = 125$

Here are some more to try. Evaluate each expression for $x = 4$, $y = -2$, $z = -3$.

1. $2x - 3$

2. $z^2 + 5$

3. $3z - 2y$

4. $xy - 4z$

5. $y - 2 + x$

6. $z - 8 - y$

7. $x^2 + 10x - 20$

8. $2\left(\frac{2+x}{y+1}\right)$

9. $y^2 - 3y + 7$

10. $2yz - x^2$

11. $-\frac{x}{3y}$

12. $(y+z) \cdot \frac{1}{4}x$

13. $2z(y + x^2 - x)$

14. $\frac{10+y}{3y(x+1)}$

15. $2\left(\frac{x+y}{y}\right)$

16. $(2x + y^2)(3 + z)$

17. $y - 5 + 3z^2$

18. $x^2 + 12z - 4y$

19. $\frac{2y^2x}{x+2}$

20. $x(3 + zy) - 2x^2$

21. $z^2 + 8zy - y^2$

22. $x^3 - 4y$

23. $6z - y^2 + \frac{x+2}{z}$

24. $\frac{-y^2(xz-5y)}{3x-4y}$

Answers

1. 5

2. 14

3. –5

4. 4

5. 0

6. –9

7. 36

8. –12

9. 17

10. –4

11. $\frac{2}{3}$

12. –5

13. –60

14. $-\frac{4}{15}$

15. –2

16. 0

17. 20

18. –12

19. $5\frac{1}{3}$

20. 4

21. 53

22. 72

23. –24

24. $\frac{2}{5}$

Checkpoint 3

Problem 3-117

Unit Rates and Proportions

Answers to problem 3-117: a: $0.84 per pound, b: 0.6 g per cm, c: $\approx$ $3.50, d: $11.88,
e: $\approx$ 169 shots, f: $3\frac{1}{3}$ teaspoons

A rate is a ratio comparing two quantities. A unit rate is simplified to have a denominator of 1. Either unit rates or proportions (equations with ratios) can be used to solve ratio problems. Solutions can also be approximated by looking at graphs of lines passing through the origin and the given information.

Example 1: Sam paid $4.95 for $\frac{3}{4}$ pound of his favorite trail-mix. What is the unit price (dollars per pound)?

Solution: The unit price is $\frac{\$4.95}{\frac{3}{4}\text{ pound}}$. To create a unit rate we need a denominator of "one."

$$\frac{\$4.95 \cdot \frac{4}{3}}{\frac{3}{4}\text{ pound} \cdot \frac{4}{3}} = \frac{\$4.95 \cdot \frac{4}{3}}{1\text{ pound}} = \$4.95 \cdot \frac{4}{3} = \$6.60 \text{ per pound}$$

Example 2: Based on the table, what is the unit growth rate (meters per year)?

Height (m)	15	17
Years	75	85

+2

+10

Solution:

$$\frac{2\text{ meters}}{10\text{ years}} = \frac{2\text{ meters} \div 10}{10\text{ years} \div 10} = \frac{\frac{1}{5}\text{ meter}}{1\text{ year}} = \frac{1}{5}\frac{\text{meter}}{\text{year}}$$

Note: This same information could be determined by looking at a graph.

Example 3: In line at the movies are 146 people in front of you. If you count 9 tickets sold in 70 seconds, how long will it take before you buy your ticket?

Solution: The information may be organized in a proportion $\frac{9\text{ tickets}}{70\text{ seconds}} = \frac{146\text{ tickets}}{x}$. Solving the proportion $\frac{9}{70} = \frac{146}{x}$ yields $9x = 10220$ so $x \approx 1135.56$ seconds or ≈ 19 minutes.

Now we can go back and solve the original problems.

a. $\dfrac{\$1.89}{2\frac{1}{4}\text{ pound}} = \dfrac{\$1.89 \cdot \frac{4}{9}}{\frac{9}{4}\text{ pound} \cdot \frac{4}{9}} = \dfrac{\$1.89 \cdot \frac{4}{9}}{1\text{ pound}} = \$1.89 \cdot \frac{4}{9} = \$0.84 \text{ per pound}$

b. For every increase of three grams, the length increases by five centimeters.
$\dfrac{3\text{ grams}}{5\text{ cm}} = \dfrac{3}{5}\dfrac{\text{gram}}{\text{cm}} = 0.6 \text{ g per cm}$

c. The graph passes through (10 bottles, \$35). $\dfrac{\$35}{10\text{ bottles}} = \$3.50 \text{ per bottle}$.

d. $\dfrac{200\text{ vitamins}}{\$4.75} = \dfrac{500\text{ vitamins}}{x} \Rightarrow 200x = 237.50 \Rightarrow x \approx \$11.88$

e. $\dfrac{72\text{ made}}{85\text{ attempts}} = \dfrac{x}{200\text{ attempts}} \Rightarrow 85x = 14400 \Rightarrow x \approx 169 \text{ made}$

f. $\dfrac{\frac{1}{2}\text{ teaspoon}}{\frac{3}{4}\text{ cup}} = \dfrac{x}{5\text{ cups}} \Rightarrow \frac{3}{4}x = \frac{5}{2} \Rightarrow x = \frac{10}{3} = 3\frac{1}{3} \text{ teaspoons}$

Here are some more to try. In problems 1 through 10 find the unit rate. In problems 11 through 20 use ratios to solve each problem.

1. Amy usually swims 20 laps in 30 minutes. What is her rate in laps per minute?

2. For $\frac{3}{4}$ of a pound of peanuts, Jimmy paid \$2.35. What is the unit rate (dollars per pound)?

3. In 7 minutes, Jack types 511 words. How many words does he type per minute?

4. Using the graph at right, determine how long it takes to mow an acre of grass.

5. If Christy and Lucas eat 4 cups of popcorn in 30 minutes, how many minutes does it take them to eat a cup of popcorn?

6. In the past year, Ana has spent \$7, 440 on her rent. What is the unit cost (dollars per month)?

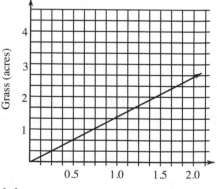

7. While constructing his house, the little piggy found that 4 bundles of sticks contained 208 sticks. How many sticks are in each bundle?

8. Meg knows that it takes 16 minutes to read $\frac{7}{8}$ of the chapter. How long will it take her to read the entire chapter?

9. At the frozen yogurt shop, Colin pays \$3.28 for his treat, which weighs $8\frac{1}{5}$ ounces. What is the unit cost (dollars per ounce)?

10. When Sarah does her math homework, she finishes 10 problems every 12 minutes. How long will it take for her to complete 35 problems?

11. Ben and his friends are having a TV marathon, and after 4 hours they have watched 5 episodes of the show. About how long will it take to complete the season, which has 24 episodes?

12. The tax on a \$400 painting is \$34. What should be the tax on a \$700 painting?

13. Use the table at right to write and solve a ratio for how long it will take Isadora to earn \$120.

\$ Earned	35	52.50	105
Days Worked	4	6	12

14. While baking, Hannah discovered a recipe for cookies that required $\frac{3}{4}$ cups of sugar for every $2\frac{1}{4}$ cups of flour. How many cups of sugar will she need for 4 cups of flour?

15. My brother grew $1\frac{3}{4}$ inches in $2\frac{1}{2}$ months. If he continues to grow at the same rate, how much should he grow in one year?

16. On his afternoon jog Chris took 42 minutes to run $3\frac{3}{4}$ miles. How many miles can he run in 90 minutes?

17. If Caitlin needs $1\frac{7}{8}$ cans of paint for each room in her house, how many cans of paint will she need to paint the 9-room house?

18. Stephen receives 6 gumballs for every two hours of homework he does. If he wants 22 gumballs, how many hours will he need to work?

Answers

1. $\frac{2}{3}\frac{\text{laps}}{\text{minute}}$

2. \$3.13 per pound

3. $73\frac{\text{words}}{\text{minute}}$

4. $\frac{3}{4}$ hour

5. $7\frac{1}{2}\frac{\text{minutes}}{\text{cup}}$

6. $\frac{\$620}{\text{month}}$

7. $52\frac{\text{sticks}}{\text{bundle}}$

8. $18\frac{2}{7}$ minutes

9. $\frac{\$0.40}{\text{ounce}}$

10. 42 minutes

11. $19\frac{1}{5}$ hours

12. \$59.50

13. 13.7 days

14. $1\frac{1}{3}$ cups

15. $8\frac{2}{5}$ inches

16. $8\frac{1}{28}$ miles

17. $16\frac{7}{8}$ cans

18. $7\frac{1}{3}$ hours

Checkpoint 4
Problem 4-71
Area and Perimeter of Circles and Complex Figures

Answers to problem 4-71: a: $A \approx 28.27$ cm^2, $C \approx 18.85$ cm , b: $A \approx 78.54$ ft^2, $C \approx 31.42$ ft ,
  c: $A \approx 150.80$ ft^2, $P \approx 49.13$ ft , d: $A \approx 452.53$ ft^2, $P \approx 85.13$ ft

For circles, the formulas for area and circumference (perimeter) are:

$$A = r^2\pi \quad \text{and} \quad C = 2r\pi \quad \text{where } r = \text{radius of the circle}$$

For complex figures (made of from circles or parts of circles with other shapes), divide the figure into more recognizable parts. Then find the sum of the area of the parts. When finding the perimeter of a complex region, be sure that the sum only includes the edges on the outside of the region.

Example 1:

3 m

Example 2:

6 cm

6 cm

2 cm

5 cm

9 cm

Area of half of a circle:
$A = \frac{1}{2} r^2 \pi = \frac{1}{2} \cdot 1.5^2 \cdot \pi \approx 3.53$ m^2

Circumference of half of a circle plus the diameter
$P = \frac{1}{2} \cdot 2r\pi + d = \frac{1}{2} \cdot 2 \cdot 1.5 \cdot \pi + 3 \approx 7.71$ m

Area of square plus triangle
$A = s^2 + \frac{1}{2} bh = 6^2 + \frac{1}{2} \cdot 3 \cdot 4 = 42$ cm^2

Add all sides for perimeter
$6 + 6 + 2 + 5 + 9 = 28$ cm

Now we can go back and solve the original problems.

a. $A = r^2\pi = 3^2 \cdot \pi \approx 28.27$ cm^2 $C = 2r\pi = 2 \cdot 3 \cdot \pi \approx 18.85$ cm

b. Radius is 5 ft: $A = r^2\pi = 5^2 \cdot \pi \approx 78.54$ ft^2 $C = 2r\pi = 2 \cdot 5 \cdot \pi \approx 31.42$ ft

c. The area of the sector is $\frac{1}{3}$ of the area of circle: $A = \frac{1}{3} r^2\pi = \frac{1}{3} \cdot 12^2 \cdot \pi \approx 150.80$ ft^2
   The perimeter is $\frac{1}{3}$ of the circumference added to the length of two radii:
      $P = \frac{1}{3} \cdot 2r\pi + 2r = \frac{1}{3} \cdot 2 \cdot 12 \cdot \pi + 2 \cdot 12 \approx 49.13$ ft

d. The area is the area of a rectangle added to the area of half a circle:
      $A = lw + \frac{1}{2} r^2\pi = 16 \cdot 22 + \frac{1}{2} \cdot 8^2 \cdot \pi \approx 452.53$ ft^2
   The perimeter is the length of the three sides added to half the circumference of the circle:
      $P = l + w + l + \frac{1}{2} \cdot 2r\pi = 16 + 22 + 22 + \frac{1}{2} \cdot 2 \cdot 8 \cdot \pi \approx 85.13$ ft

504

Core Connections, Course 3

Here are some more to try. Find the area and perimeter of the following figures.
Note: All angles that look like right angles are right angles.

1. Circle with a radius of 7.3 m

2. Circle with a diameter of 8.5 ft.

3. Circle with a radius of 11 yds

4. Circle with a diameter of 52 mm

5. Circle with a radius of 2.12 cm

6. Circle with a diameter of 15 in.

7. Find the area of the shaded region.

8. Semi-circle

9.

10. Trapezoid on a rectangle

11. Rectangle and a semi-circle

12.

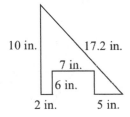

13. Find the area of the shaded region.
     The diameter of the circle is 4 ft.

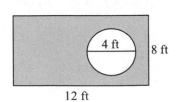

14. Semi-circle on a rectangle

15. Quarter-circle

5 in.

16.

8 cm

5.1 cm   5 cm   5.1 cm

5 cm

10 cm

17.

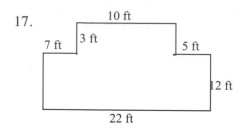

10 ft

7 ft   3 ft   5 ft

12 ft

22 ft

18.

8 in.

6 in.

10 in.

6.4 in.

13 in.

19. Find the area of the shaded region.

7 in.

12 in.   8 in.

10 in.

20. Circle with diameter = 60 cm

60 cm

21.

12.8 m

19.2 m   18.6 m

27.2 m

18.6 m   19.2 m

12.8 m

22. Find the area of the center region bounded by four congruent quarter circles.

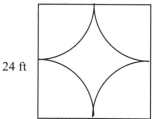

24 ft

24 ft

23. Find the area of the shaded region. bounded by a square and a circle.

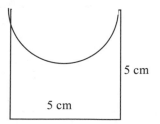

5 in.

24. A half-circle cut out of a square.

5 cm

5 cm

Answers

1. $A = 167.4 \text{ m}^2$, $P = 45.9 \text{ m}$

2. $A = 56.7 \text{ ft}^2$, $P = 26.7 \text{ ft}$

3. $A = 380.1 \text{ yds}^2$, $P = 69.1 \text{ yds}$

4. $A = 2123.7 \text{ mm}^2$, $P = 163.4 \text{ mm}$

5. $A = 14.1 \text{ cm}^2$, $P = 13.3 \text{ cm}$

6. $A = 176.7 \text{ in.}^2$, $P = 47.1 \text{ in.}$

7. $A = 184.5 \text{ m}$

8. $A = 628.3 \text{ in.}^2$, $P = 102.8 \text{ in.}$

9. $A = 192 \text{ ft}^2$, $P = 68 \text{ ft}$

10. $A = 41 \text{ cm}^2$, $P = 28.4 \text{ cm}$

11. $A = 100.3 \text{ m}^2$, $P = 48.8 \text{ m}$

12. $A = 28 \text{ in.}^2$, $P = 53.2 \text{ in.}$

13. $A = 83.4 \text{ ft}^2$

14. $A = 265.9 \text{ m}^2$, $P = 73.98 \text{ m}$

15. $A = 19.6 \text{ in.}^2$, $P = 17.85 \text{ in.}$

16. $A = 95 \text{ cm}^2$, $P = 38.2 \text{ cm}$

17. $A = 294 \text{ ft}^2$, $P = 74 \text{ ft}$

18. $A = 90 \text{ in.}^2$, $P = 43.4 \text{ in.}$

19. $A = 64 \text{ in.}^2$

20. $A = 2827.4 \text{ cm}^2$, $P = 188.5 \text{ cm}$

21. $A = 744 \text{ m}^2$, $P = 102.4 \text{ m}$

22. $A = 123.6 \text{ ft}^2$

23. $A = 5.7 \text{ in.}^2$

24. $A = 5.34 \text{ cm}^2$, $P = 30.7 \text{ cm}$

Checkpoint 5

Problem 5-61

Solving Equations

Answers to problem 5-61: a: $x = -2$, b: $x = 1\frac{1}{2}$, c: $x = 3$, d: no solution

Equations may be solved in a variety of ways. Commonly, the first steps are to remove parenthesis using the Distributive Property and then simplify by combining like terms. Next isolate the variable on one side and the constant terms on the other. Finally, divide to find the value of the variable. Note: When the process of solving an equation ends with different numbers on each side of the equal sign (for example, $2 = 4$), there is *no solution* to the problem. When the result is the same expression or number on each side of the equation (for example, $x + 3 = x + 3$) it means that *all real numbers* are solutions.

Example 1: Solve $4x + 4x - 3 = 6x + 9$

Solution:

$4x + 4x - 3 = 6x + 9$	problem
$8x - 3 = 6x + 9$	simplify
$2x = 12$	add 3, subtract $6x$ on each side
$x = 6$	divide

Check: $4(6) + 4(6) - 3 = 6(6) + 9$

$24 + 24 - 3 = 36 + 9$

$48 - 3 = 45$

$45 = 45$

Example 2: Solve $-4x + 2 - (-x + 1) = -3 + (-x + 5)$

Solution:

$-4x + 2 - (-x + 1) = -3 + (-x + 5)$	problem
$-4x + 2 + x - 1 = -3 - x + 5$	remove parenthesis (distribute)
$-3x + 1 = -x + 2$	simplify
$-2x = 1$	add x, subtract 1 from each side
$x = -\frac{1}{2}$	divide

Check:

$$-4\left(-\frac{1}{2}\right) + 2 - \left(-\left(-\frac{1}{2}\right) + 1\right) = -3 + \left(-\left(-\frac{1}{2}\right) + 5\right)$$

$$2 + 2 - \left(\frac{1}{2} + 1\right) = -3 + \left(\frac{1}{2} + 5\right)$$

$$4 - \left(1\frac{1}{2}\right) = -3 + \left(5\frac{1}{2}\right)$$

$$2\frac{1}{2} = 2\frac{1}{2}$$

Now we can go back and solve the original problems.

a. $3x + 7 = -x - 1$
$$4x = -8$$
$$x = -2$$

b. $1 - 2x + 5 = 4x - 3$
$$-2x + 6 = 4x - 3$$
$$9 = 6x$$
$$1\frac{1}{2} = x$$

c. $-2x - 6 = 2 - 4x - (x - 1)$
$$-2x - 6 = 2 - 4x - x + 1$$
$$-2x - 6 = -5x + 3$$
$$3x = 9$$
$$x = 3$$

d. $3x - 4 + 1 = -2x - 5 + 5x$
$$3x - 3 = 3x - 5$$
$$-3 = -5$$
$$-3 \neq -5 \Rightarrow \text{no solution}$$

Here are some more to try. Solve each equation.

1. $2x - 3 = -x + 3$

2. $3x + 2 + x = x + 5$

3. $6 - x - 3 = 4(x - 2)$

4. $4x - 2 - 2x = x - 5$

5. $-(x + 3) = 2x - 6$

6. $-x + 2 = x - 5 - 3x$

7. $1 + 3x - x = x - 4 + 2x$

8. $5x - 3 + 2x = x + 7 + 6x$

9. $4y - 8 - 2y = 4$

10. $-x + 3 = 6$

11. $-2 + 3y = y - 2 - 4y$

12. $2(x - 2) + x = 5$

13. $-x - 3 = 2x - 6$

14. $10 = x + 5 + x$

15. $2x - 1 - 1 = x - 3 - (-5 + x)$

16. $3 + 3x - x + 2 = 3x + 4$

17. $-4 + 3x - 1 = 2x + 1 + 2x$

18. $2x - 7 = -x - 1$

19. $7 = 3x - 4 - (x + 2)$

20. $5y + (-y - 2) = 4 + y$

Answers

1. $x = 2$

2. $x = 1$

3. $x = 2\frac{1}{5}$

4. $x = -3$

5. $x = 1$

6. $x = -7$

7. $x = 5$

8. no solution

9. $y = 6$

10. $x = -3$

11. $y = 0$

12. $x = 3$

13. $x = 1$

14. $x = 2\frac{1}{2}$

15. $x = 2$

16. $x = 1$

17. $x = -6$

18. $x = 2$

19. $x = 6\frac{1}{2}$

20. $y = 2$

Multiple Representations of Linear Equations

Answers to problem 6-109:

a:

Figure #	0	1	2	3
# of Tiles	2	4	6	8

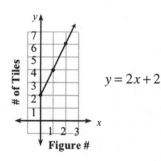

$y = 2x + 2$

b:

x	0	1	2	3
y	7	4	1	-2

c: $y = 3x + 1$

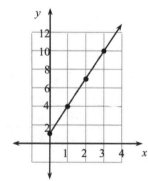

d:

x	0	1	2	3
y	6	4	2	0

$y = -2x + 6$

If you know one representation of a linear pattern, it can also be represented in three other different ways. Linear representations may be written as equations in the form $y = mx + b$ where m is the growth pattern and b is the starting value.

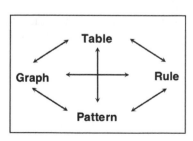

Example 1: Using the pattern at right, create an $x \to y$ table, a graph, and write the rule as an equation.

Figure 0   Figure 1   Figure 2   Figure 3

Solution: The number of tiles matched with the figure number gives the $x \to y$ table. Plotting those points gives the graph. Using the starting value for b and the growth pattern for m gives the information to write the equation in $y = mx + b$ form.

Figure # (x)	0	1	2	3
# of Tiles (y)	3	5	7	9

The starting number is 3 tiles and the pattern grows by 2 tiles each figure so the equation is $y = 2x + 3$.

Figure Number

Example 2:   Create an $x \to y$ table and the rule (equation) based on the graph at right.

Solution:

Place the given points in a table:

x	0	1	2	3
y	12	9	6	3

The starting value is 12 and the growth pattern is –3. The equation is $y = -3x + 12$.

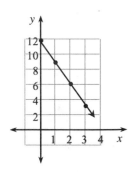

Now we can go back and solve the original problems.

a. Start by making a table from the tile pattern.

Figure #	0	1	2	3
# of Tiles	4	6	8	10

Since the starting value is 4 and the growth pattern is 2 the equation is $y = 2x + 4$.

b. Make a table by replacing x in the rule with $0, 1, 2$, and then computing y. See the table above. Plot the points from the table to get the graph shown with the given answers.

c. Looking at the table, the y-value changes by 9 when the the x-value changes by 3. Therefore the y-value is changing by 3 when the x-value is changing by 1. A completed table is shown below. Since the starting value is 1 and the growth pattern is 3, the table and equation are: See the graph given with the answers.

x	0	1	2	3
y	1	4	7	10

$y = 3x + 1$

d. Again the table above is determined from the points on the graph. Looking at the table, the starting value is 6 and the growth pattern is -2 so the equation is $y = -2x + 6$.

x	0	1	2	3
y	6	4	2	0

Here are some more to try. For each situation, complete a Multiple Representations of Linear Equations web by finding the missing $x \rightarrow y$ table, graph, and/or rule. Since there are many possible patterns, it is not necessary to create one.

1.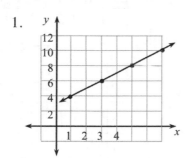

2.

x	0			3
y	2			11

3. $y = 3x - 2$

4.

Figure 1   Figure 2   Figure 3

5.

x	1			4
y	1.5			3

6. $y = -4x + 12$

7.

8.

      Figure 1   Figure 2   Figure 3

9. $y = -2x + 7$

10.

x	1	2		
y	$4\frac{1}{4}$	$6\frac{1}{2}$		

Answers

1.

x	1	2	3	4
y	4	5	6	7

$y = x + 3$

2.

$y = 3x + 2$

3.

x	0	1	2	3
y	−2	1	4	7

4.

x	0	1	2	3
y	2	5	8	11

$y = 3x + 2$

5.

$$y = \tfrac{1}{2}x + 1$$

6.

x	0	1	2	3
y	12	8	4	0

7.

x	0	1	2	3
y	0	2	4	6

$$y = 2x$$

8.

x	0	1	2	3
y	0	3	5	7

$$y = 2x + 1$$

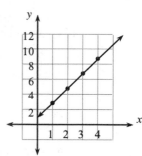

9.

x	0	1	2	3
y	7	5	3	1

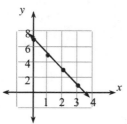

10. $y = \tfrac{3}{4}x + 5$

Checkpoint 7

Problem 7-115

Solving Equations with Fractions (Fraction Busters)

Answers to problem 7-115: a: $x = \frac{15}{4} = 3\frac{3}{4}$, b: $x \approx \$1.74$, c: $x = -5$, d: $(12, 16)$

Equations are often easier to solve if there are no fractions. To eliminate fractions from an equation, multiply both sides of the equation by the common denominator.

Example 1: Solve $\frac{1}{2}x + \frac{2}{3} = \frac{3}{4}$

Solution: Start by multiplying both sides of the equation by 12 (the common denominator.) Simplify and then solve as usual.

$$12\left(\frac{1}{2}x + \frac{2}{3}\right) = 12\left(\frac{3}{4}\right)$$
$$6x + 8 = 9$$
$$6x = 1$$
$$x = \frac{1}{6}$$

Example 2: Solve $1.1x + 0.35x = 29$

Solution: Two decimal places means that the common denominator is 100. Multiply both sides by 100 and solve as usual.

$$100(1.1x + 0.35x) = 100(29)$$
$$110x + 35x = 2900$$
$$145x = 2900$$
$$x = 20$$

Now we can go back and solve the original problems.

a.
$$\frac{1}{5}x + \frac{1}{3}x = 2$$
$$15\left(\frac{1}{5}x + \frac{1}{3}x\right) = 15(2)$$
$$3x + 5x = 30$$
$$8x = 30$$
$$x = \frac{30}{8} = \frac{15}{4} = 3\frac{3}{4}$$

b.
$$x + 0.15x = \$2$$
$$100(x + 0.15x) = 100(\$2)$$
$$100x + 15x = \$200$$
$$115x = \$200$$
$$x \approx \$1.74$$

c.
$$\frac{x+2}{3} = \frac{x-2}{7}$$
$$21\left(\frac{x+2}{3}\right) = 21\left(\frac{x-2}{7}\right)$$
$$7(x+2) = 3(x-2)$$
$$7x + 14 = 3x - 6$$
$$4x = -20$$
$$x = -5$$

d.
$$y = \frac{2}{3}x + 8$$
$$y = \frac{1}{2}x + 10$$
$$\frac{2}{3}x + 8 = \frac{1}{2}x + 10$$
$$6\left(\frac{2}{3}x + 8\right) = 6\left(\frac{1}{2}x + 10\right)$$
$$4x + 48 = 3x + 60$$
$$x = 12$$
$$y = \frac{2}{3}(12) + 8 = 16$$
$$(12, 16)$$

Here are some more to try. Solve each equation or system of equations.

1. $\frac{1}{6}x + \frac{2}{3}x = 5$

2. $y = 32x + 16$
   $y = 80x + 4$

3. $\frac{6}{15} = \frac{x-2}{40}$

4. $y = \frac{x}{3}$
   $y = \frac{4}{3}x - 9$

5. $\frac{r}{2} - 4 = \frac{x}{3}$

6. $\frac{x}{4} - 3 = \frac{x+4}{6} - 2$

7. $\frac{x}{10} + \frac{5}{12} = 3x - 1$

8. $\frac{2x-2}{6} - \frac{1}{2} = \frac{x}{2} - 2$

9. $0.2x + x = 30$

10. $y = \frac{x}{6} + \frac{1}{4}$
    $y = x - \frac{9}{4}$

11. $y = -3x + 2$
    $y = -\frac{15}{4}x + 3$

12. $x + 3\frac{2}{3} = 2x + \frac{1}{3}$

13. $\frac{x}{2} + \frac{4x}{3} = 2x - 1.5$

14. $\frac{x+1}{4x} = \frac{5}{16}$

15. $y = \frac{1}{3}x + 8$
    $y = -\frac{1}{2}x - 2$

16. $y = 7x + 2$
    $y = 2x - 10\frac{1}{2}$

17. $y = \frac{x}{2} - 1$
    $y = \frac{x+3}{12}$

18. $y = \frac{3}{2}x - 10$
    $y = \frac{x}{3} - \frac{x}{2}$

19. $\frac{x-1}{4} = \frac{7}{8}$

20. $\frac{2}{3}x = x - \frac{10}{3}$

Answers

1. $x = 6$

2. $x = \frac{1}{4}$, $y = 24$

3. $x = 18$

4. $x = 9$, $y = 3$

5. $x = 24$

6. $x = 20$

7. $x = \frac{85}{174}$

8. $x = 7$

9. $x = 25$

10. $x = 3$, $y = \frac{3}{4}$

11. $x = \frac{4}{3}$, $y = -2$

12. $x = 3\frac{1}{3}$

13. $x = 9$

14. $x = 4$

15. $x = -12$, $y = 4$

16. $x = -2\frac{1}{2}$, $y = -15\frac{1}{2}$

17. $x = 3$, $y = \frac{1}{2}$

18. $x = 6$, $y = -1$

19. $x = 4.5$

20. $x = 10$

Checkpoint 8

Problem 8-135

Transformations

Answers to problem 8-135: (Given in the order *X, Y, Z*) a: $(-2, 2), (-2, 0), (1, 2)$,
b: $(4, -1), (4, -3), (1, -1)$, c: $(-1, 4), (-3, 4), (-1, 1)$, d: $(-8, -2), (-8, 6), (-2, 2)$

Rigid transformations are ways to move an object while not changing its shape or size.
A translation (slide) moves an object vertically, horizontally or both. A reflection (flip)
moves an object across a line of reflection as in a mirror. A rotation (turn) moves an
object clockwise or counterclockwise around a point.

A dilation is a non-rigid transformation. It produces a figure that is similar to the original
by proportionally shrinking or stretching the figure from a point.

**Example 1: Translate (slide) △*ABC* left six units and down
three units. Give the coordinates of the new △*XYZ*.**

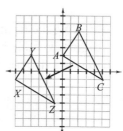

Solution: The original vertices are *A* $(0, 2)$, *B* $(2, 5)$, and *C* $(5, -1)$.
The new vertices are *X* $(-6, -1)$, *Y* $(-4, 2)$, and *Z* $(-1, -4)$.

**Example 2: Reflect (flip) △*ABC* across the *x*-axis to get △*PQR*.
Give the coordinates of the new △*PQR*.**

**Now reflect (flip) △*ABC* across the *y*-axis to get △*XYZ*. Give the
coordinates of the new △*XYZ*.**

Solution: The key is that the reflection is the same distance from the
axis as the original figure. For the first reflection the points are
P $(4, -2)$, *Q* $(1, -4)$, and *R* $(3, -6)$. For the second reflection the
points are *X* $(-4, 2)$, *Y* $(-1, 4)$, and *Z* $(-3, 6)$.

**Example 3: Rotate (turn) △*ABC* counterclockwise 90° about
the origin to get △*MNO*. Give the coordinates of the new
△*MNO*. Then rotate △*MNO* counterclockwise another 90° to
get △*XYZ*. Give the coordinates of the new △*XYZ*.**

Solution: After the first 90° rotation, the coordinates of *A* $(2, 0)$, *B*
$(6, 0)$, and *C* $(5, 4)$ became *M* $(0, 2)$, *N* $(0, 6)$, and *O* $(-4, 5)$. Note
that each original point (x, y) became $(-y, x)$. After the next 90° rotation, the coordinates
of the vertices are now *X* $(-2, 0)$, *Y* $(-6, 0)$, and *Z* $(-5, -4)$. After the 180° rotation each of
the points (x, y) in the original △*ABC* became $(-x, -y)$. Similarly a 270°
counterclockwise rotation or a 90° clockwise rotation about the origin takes each point
(x, y) to the point $(y, -x)$.

Example 4: Dilate (enlarge/reduce) △*ABC* **by a scale factor of**
$\frac{1}{2}$ **from the origin to get** △*XYZ* **. Give the coordinates of the**
new △*XYZ* **.**

Solution: Multiplying the coordinates of the vertices of △*ABC* by
the scale factor gives the coordinates of the vertices of the new
△*XYZ* . They are *X* (−2,0), *Y* (0,3) and *Z* (1,−1).

Now we can go back and solve the original problems.

a. Sliding the triangle two units to the right and three units up increases the *x*-values by 2
    and the *y*-values by 3. See the answers above.

b. Reflecting the triangle across the *y*-axis changes the *x*-values to the opposite and keeps
    the *y*-values the same. See the answers above.

c. Rotating the triangle 90° clockwise moves the triangle into the second quadrant. The
    original *y*-value becomes the new *x*-value and the opposite of the original *x*-value
    becomes the *y*-value. See the answers above.

d. Dilating the triangle by a scale factor of two multiplies all of the coordinates by two.
    See the answers above.

Here some more to try. For the following problems, refer to the figures below:

| Figure A | Figure B | Figure C |

  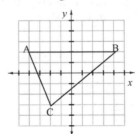

State the new coordinates after each transformation.

      1. Translate figure A left 2 units and down 2 units.

      2. Rotate figure C 180° counterclockwise about the origin.

      3. Reflect figure B across the *y*-axis.

      4. Reflect figure B across the *x*-axis.

      5. Translate figure A right 4 units and up 1 unit.

      6. Reflect figure C across the *y*-axis.

Core Connections, Course 3

7. Rotate figure B 270° counterclockwise about the origin.

8. Translate figure C left 1 unit and up 2 units.

9. Rotate figure A 90° clockwise about the origin.

10. Reflect figure B across the line $y = 3$.

11. Dilate figure B by a scale factor of 3.

12. Rotate figure A 180° counterclockwise about the origin.

13. Translate figure B 4 units down and 4 units to the right.

14. Dilate figure A by a scale factor of 4.

15. Rotate figure C 90° clockwise about the origin.

16. Reflect figure A across the y-axis.

17. Dilate figure C by a scale factor of $\frac{1}{2}$.

18. Translate figure C 3 units right and 2 units down.

19. Rotate figure C 180° about the origin clockwise.

20. Dilate figure A by a scale factor of 2.

Answers

1. $(-1, -2), (1, 2), (3, 0)$ 2. $(4, -2), (-4, -2), (2, 3)$

3. $(5, 2), (1, 2), (0, 5)$ 4. $(-5, -2), (-1, -2), (0, -5)$

5. $(5, 1), (7, 5), (9, 3)$ 6. $(4, 2), (-4, 2), (2, -3)$

7. $(2, 5), (2, 1), (5, 0)$ 8. $(-5, 4), (3, 4), (-3, -1)$

9. $(0, -1), (4, -3), (2, -5)$ 10. $(5, 4), (1, 4), (0, 1)$

11. $(-15, 6), (-3, 6), (0, 15)$ 12. $(-1, 0), (-3, -4), (-5, -2)$

13. $(-1, -2), (3, -2), (4, 1)$ 14. $(4, 0), (12, 16), (20, 8)$

15. $(2, 4), (2, -4), (-3, 2)$ 16. $(-1, 0), (-3, 4), (-5, 2)$

17. $(-2, 1), (2, 1), (-1, -1.5)$ 18. $(-1, 0), (7, 0), (1, -5)$

19. $(4, -2), (-4, -2), (2, 3)$ 20. $(2, 0), (6, 8), (10, 4)$

Checkpoint 9

Problem 9-50

Scatterplots and Association

Answers to problem 9-50:

a: box plot

b: scatterplot

c: See graph at right.

d: strong linear negative association

e: $y = -3x + 35$

f: $17,000

g: A slope of –3 means the car is losing $3000 in value each year, y-intercept of 35 means the cost when new was $35,000.

An association (relationship) between two numerical variables on a graph can be described by its form, direction, strength, and outliers. When the association has a linear form, a line a best fit can be drawn and its equation can be used to make predictions about other data.

Example 1: Describe the association in the scatterplot at right.

Solution: Looking from left to right, except for point (e), the points are fairly linear and increasing. This is a moderate, positive linear association. Point (e) is an outlier.

Example 2: For the scatterplot, draw a line of best fit and determine the equation of the line.

Solution: Use a ruler or straightedge to draw the line that approximates the trend of the points. If it is not a perfect line, approximately the same number of points will be above and below the line of best fit.

To determine the equation of the line, draw in a slope triangle and determine the ratio of the vertical side to the horizontal side. In this case it is $\frac{-30}{5} = -6$. Estimate the y-intercept by looking at where the line intersects the y-axis. In this case, it is approximately 30. The equation of any non-vertical line may be written in the form $y = mx + b$ where m is the slope and b is the y-intercept.

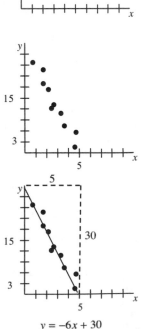

$$y = -6x + 30$$

522

Now we can go back and solve the original problem.

a. Since the costs are a single set of data, a box plot is a convenient way to show the distribution.

b. Age and cost are two sets of related data so a scatterplot is appropriate.

c. See the graph given in the answers.

d. Reading from left to right, the scatterplot is decreasing, linear and the points are close to the line of best fit. This is a strong, linear, negative association.

e. Looking at the line of best fit, the slope triangle has a ratio of $-\frac{3}{1}$ and the y-intercept is approximately 35. Placing that information into the equation of a line, $y = mx + b$, yields $y = -3x + 35$.

f. Substituting $x = 6$ into the equation of part (e) yields $y = -3(6) + 35 = 17$, $17,000.

g. Slope represents the rate of change. A rate of change of –3 means that the value is decreasing by 3 units (in this case each unit is $1000) per year. The y-intercept represents the value at year zero or a new car.

Here are some more to try.

In problems 1 through 4, describe the association.

1.

2.

3.

4.

In problems 5 through 8 plot the data, draw a line of best fit, and approximate the equation of the line.

5.

Distance to Airport (mi)	5	10	15	20	25	30
Cost of Shuttle ($)	14	17	21	31	33	40

6.

Exercise/Month (hours)	3	6	9	12	15	18
Rate of Heart Attack/1000	24	21	18	12	6	0

7.

Time Spent Studying (hours)	0	2	2.5	2.8	3	4.5	5
Score on Test	65	70	70	85	80	95	100

8.

Time Since Purchase (hours)	0	2	4	6	8	10
Number of Cookies	24	20	14	11	5	0

Answers

1. strong positive association

2. no association

3. strong positive association

4. strong negative association

5.

$\approx y = 1x + 8$

6.

$\approx y = -1.5x + 30$

7.

$\approx y = 6x + 63$

8.

$\approx y = 2.4x + 10$

Puzzle Investigator Problems

Dear Students,

Puzzle Investigator problems (PIs) present you with an opportunity to investigate complex, interesting problems. Their purpose is to focus on the process of solving complex problems. **You will be evaluated on your ability to show, explain, and justify your work and thoughts**. Save *all* of your work, including what does not work, in order to write about the processes you used to reach your answer.

Completion of a Puzzle Investigator problem includes four parts:

- **Problem Statement:** State the problem clearly in your own words so that anyone reading your paper will understand the problem you intend to solve.

- **Process and Solutions:** Describe in detail your thinking and reasoning as you work from start to finish. Explain your solution and how you know it is correct. Add diagrams when it helps your explanation. Include what you do that does not work and changes you make along the way. If you do not complete this problem, describe what you <u>do</u> know and where and why you are stuck.

- **Reflection:** Reflect about your learning and your reaction to the problem. What mathematics did you learn from it? What did you learn about your math problem solving strategies? Is this problem similar to any other problems you have done before? If yes, how?

- **Attached work:** Include <u>all</u> your work and notes. Your scratch work is important because it is a record of your thinking. Do not throw anything away.

PI-1.   WHICH IS THE FAKE?

Josiah is in charge of the historical museum's rare coin collection. Recently, there were rumors that one of a special collection of identical coins is a fake and that it weighs less than the others.

Josiah has a balance pan, which can compare the weights of two sets of objects and tell you which is heavier and lighter. Assume that only one coin is fake.

a.   What if the collection only has 3 coins? How many different times do you need to use the balance pan to figure out which coin is fake?

b.   Assume the coin collection has 8 coins. Josiah claims he can find the fake by using the balance pan only twice. Is this possible? If so, explain how it works. If it is not possible, explain why not.

c.   If the collection has 12 coins, how could Josiah use the balance to find the fake? Find a strategy that will find the fake by using the balance pan the fewest number of times.

PI-2.   NUMBER PUZZLES

For this challenge, you will solve multiple number puzzles. For each puzzle, show all of your work (even that which leads to a "dead end"). For each part below, describe in a paragraph what strategy worked and any observations you made that made the puzzle easier.

a. Figure out which number from 0 through 9 each letter at right stands for so that the addition works. Assume $T \neq 0$ and $F \neq 0$. If $U = 0$, what are the values of the other letters?

$$\begin{array}{r} TWO \\ +\,TWO \\ \hline FOUR \end{array}$$

b. Is there a value of U for which you can find two different solutions? Is there any value of U that will not work, that is, for which you cannot find a solution?

c. This time, figure out which numbers 0 through 7 each letter stands for in the puzzle at right so that the multiplication is true.

$$\begin{array}{r} AAA \\ \times\,BC \\ \hline DDDE \\ FFF \\ \hline GGGE \end{array}$$

PI-3.   RUMORS, RUMORS, RUMORS

Stevens Middle School has 1500 students. During first period, a rumor is started when Susan tells three friends a secret. Each of Susan's three friends tells three of their friends during second period, who then tell three different friends during third period. Assume each person tells the rumor to only three others, and that each new person who is told the rumor has not heard it yet.

a. Find the number of students who have heard the rumor by the end of school. (Stevens Middle School has 6 periods.)

b. What if every friend only told 2 other people? How many people would hear the rumor by the end of school?

c. How many people would each friend need to tell so that all the students at the school have heard the rumor by the end of school?

PI-4.   FIBONACCI RECTANGLES

The Fibonacci Numbers are those numbers found in the following sequence:

$$1, 1, 2, 3, 5, 8, 13, ...$$

a.   Describe how this sequence is growing. Continue it until you have the first 15 Fibonacci numbers.

b.   If the measures of the sides of a rectangle are consecutive Fibonacci numbers, it is called a "Fibonacci rectangle." Here are the first four Fibonacci rectangles:

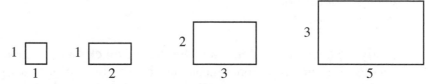

Verify that the sum of the areas of the first two Fibonacci rectangles is 3 square units and that the sum of the first three Fibonacci rectangles is 9 square units.

c.   Copy and complete the table at right that shows how the sum of the areas of the Fibonacci rectangles grows for the first 8 rectangles.

d.   Look for any special numbers in your table. Can you find any patterns? For example, what seems special about the sum of the areas for an odd number of Fibonacci rectangles? How are these numbers connected to the Fibonacci numbers? Extend the table if you need more data.

Number of Fibonacci Rectangles	Sum of the Areas (in sq. units)
2	3
3	9
4	
5	
6	
7	
8	

e.   How can you predict the sum of the areas of Fibonacci rectangles? Use your patterns to predict the sum of the areas of the first 15 Fibonacci rectangles. Then find out if your pattern worked.

PI-5.   THREE VIEWS

Architects and designers often use three views, like the top, front, and right, to show the shape of a solid geometric object. See the example at right. If the solid contains no hidden cavities or hollow spaces, then views from the top, front, and right side give enough information to convey the shape and size.

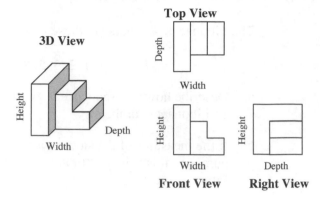

Study the three views of the staircase-shaped block above. Look for relationships and common dimensions between the various views. It may help to build the shape if you have blocks available, or to copy the diagrams on your paper and use color or letters to show which faces are the same.

a.   Anson drew three views for the blocks at right, but he forgot to label which view is which. Identify to Anson which is the top, front, and right view, and explain how you know.

i.   ii.   iii.

b.   On graph paper, draw the three views for the shape at right. Be sure to label your diagrams with the words "height," "width," and "depth." Also label the views as top, right, or front.

c.   Is it possible to add a cube to the shape and not change the right view? If so, describe all the possible ways.

d.   Is it possible to remove a cube (or several cubes) without changing the front view? Explain.

e.   Anson designed a new solid and drew the top, right, and front views at right. Describe his solid. Then find its volume and surface area. Assume there are no floating cubes.

PI-6.   POOL, ANYONE?

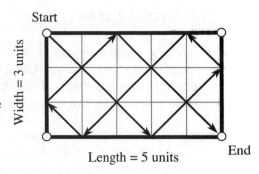

Start

Width = 3 units

Length = 5 units   End

Paper pool is a game played with rectangles like the one at right. We assume that a ball is hit from a corner and that it always hits the side at a 45° angle. We also assume that the "pockets" (the cups the ball drops into) are located only in the corners.

The goal is to find a way to predict how many times the ball will rebound (bounce off of) the side of the table before going into a corner pocket.

a.   An example of a ball on a 3×5 table is shown above. Confirm that the ball shown above will bounce off a side 6 times before entering the pocket in the lower right-hand corner.

b.   What happens for rectangles of other sizes? On graph paper, set up the paper pool tables described below and look for patterns. Assume the ball starts in the upper left-hand corner. For each paper pool table, record how many times the ball hits the sides of the table before landing in a pocket. Also record the pocket in which the ball lands.

   i. 2×2 ii. 2×3 iii. 2×4

   iv. 2×6 v. 2×7 vi. 3×3

   vii. 3×4 viii. 3×5 ix. 3×6

   x. 3×7 xi. 4×4 xii. 4×5

c.   Is there a corner pocket where the ball will never end up? Why do you think this is?

d.   When will there be no rebounds? Explain.

e.   On which tables will the ball hit a side only 1 time? On which paper tables will the ball hit a side 2 times? Explain how you can tell how many times the ball will hit a side if you know the length and width of the table. For example, can you tell how many times the ball will hit a side on a 31×62 table without drawing a picture?

PI-7.   CUSTOMER SERVICE

Patti the Plumber wants to be ready to repair broken pipes of any whole-number length up to 30 feet long. Unfortunately, her truck has a rack that only allows her to transport 5 pipes. To make new lengths, she can join any pieces end-to-end. Assume her truck can carry pipes of any length.

a.   Patti does not want to cut the pipe on location. Help Patti figure out which five lengths of pipe she should carry in the truck to be able to produce lengths of 1, 2, 3, 4, 5, …, 29, and 30 feet. Show how Patti can produce each length using one or more of the lengths of pipe you propose.

b.   What is the longest length Patti can produce with her pipes from part (a)?

c.   When solving this problem, Patti remembered a game she used to play as a child. After asking her friend to silently pick a number from 1 to 15, she would then have the friend indicate which cards below had his number on it. She would then instantly know which number her friend had picked. For example, if her friend said his number was on cards B, C, and D, she would quickly know the number was 14. How does this game work? And what is its connection to her problem with pipe lengths?

1	3	5	7
9	11	13	15
17	19	21	23
25	27	29	31

Card A

2	3	6	7
10	11	14	15
18	19	22	23
26	27	30	

Card B

4	5	6	7
12	13	14	15
20	21	22	23
28	29	30	31

Card C

8	9	10	11
12	13	14	15
24	25	26	27
28	29	30	31

Card D

16	17	18	19
20	21	22	23
24	25	26	27
28	29	30	31

Card E

PI-8.   SIERPINSKI TRIANGLES

Fractals are geometric structures developed by repeating a process over and over. A famous example of a fractal is the **Sierpinski Triangle**, shown below. To create this design, start with a triangle, as shown in Figure 1. Then find and connect the midpoints of all of the sides of the triangle, subdividing it into four smaller triangles. Shade all but the central triangle as shown in Figure 1.

Then repeat the process by finding and connecting the midpoints of the shaded triangles of Figure 1. Shade all but the center triangles, as shown in Figure 2. If this process is continued infinitely, the result is the Sierpinski Triangle.

Figure 0   Figure 1   Figure 2   Figure 3

a.   On the PI-8 Resource Page (which can be downloaded at www.cpm.org), shade in the next figure in the sequence.

b.   For Figures 1 through 4, write a fraction to represent the amount of the entire triangle that is shaded. As you work, look for patterns. What is happening to the numerator and denominator of the fraction? What is happening to the amount shaded?

c.   Use your pattern to predict what portion of Figure 5 and Figure 6 in the sequence will be shaded.

d.   The shaded portion of Figure 2 could be written as $\left(\frac{3}{4}\right)^2$. Rewrite the other figures in this form. According to this pattern, what should the value of $\left(\frac{3}{4}\right)^0$ to be? Explain why.

e.   Is there any figure that will have less than 10% shaded? If so, use your pattern to explain how you know.

PI-9.   WEIGHING PUMPKINS

Every year at Half Moon Bay, there is a pumpkin contest to see who has grown the largest pumpkin for that year.

Last year, one pumpkin grower (who was also a mathematician) brought 5 pumpkins to the contest. Instead of weighing them one at a time, he informed the judges, "*When I weighed them two at a time, I got the following weights: 110, 112, 113, 114, 115, 116, 117, 118, 120, and 121 pounds.*"

Your Task: Find how much each pumpkin weighed.

PI-10.   MAKING TRACKS!

Vu got a new bicycle for her birthday and cannot wait to ride it all around her favorite park. To find out which paths are best, she wants to ride each of them exactly once, without repeating any path and without missing any. When she can do this, it is called an "Euler" (pronounced "oy-ler") path after a mathematician who investigated similar paths.

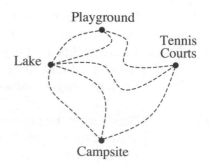

The map of the park is shown at right. Vu needs to decide where her mother should drop her off to begin her ride.

a.   Is it possible for Vu to ride each trail exactly once without repeating any path and without missing any?

   • If it is possible, show all the possible ways for her to do this.

   • If none exist, find a new path you could add to the park to create an Euler path.

b.   The park manager is planning to add a parking lot as a new point on the map. It will need to be connected to at least one of the other locations in the park with a path. Propose a location of a parking lot and at least one other path so that the park will have an Euler path. Remember that to be an Euler path, it must use all the paths exactly once.

c.   Vu is thinking about going to one of the parks shown below. Which of them have Euler paths? Which do not? If an Euler path exists, show where Vu could start and stop her ride, and use arrows to show the direction she should travel. Look for reasons why some parks have Euler paths and others do not.

i.   *ii.*   *iii.*   *iv.*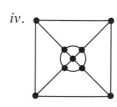

d.   Draw two new parks that have Euler paths and two that do not.

e.   Why do some parks have Euler paths and others do not?

PI-11. WHAT'S MY NUMBER?

Francesca has a game for you. She decided to show the rules of the game using a flowchart, at right.

a. Show that if you start with the number 60, you will lose.

b. How many starting numbers less than 100 will win? List the possible winning numbers and show how you know they will win.

c. What if Francesca changed the rules so that you win if you end up with the number 1? What numbers would win?

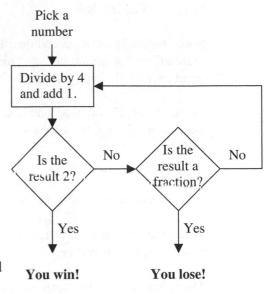

PI-12. GOING BANANAS!

This year's harvest from a small, remote banana plantation consists of 3000 bananas. The farmer's camel can carry up to 1000 bananas at a time. The market place where the bananas are sold is 1000 miles away. Unfortunately, the camel eats one banana each and every mile she walks.

Your Task: Of the three thousand bananas harvested, what is the greatest number of bananas the farmer can get to market?

PI-13.   HAPPY NUMBERS

Some numbers have special qualities that earn them a title, such as "square number" or "prime number." This problem will explore another type of number, called "happy numbers."

The number 23 is a happy number. To determine if a number is a happy number, square each of its digits and add.

$$2^2 + 3^2 = 13$$
$$1^2 + 3^2 = 10$$

Repeat this process several times until you get 1, or until you get the same number twice (see below).

$$1^2 + 0^2 = 1$$

When the final answer is 1, the original number is called a **happy number**.

The number 34 is not happy number, as demonstrated below:

Step #1 $3^2 + 4^2 = 25$
Step #2 $2^2 + 5^2 = 29$
Step #3 $2^2 + 9^2 = 85$
Step #4 $8^2 + 5^2 = \mathbf{89}$
Step #5 $8^2 + 9^2 = 145$
Step #6 $1^2 + 4^2 + 5^2 = 42$
Step #7 $4^2 + 2^2 = 20$
Step #8 $2^2 + 0^2 = 4$
Step #9 $4^2 + 0^2 = 16$
Step #10 $1^2 + 6^2 = 37$
Step #11 $3^2 + 7^2 = 58$
Step #12 $5^2 + 8^2 = \mathbf{89}$

Since 89 is repeated, the final answer will be in a never-ending loop and, therefore, will never equal 1. This means that 34 *is not* a happy number.

a.   There are 17 two-digit happy numbers. Find as many as you can. Remember to keep all your work and ideas organized so you can refer back when writing up what you discovered.

b.   Find 5 three-digit happy numbers.

c.   Eve found out that 478 is a happy number. Based on this, what other numbers must be happy numbers? How do you know? Find at least 10 new happy numbers.

PI-14.   MAKING DECISIONS

Carlos wanted to get a part-time job to have
extra money for the holidays. After reading
the advertisement at right, he applied. His
interview went well, and he was offered the
job. He had to choose between the following
two pay scales:

**HELP
WANTED**
CABANA'S
DEPT. STORE
Nov. 25 – Dec. 24
Wrapping Gifts
6pm – 9pm daily

Pay Scale # 1

He would earn $10 per hour.

Pay Scale # 2

On day # 1, he would earn a total of 1¢
On day # 2, he would make a total of 2¢
On day # 3, he would make a total of 4¢

Each day, his salary rate would double
from the day before.

a.   Before starting the problem, guess which pay scale Carlos chose. Explain
why you think this.

b.   If the store is closed on Thanksgiving (November 27th), and Carlos works
every day that the store is open through December 24th, make a table that
shows how much he makes each day using both pay scales.

c.   If you had a job offer like this one, which pay scale would you choose?
Why?

Glossary

5-D Process An organized method to solve problems. The 5 D's stand for Describe/Draw, Define, Do, Decide, and Declare. This is a problem-solving strategy for which solving begins by making a prediction about the answer or one element of it (a trial), and then confirming whether the result of the trial is correct. If not, information is gained about how close the trial is to the correct value, so that adjustments to the trial value may be made. Being organized is extremely important to the success of this method, as well as writing a usable table. The 5-D Process leads to writing equations to represent word problems. (p. 16)

AA ~ (Triangle Similarity) If two angles of one triangle are congruent to the two corresponding angles of another triangle, then the triangles are similar. For example, given $\triangle ABC$ and $\triangle A'B'C'$ with $\angle A \cong \angle A'$ and $\angle B \cong \angle B'$, then $\triangle ABC \sim \triangle A'B'C'$. You can also show that two triangles are similar by showing that *three* pairs of corresponding angles are congruent (which would be called AAA~), but two pairs are sufficient to demonstrate similarity. (p. 413)

absolute value The absolute value of a number is the distance of the number from zero. Since the absolute value represents a distance, without regard to direction, absolute value is always non-negative. Thus, the absolute value of a negative number is its opposite, while the absolute value of a non-negative number is just the number itself. The absolute value of x is usually written "$|x|$." For example, $|-5| = 5$ and $|22| = 22$.

acute angle An angle with a measure greater than 0° and less than 90°. An example is shown at right.

acute triangle A triangle with all three angle measures less than 90°. (p. 420)

additive identity The number 0 is called the additive identity because adding 0 to any number does not change the number. For example, $7 + 0 = 7$. (p. 74)

Additive Identity Property The Additive Identity Property states that adding zero to any expression leaves the expression unchanged. That is, $a + 0 = a$. For example, $-2 + 0 = -2$. (p. 74)

additive inverse The number you need to add to a given number to get a sum of 0. For example, the additive inverse of –3 is 3. It is also called the opposite. (p. 78)

Additive Inverse Property The Additive Inverse Property states that for every number a there is a number $-a$ such that $a = -a = 0$. For example, the number 5 has an additive inverse of –5; 5 + (–5) = 0. The additive inverse of a number is often called its opposite. For example, 5 and –5 are opposites. (p. 78)

adjacent angles   For two angles to be adjacent, they must satisfy these three conditions: (1) The two angles must have a common side; (2) They must have a common vertex; and (3) They can have no interior points in common. This means that the common side must be between the two angles; no overlap between the angles is permitted. In the example at right, ∡*ABC* and ∡*CBD* are adjacent angles. (p. 396)

algebra   A branch of mathematics that uses variables to generalize the rules of numbers and numerical operations.

algebra tiles   An algebra tile is a manipulative whose area represents a constant or variable quantity. The algebra tiles used in this course consist of large squares with dimensions x-by-x; rectangles with dimensions x-by-1; and small squares with dimensions 1-by-1. These tiles are named by their areas: x^2, x, and 1, respectively. The smallest squares are called "unit tiles." In this text, shaded tiles will represent positive quantities while unshaded tiles will represent negative quantities. (p. 139)

algebraic expression   See *expression*.

alternate interior angles   Angles between a pair of lines that switch sides of a third intersecting line (called a transversal). For example, in the diagram at right the shaded angles are alternate interior angles. If the lines intersected by the transversal are parallel, the alternate interior angles are congruent. Conversely, if the alternate interior angles are congruent, then the two lines intersected by the transversal are parallel. (p. 401)

angle   Generally, an angle is formed by two rays that are joined at a common endpoint. Angles in geometric figures are usually formed by two segments that have a common endpoint (such as the angle shaded in the figure at right). Also see *acute angle*, *obtuse angle*, and *right angle*. (p. 396)

annual   Occurring once every year.

area   For this course, area is the number of square units needed to fill up a region on a flat surface. In later courses, the idea will be extended to cones, spheres, and more complex surfaces. Also see *surface area*.

Area = 15 square units

association   A relationship between two (or more) variables. An association between numerical variables can be displayed on a scatterplot, and described by its form, direction, strength, and outliers. Possible association between two categorical variables can be studied in a relative frequency table. Also see *scatterplot*. (p. 290)

Associative Property of Addition   The Associative Property of Addition states that if a sum contains terms that are grouped, then the sum may be grouped differently with no effect on the total, that is, $a + (b + c) = (a + b) + c$. For example, $3 + (4 + 5) = (3 + 4) + 5$. (p. 74)

Associative Property of Multiplication   The Associative Property of Multiplication states that if a product contains terms that are grouped, then the product may be grouped differently with no effect on the result, that is, $a(bc) = (ab)c$. For example, $2 \cdot (3 \cdot 4) = (2 \cdot 3) \cdot 4$. (p. 74)

average   The sum of given values divided by the number of values used in computing the sum. For example, the average of 1, 4, and 10 is $\frac{1+4+10}{3} = 5$. See *mean*.

axis (plural: axes)   On a coordinate plane, two number lines that meet at right angles at the origin $(0, 0)$. The x-axis runs horizontally and the y-axis runs vertically. (p. 11)

b   When the equation of a line is expressed in $y = mx + b$ form, the constant b gives the y-intercept of the line. For example, the y-intercept of the line $y = -\frac{1}{3}x + 7$ is 7. (p. 162)

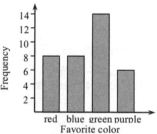

bar graph   A bar graph is a set of rectangular bars that have height proportional to the number of data elements in each category. Each bar stands for all of the elements in a single distinguishable category (such as "red"). Usually all of the bars are the same width and separated from each other. Also see *histogram*.

base of a geometric figure   (a) The base of a triangle: any side of a triangle to which a height is drawn. There are three possible bases in each triangle. (b) The base of a trapezoid: either of the two parallel sides. (c) The base of a parallelogram (including rectangle, rhombus, and square): any side to which a height is drawn. There are four possible bases. (d) The base of a three-dimensional figure. Also see *prism* and *pyramid*.

base of an exponent   When working with an exponential expression in the form b^a, b is called the base. For example, 2 is the base in 2^5. (5 is the exponent, and 32 is the value.) See *exponent*. (p. 347)

box plot   A graphic way of showing a summary of data using the median, quartiles, and extremes of the data.

categorical data   Data that can be put into categories (like what color you prefer, your gender, or the state you were born in), as opposed to numerical data that can be placed on a number line. (p. 324)

center of a circle On a flat surface, the fixed point from which all points on the circle are equidistant. *See* circle. (p. 128)

central angle An angle with its vertex at the center of a circle. (p. 273)

chord A line segment with its endpoints on a circle. A chord that passes through the center of a circle is called a "diameter." *See* circle. (p. 128)

circle The set of all points on a flat surface that are the same distance from a fixed point. If the fixed point (center) is O, the symbol $\odot\, O$ represents a circle with center O. If r is the length of a circle's radius and d is the length of its diameter, the circumference of the circle is $C = 2\pi r$ or $C = \pi d$. The area of the circle is $A = \pi r^2$. (p. 128)

circle graph A way of displaying data that can be put into categories (like what color you prefer, your gender, or the state you were born in). A circle graph shows the proportion each category is of the whole. (p. 276)

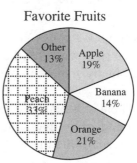

circumference The perimeter (distance around) of a circle. (p. 128)

coefficient (numerical) A number multiplying a variable or product of variables. For example, -7 is the coefficient of $-7x$. (p. 52)

coincide Two graphs coincide if they have all their points in common. For example, the graphs of $y = 2x + 4$ and $3y = 6x + 12$ coincide; both graphs are lines with a slope of 2 and a y-intercept of 4. When the graphs of two equations coincide, those equations share all the same solutions and have an infinite number of intersection points. (p. 210)

combining like terms Combining two or more like terms simplifies an expression by summing constants and summing those variable terms in which the same variables are raised to the same power. For example, combining like terms in the expression $3x + 7 + 5x - 3 + 2x^2 + 3y^2$ gives $8x + 4 + 2x^2 + 3y^2$. When working with algebra tiles, combining like terms involves putting together tiles with the same dimensions. (p. 56)

Commutative Property of Addition The Commutative Property of Addition states that if two terms are added, then the order may be reversed with no effect on the total. That is, $a + b = b + a$. For example, $7 + 12 = 12 + 7$. (p. 66)

Commutative Property of Multiplication The Commutative Property of Multiplication states that if two expressions are multiplied, then the order may be reversed with no effect on the result. That is, $ab = ba$. For example, $5 \cdot 8 = 8 \cdot 5$. (p. 66)

complementary angles   Two angles whose measures add up to 90°. Angles T and V are complementary because $m\angle T + m\angle V = 90°$. Complementary angles may also be adjacent, like $\angle ABC$ and $\angle CBD$ in the diagram at far right. (p. 396)

complete graph   A complete graph is one that includes everything that is important about the graph (such as intercepts and other key points, asymptotes, or limitations on the domain or range), and that makes the rest of the graph predictable based on what is shown. (p. 124)

compound interest   Interest that is paid on both the principal and the previously accrued interest. (p. 351)

cone   A three-dimensional figure that consists of a circular face, called the "base," a point called the "apex," that is not in the flat surface (plane) of the base, and the lateral surface that connects the apex to each point on the circular boundary of the base. (p. 465)

congruent   Two shapes are congruent if they have exactly the same shape and size. Congruent shapes are similar and have a scale factor of 1. (p .245)

conjecture   An educated guess that often results from noticing a pattern. (p. 240)

constant of proportionality (k)   In a proportional relationship, equations are of the form $y = kx$, where k is the constant of proportionality. (p. 315)

constant term   A number that is not multiplied by a variable. In the expression $2x + 3(5 - 2x) + 8$, the number 8 is a constant term. The number 3 is not a constant term, because it is multiplied by a variable inside the parentheses. (p. 52)

continuous graph   For this course, when the points on a graph are connected and it makes sense to connect them, then the graph is continuous. Such a graph will have no holes or breaks in it. This term will be more completely defined in a later course. (p. 105)

converse   The converse of a conditional statement can be found by switching the hypothesis (the "if" part) and the conclusion (the "then" part). For example, the converse of "*If P, then Q*" is "*If Q, then P*." (p. 444)

converse of the Pythagorean Theorem   The converse of the Pythagorean Theorem can be used to determine if a triangle is a right triangle. If $(\text{leg } \#1)^2 + (\text{leg } \#2)^2 = \text{hypotenuse}^2$ then the triangle is a right triangle. (p. 425)

coordinate   The number corresponding to a point on the number line or an ordered pair (x, y) that corresponds to a point in a two-dimensional coordinate system. In an ordered pair, the x-coordinate appears first and the y-coordinate appears second. For example, the point $(3,5)$ has an x-coordinate of 3 and a y-coordinate of 5. See *ordered pair*. (p. 11)

coordinate graph (system)   A system of graphing ordered pairs of numbers on a coordinate plane. An ordered pair represents a point, with the first number giving the horizontal position relative to the x-axis and the second number giving the vertical position relative to the y-axis. Also see *ordered pair*. (p. 14)

coordinate plane   A flat surface defined by two number lines meeting at right angles at their zero points. A coordinate plane is also sometimes called a "Cartesian Plane." (p. 11)

corresponding angles   (a) When two lines are intersected by a third line (called a transversal), angles on the same side of the two lines and on the same side of the transversal are called corresponding angles. For example, the shaded angles in the diagram at right are corresponding angles. Note that if the two lines cut by the transversal are parallel, the corresponding angles are congruent. Conversely, if the corresponding angles are congruent, then the two lines intersected by the transversal are parallel. (p. 401)

corresponding parts   Points, sides, edges, or angles in two or more figures that are images of each other with respect to a transformation. If two figures are congruent, then the corresponding parts of the figures are congruent to each other. See *similar* and *congruent*. (p. 245)

counterexample   An example showing that a statement has at least one exception; that is, a situation in which the statement is false. For example, the number 4 is a counterexample to the statement that all even numbers are greater than 7. (p. 194)

cube   A polyhedron of six faces, each of which is a square. (p. 457)

cube root   In the equation $a = b^3$, the value b that is multiplied by itself three times to give the value a. For example, the cube root of 8 is 2 because $8 = 2 \cdot 2 \cdot 2 = 2^3$. This is written $\sqrt[3]{8} = 2$. (p. 457)

cubic unit   A cube, each of whose edges measure 1 unit in length. Volume is measured in cubic units.

cylinder (circular)   A three-dimensional figure that consists of two parallel congruent circular regions (called *bases*) and a lateral surface containing segments connecting each point on the circular boundary of one base to the corresponding point on the circular boundary of the other. (p. 468)

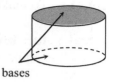

bases

degree   A unit for measuring angles. Usually denoted by ° (the degree symbol). There are 360° in one full rotation.

dependent variable   When one quantity depends for its value on one or more others, it is called the dependent variable. For example, the speed of a car might be related to the amount of force you apply to the gas pedal. Here, the speed of the car is the dependent variable; it depends on how hard you push the pedal. The dependent variable appears as the output value in an $x \rightarrow y$ table, and is usually placed relative to the vertical axis of a graph. You often use the letter y and the vertical y-axis for the dependent variable. When working with functions or relations, the dependent variable represents the output value. In Statistics, the dependent variable is often called the response variable. Also see *independent variable*. (p. 113, 378)

diameter   A line segment drawn through the center of a circle with both endpoints on the circle. The length of a diameter is usually denoted d. Note that the length of a circle's diameter is twice the length of its radius. *See* circle. (p. 128)

dilation   A transformation which produces a figure similar to the original by proportionally shrinking or stretching the figure. In a dilation, a shape is stretched (or compressed) proportionally from a point, called the point of dilation. (p. 239)

direction (of an association)   If one variable in a relationship increases as the other variable increases, the direction is said to be a positive association. If one variable decreases as the other variable increases, there is said to be a negative association. If there is no apparent pattern in the scatterplot, then the variables have no association. When describing a linear association, you can use the slope, and its numerical interpretation in context, to describe the direction of the association. (p. 287)

discrete graph   A graph that consists entirely of separated points is called a discrete graph. For example, the graph shown at right is discrete. Also see *continuous*. (p. 105)

Distributive Property   For any a, b, and c, $a(b+c) = ab + ac$. For example, $10(7+2) = 10 \cdot 7 + 10 \cdot 2$. (p. 139)

edge   In three dimensions, a line segment formed by the intersection of two faces of a polyhedron.

endpoint   A point that mark the ends of a line segment or ray.

enlarge   To make larger. (p. 262)

Equal Values Method   A method for solving a system of equations.
To use the equal values method, take two expressions that are each equal to
the same variable and set those expressions equal to each other.   For
example, in the system of equations at right, $-2x+5$ and $x-1$ each equal y. So you write
$-2x+5 = x-1$, then solve that equation to find x. Once you have x, you substitute that
value back into either of the original equations to find the value of y. (p. 205)

$$y = -2x + 5$$
$$y = x - 1$$

equation   A mathematical sentence in which two expressions have an "equals" sign ($=$)
between them indicating that they have an equal value. For example, the equation
$7x+4.2=-8$ states that the expression $7x+4.2$ has the value -8. In this course, an
equation is often used to represent a rule relating two quantities.

Equation Mat   An Equation Mat puts two Expression Mats side-
by-side to find the value(s) which make the expressions equal.
Legal moves are used to find the value(s) that makes the expressions
equal. For example, the Equation Mat at right represents the
equation $2(x + 1) - 1 = x + 4$. The two sides of the mat are equal
when $x = 3$. Also see *"legal" moves*. (p. 81)

equivalent   Two expressions are equivalent if they have the same value. For example,
$2+3$ is equivalent to $1+4$. Two equations are equivalent if they have all the same
solutions. For example, $y = 3x$ is equivalent to $2y = 6x$. Equivalent equations have the
same graph. (p. 194)

evaluate (an expression)   To find the numerical value of. To evaluate an expression,
substitute the value(s) given for the variable(s) and perform the operations according to
the order of operations. For example, evaluating $2x + y - 10$ when $x = 4$ and $y = 3$ gives
the value 1. Also see *expression*. (p. 61)

exponent   In an expression of the form b^a, a is called the exponent. For example, in the
expression 2^5, 5 is called the exponent (2 is the base, and 32 is the value). The exponent
indicates how many times to use the base as a multiplier. For example, in 2^5, 2 is used 5
times: $2^5 = 2 \cdot 2 \cdot 2 \cdot 2 \cdot 2 = 32$. For exponents of zero, the rule is: for any number $x \neq 0$,
$x^0 = 1$. (p. 61)

expression   An expression is a combination of individual terms separated by plus or
minus signs. Numerical expressions combine numbers and operation symbols; algebraic
(variable) expressions include variables. For example, $4 + (5 - 3)$ is a numerical
expression. In an algebraic expression, if each of the following terms, $6xy^2$, 24, and $\frac{y-3}{4+x}$,
are combined, the result may be $6xy^2 + 24 - \frac{y-3}{4+x}$. An expression does not have an
"equals" sign. (p. 52)

Expression Comparison Mat   An Expression Comparison Mat puts two Expression Mats side-by-side so they can be compared to see which represents the greater value. For example, in the Expression Comparison Mat at right, Mat A represents –3, while Mat B represents –2. Since –2 > –3 Mat B is greater. (p. 64)

Expression Mat   An organizing tool used to visually represent an expression with algebra tiles. (p. 64)

exterior angle (of a triangle)   When a side of a triangle is extended to form an angle outside of the triangle, that angle is called an exterior angle. The exterior angle is adjacent to the angle inside the triangle. For example, ∠4 in the diagram at right is an exterior angle of the triangle. (p. 409)

Exterior Angle Theorem   The measure of an exterior angle of a triangle is equal to the sum of the measures of the two remote (non-adjacent) interior angles of the triangle. In the diagram above, m∠1 + m∠2 = m∠4. (p. 409)

face   One of the flat surfaces of a polyhedron, including the base(s). (p. 460)

factor   (1) In arithmetic: when two or more integers are multiplied, each of the integers is a factor of the product. For example, 4 is a factor of 24, because $4 \cdot 6 = 24$.
(2) In algebra: when two or more algebraic expressions are multiplied together, each of the expressions is a factor of the product. For example, x^2 is a factor of $-17x^2y^3$, because $(x^2)(-17y^3) = -17x^2y^3$. (3) To factor an expression is to write it as a product. For example, the factored form of $3x - 18$ is $3(x - 6)$. (p. 52)

Fibonacci numbers   The sequence of numbers 1, 1, 2, 3, 5, 8, 13, …. Each term of the Fibonacci sequence (after the first two terms) is the sum of the two preceding terms. (p. 95)

first quartile (Q1)   The median of the lower half of an ordered set of data is the lower quartile.

flip   See *reflection*.

form (of an association)   The form of an association can be linear of non-linear. The form can contain cluster of data. (p. 920)

formula   An equation that shows a mathematical relationship.

fraction   The quotient of two quantities in the form $\frac{a}{b}$ where b is not equal to 0.

Fraction Busters   "Fraction Busting" is a method of simplifying equations involving fractions that uses the Multiplicative Property of Equality to rearrange the equation so that no fractions remain. To use this method, multiply both sides of an equation by the common denominator of all the fractions in the equation. The result will be an equivalent equation with no fractions. For example, when given the equation $\frac{x}{7} + 2 = \frac{x}{3}$, you can multiply both sides by the "Fraction Buster" 21. The resulting equation, $3x + 42 = 7x$, is equivalent to the original but contains no fractions. (p. 198)

frequency   The number of times that something occurs within an interval or data set.

frequency table   A table that displays counts, or frequencies, of data. (p. 324)

function   A relationship in which for each input value there is one and only one output value. For example, the relationship $y = x + 4$ is a function; for each input value (x) there is exactly one output value (y). In terms of ordered pairs (x, y), no two ordered pairs of a function have the same first member (x). (p. 378)

generic rectangle   A type of diagram used to visualize multiplying expressions without algebra tiles. Each expression to be multiplied forms a side length of the rectangle, and the product is the sum of the areas of the sections of the rectangle. For example, the generic rectangle at right may be used to multiply $(2x + 5)$ by $(x + 3)$. (p. 139)

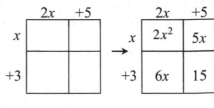

$$(2x + 5)(x + 3) = 2x^2 + 11x + 15$$

area as a product   area as a sum

Giant One   A fraction that is equal to 1. Multiplying any fraction by a Giant One will create a new fraction equivalent to the original fraction. (p. 35)

graph   A graph represents numerical information in a visual form. The numbers may come from a table, situation (pattern), or rule (equation or inequality). Most of the graphs in this course show points, lines, and/or curves on a two-dimensional coordinate system like the one at right or on a single axis called a number line (see diagram below right). (p. 124)

growth   One useful way to analyze a mathematical relationship is to examine how the output value grows as the input value increases. You can see this growth on a graph of a linear relationship by using a growth triangle.

Core Connections, Course 3

growth triangle A growth triangle is a right triangle drawn on a graph of a line so that the hypotenuse of the triangle is part of the line. The vertical leg length is the change in the *y*-value (+ 4); the horizontal leg length is the change in the *x*-value (+ 1). We use the lengths of the legs in the triangle describe the pattern of growth. For example, the diagram at right shows a growth pattern of adding 4 to each *y*-value for every increase of 1 in the *x*-value. In a tile pattern, each figure grows by adding 4 tiles.

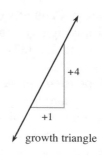

growth triangle

height (a) Triangle: the length of a segment that connects a vertex of the triangle to a line containing the opposite base (side) and is perpendicular to that line. (b) Trapezoid: the length of any segment that connects a point on one base of the trapezoid to the line containing the opposite base and is perpendicular to that line. (c) Parallelogram (includes rectangle, rhombus, and square): the length of any segment that connects a point on one base of the parallelogram to the line containing the opposite base and is perpendicular to that line. (d) Pyramid and cone: the length of the segment that connects the apex to a point in the plane containing the base of a figure and is perpendicular to that plane. (e) Prism or cylinder: the length of a segment that connects one base of the figure to the plane containing the other base and is perpendicular to that plane.

histogram A way of displaying data that is much like a bar graph in that the height of the bars is proportional to the number of elements. The difference is that each bar of a histogram represents the number of data elements in a range of values, such as the number of people who weigh from 100 pounds up to, but not including, 120 pounds. Each range of values should have the same width. Also see *bar graph*.

horizontal Parallel to the horizon. The *x*-axis of a coordinate graph is the horizontal axis. (p. 310)

horizontal lines Horizontal lines are "flat" and run left to right in the same direction as the *x*-axis. Horizontal lines have equations of the form $y = b$, where *b* can be any number. For example, the graph at right shows the horizontal line $y = 3$. The slope of any horizontal line is 0. The *x*-axis has the equation $y = 0$ because $y = 0$ everywhere on the *x*-axis. (p. 310)

hypotenuse The longest side of a right triangle (the side opposite the right angle). (p. 425)

Identity Property of Addition The Identity Property of Addition states that adding zero to any expression leaves the expression unchanged. That is, $a + 0 = a$. For example, $7 + 0 = 7$, and $-2y + 0 = -2y$. (p. 74)

Identity Property of Multiplication The Identity Property of Multiplication states that multiplying any expression by 1 leaves the expression unchanged. That is, $a(1) = a$. For example, $437x \cdot 1 = 437x$. (p. 74)

independent variable When one quantity changes in a way that does not depend on the value of another quantity, the value that changes independently is represented with the independent variable. For example, you might relate the speed of a car to the amount of force you apply to the gas pedal. Here, the amount of force applied may be whatever the driver chooses, so it represents the independent variable. The independent variable appears as the input value in an $x \rightarrow y$ table, and is usually placed relative to the horizontal axis of a graph. You often use the letter x and the horizontal x-axis for the independent variable. When working with functions or relations, the independent variable represents the input value. In Statistics, the independent variable is often called the explanatory variable. Also see *dependent variable*. (p. 11, 378)

indirect measurement A technique that uses proportionality to determine a measurement when directly measuring the object is not possible. (p. 482)

inequality An inequality consists of two expressions on either side of an inequality symbol. For example, the inequality $7x + 4.2 < -8$ states that the expression $7x + 4.2$ has a value less than –8.

inequality symbols The symbol $\leq$ read from left to right means "less than or equal to," the symbol $\geq$ read from left to right means "greater than or equal to," and the symbols $<$ and $>$ mean "less than" and "greater than," respectively. For example, "$7 < 13$" means that 7 is less than 13.

input value The input value is the independent variable in a relation. Substitute the input value into our rule (equation) to determine the output value. For example, if you have a rule for how much your phone bill will be if you talk a certain number of minutes, the number of minutes you talk is the input value. The input value appears first in an $x \rightarrow y$ table, and is represented by the variable x. When working with functions, the input value is the value put into the function. (p. 14)

integers The set of numbers $\{\ldots, -3, -2, -1, 0, 1, 2, 3, \ldots\}$.

intercepts Points where a graph crosses the axes. x-intercepts are points at which the graph crosses the x axis and y-intercepts are points at which the graph crosses the y axis. On the graph at right the x-intercept is $(3, 0)$ and the y-intercept is $(0, 6)$. (p. 124)

interest An amount paid which is a percentage of an initial value (principal). For example, a savings account may offer 4% annual interest rate, which means they will pay $4.00 in interest for a principal of $100 kept in the account for one year. (p. 304)

inverse operation An operation that undoes another operation. For example, multiplication is the inverse operation for division.

irrational numbers The set of numbers that cannot be expressed in the form $\frac{a}{b}$, where a and b are integers and $b \neq 0$. For example, π and $\sqrt{2}$ are irrational numbers. (p. 429)

lateral face A (flat) sides of a polyhedron. It is always a polygon. (p. 468)

lattice points The points on a coordinate grid where the grid lines intersect. The diagram at right shows two lattice points. The coordinates of lattice points are integers. (p. 302)

laws of exponents The laws of exponents studied in this course are: (p. 373)

Law	Examples	
$x^m x^n = x^{m+n}$ for all x	$x^3 x^4 = x^{3+4} = x^7$	$2^5 \cdot 2^{-1} = 2^4$
$\frac{x^m}{x^n} = x^{m-n}$ for $x \neq 0$	$x^{10} \div x^4 = x^{10-4} = x^6$	$\frac{5^4}{5^7} = 5^{-3}$
$(x^m)^n = x^{mn}$ for all x	$(x^4)^3 = x^{4 \cdot 3} = x^{12}$	$(10^5)^6 = 10^{30}$
$x^0 = 1$ for $x \neq 0$	$\frac{y^2}{y^2} = y^0 = 1$	$9^0 = 1$
$x^{-1} = \frac{1}{x}$ for $x \neq 0$	$\frac{1}{x^2} = (\frac{1}{x})^2 = (x^{-1})^2 = x^{-2}$	$3^{-1} = \frac{1}{3}$

legs The two sides of a right triangle that form the right angle. Note that legs of a right triangle are always shorter than its hypotenuse. (p. 425)

"legal" moves When working with an Equation Mat or Expression Comparison Mat, there are certain "legal" moves you can make with the algebra tiles that keep the relationship between the two sides of the mat intact. For example, removing an x tile from the positive region of each side of an equation mat is a legal move; it keeps the expressions on each side of the mat equal. The legal moves are those justified by the properties of the real numbers. (p. 72)

like terms Two or more terms that contain the same variable(s), with corresponding variables raised to the same power. For example, $5x^2$ and $2x^2$ are like terms. See *combining like terms*. (p. 56)

line A line is an undefined term in geometry. A line is one-dimensional and continues without end in two directions. A line is made up of points and has no thickness. A line may be named with a letter (such as l), but also may be labeled using two points on the line, such as $\overleftrightarrow{AB}$ shown the right.

$A \qquad B$

line segment   The portion of a line between two points. A line segment is named using its endpoints. For example, the line segment at right may be named either $\overline{AB}$ or $\overline{BA}$.

A B

line of best fit   A line that represents, in general, data on a scatterplot. The line of best fit is a model of numerical two-variable data that helps describe the data. It is also used to make predictions for other data. (p. 282)

linear association   See *association*. (p. 290)

linear equation   An equation in two variables whose graph is a line. For example, $y = 2.1x - 8$ is a linear equation. The standard form for a linear equation is $ax + by = c$, where a, b, and c are constants and a and b are not both zero. Most linear equations can be written in $y = mx + b$ form, which is more useful for determining the line's slope and y-intercept. (p. 189)

lowest common denominator (LCD)   The smallest common multiple of the denominators of two or more fractions. For example, the LCD of $\frac{5}{12}$ and $\frac{3}{8}$ is 24. (p. 192)

m   When the equation of a line is expressed in $y = mx + b$ form, the parameter m gives the slope of the line. For example, the slope of the line $y = -\frac{1}{3}x + 7$ is $-\frac{1}{3}$. (p. 162)

mean   The mean, or average, of several numbers is one way of defining the "middle" of the numbers. To find the average of a group of numbers, add the numbers together then divide by the number of numbers in the set. For example, the average of the numbers $1, 5$, and 6 is $(1 + 5 + 6) \div 3 = 4$. The mean is generally the best measure of central tendency when there are not outliers in the data set. See *average*.

measure of central tendency   Mean and median are measures of central tendency, reflecting special statistical information about a set of data. See *center (of a data distribution)*.

measurement   For the purposes of this course, a measurement is an indication of the size or magnitude of a geometric figure. For example, an appropriate measurement of a line segment would be its length. Appropriate measurements of a square would include not only the length of a side, but also its area and perimeter. The measure of an angle represents the number of degrees of rotation from one ray to the other about the vertex.

median   The middle number of an ordered set of data. If there is no distinct middle, then the average of the two middle numbers is the median. The median is generally more accurate than the mean as a measure of central tendency when there are outliers in the data set.

model A mathematical summary (often an equation) of a trend in data, after making assumptions and approximations to simplify a complicated situation. Models allow us to describe data to others, compare data more easily to other data, and allow us to make predictions. For example, mathematical models of weather patterns allow us to predict the weather. No model is perfect, but some models are better at describing trends than other models. (p. 492)

multiple representations web An organizational tool used to keep track of connections between the four representations of relationships between quantities emphasized in this course. In this course, four different ways of representing a numerical relationship are emphasized: with a graph, table, situation (pattern), or rule (equation or inequality).

multiplicative identity The number 1 is called the multiplicative identity because multiplying any number by 1 does not change the number. For example, $7(1) = 7$. (p. 74)

Multiplicative Identity Property The Multiplicative Identity Property states that multiplying any expression by 1 leaves the expression unchanged. That is, $a(1) = a$. For example, $437x \cdot 1 = 437x$. (p. 74)

multiplicative inverse The multiplicative inverse for a non-zero number is the number you can multiply by to get the multiplicative identity, 1. For example, for the number 5, the multiplicative inverse is $\frac{1}{5}$; for the number $\frac{2}{3}$ the multiplicative inverse is $\frac{3}{2}$. (p. 78)

non-commensurate Two measurements are called non-commensurate if no whole number multiple of one measurement can ever equal a whole number multiple of the other. For example, measures of 1 cm and $\sqrt{2}$ cm are non-commensurate, because no combination of items 1 cm long will ever have exactly the same length as a combination of items $\sqrt{2}$ cm long. (p. 48)

number line A diagram representing all real numbers as points on a line. All real numbers are assigned to points. The numbers are called the coordinates of the points and the point for which the number 0 is assigned is called the origin. Also see *boundary point*. (p. 18)

obtuse angle Any angle that measures between (but not including) 90° and 180°.

obtuse triangle A triangle with one obtuse angle. (p. 420)

one-dimensional Something that does not have any width or depth. Lines and curves are one-dimensional.

operation A mathematical process such as addition, subtraction, multiplication, division, raising to a power, or taking a root.

opposite (of a number)   The same number but with the opposite sign (+ or –).
The additive inverse. (p. 78)

Order of Operations   The specific order in which certain operations are to be carried out
to evaluate or simplify expressions: parentheses (or other grouping symbols), exponents
(powers or roots), multiplication and division (from left to right), and addition and
subtraction (from left to right). (p. 61)

ordered pair   Two numbers written in order as follows: (x, y). The
primary use of ordered pairs in this course is to represent points in an
xy-coordinate system. The first coordinate (x) represents the distance
from the x-axis. The second coordinate (y) represents the distance from
the y-axis. For example, the ordered pair $(3, 5)$ represents the point
shown in bold at right. (p. 11)

origin   The point on a coordinate plane where the x-axis and y-axis intersect is called the
origin. This point has coordinates $(0, 0)$. The point assigned to zero on a number line is
also called the origin. See *axis*. (p. 11)

outlier   A number in a set of data that is much larger or much smaller than the other
numbers in the set. (p. 322)

output value   The output value is the dependent variable in a relation. When you
substitute the input value into our rule (equation), the result is the output value. For
example, if you have a rule for how much your phone bill will be if you talk a certain
number of minutes, the amount of your phone bill is the output value. The output value
appears second in an $x \rightarrow y$ table, and is represented by the variable y. When working with
functions, the output value is the value that results from applying the rule for the function
to an input value. (p. 14)

parabola   A parabola is a particular kind of
mathematical curve. In this course, a parabola is always
the graph of a quadratic function $y = ax^2 + bx + c$ where a
does not equal 0. The diagram at right shows some
examples of parabolas. The highest or lowest point on
the graph is called the vertex. (p. 109)

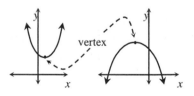

parallel   Two or more straight lines on a flat surface that do not
intersect (no matter how far they are extended) are parallel. The
matching arrows on the parallelogram (see below) indicate that
those segments are parallel. (p. 210)

parameter   In a general equations where x and y represent the inputs and outputs of the function, variables such as b and m, are often referred to as parameters, and they are often replaced with specific values. For example: in the equation $y = mx + b$ representing all lines, the b and m are (variable) parameters that give the slope and y-intercept, while x and y are the independent and dependent variables. (p. 162)

pattern   A pattern is a set of things in order that change in a regular way. For example, the numbers $1, 4, 7, 10, \ldots$ form a pattern, because each number increases by 3. The numbers $1, 4, 9, 16, \ldots$ form a pattern, because they are squares of consecutive integers. In this course, you often look at tile patterns, whose figure numbers and areas are represented with a table, a rule (equation), or a graph.

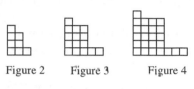

Figure 2   Figure 3   Figure 4

percent (%)   A ratio that compares a number to 100. Percents are often written using the "%" symbol. For example, 0.75 is equal to $\frac{75}{100}$ or 75%. (p. 5)

perfect square   A number that is the product of an integer and itself. For example, 25 is a perfect square because it is the product of 5 and 5. (p. 422)

perimeter   The distance around a figure on a flat surface. (p. 50)

Perimeter =
$5 + 8 + 4 + 6 = 23$ units

perpendicular   Two rays, line segments, or lines that meet (intersect) to form a right angle (90°) are called perpendicular. A line and a flat surface may also be perpendicular if the line does not lie on the flat surface but intersects the surface and forms a right angle with every line on the flat surface passing through the point of intersection. A small square at the point of intersection of two lines or segments indicates that the lines form a right angle and are therefore perpendicular. (p. 391)

pi (π)   The ratio of the circumference (C) of the circle to its diameter (d). For every circle, $\pi = \frac{\text{circumference}}{\text{diameter}} = \frac{C}{d}$. Numbers such as 3.14, 3.14159, or $\frac{22}{7}$ are approximations of π. (p. 128)

plane   A plane is a two-dimensional flat surface that extends without end. It is made up of points and has no thickness.

point   An exact location in space. In two dimensions, an ordered pair specifies a point on a coordinate plane. See *ordered pair*.

point of intersection A point of intersection is a point that the graphs of two equations have in common. For example, (3, 4) is a point of intersection of the two graphs shown at right. Two graphs may have one point of intersection, several points of intersection, or no points of intersection. The ordered pair representing a point of intersection gives a solution to the equations of each of the graphs. (p. 197)

polygon A two-dimensional closed figure of three or more line segments (sides) connected end to end. Each segment is a side and only intersects the endpoints of its two adjacent sides. Each point of intersection is a vertex. At right are two examples of polygons.

portion A part of something; a part of a whole.

portions web The web diagram at right illustrates that fractions, decimals, and percents are different ways to represent a portion of a number. Portions may also be represented in words, such as "four-fifths" or "seven-fourths," or as diagrams. (p. 5)

power A number or variable raised to an exponent in the form x^n. See *exponent*.

> fraction
>
> words or pictures
>
> decimal   percent
>
> **Representations of a Portion**

predicted value (of an association) The dependent (y-value) that is predicted for an independent (x-value) by the best-fit model for an association.

prime number A positive integer with exactly two factors. The only factors of a prime number are 1 and itself. For example, the numbers 2, 3, 17, and 31 are all prime.

principal Initial investment or capital. An initial value. (p. 341, 351)

prism A three-dimensional figure that consists of two parallel congruent polygons (called *bases*) and a vertical surface containing segments connecting each point on each side of one base to the corresponding point on the other base. The lateral surface of a prism consists of parallelograms.

product The result of multiplying. For example, the product of 4 and 5 is 20.

proportion An equation stating that two ratios (fractions) are equal. For example, the equation at right is a proportion. A proportion is a useful type of equation to set up when solving problems involving proportional relationships. (p. 315)

$$\frac{68 \text{ votes for Mr. Mears}}{100 \text{ people surveyed}} = \frac{34 \text{ votes for Mr. Mears}}{50 \text{ people surveyed}}$$

proportional equation   An equation stating that two ratios (fractions) are equal. (p. 313)

proportional relationship   Two values are in a proportional relationship if a proportion may be set up that relates the values. (p. 313)

pyramid   A three-dimensional figure with a base that is a polygon. The lateral faces are formed by connecting each vertex of the base to a single point (the vertex of the pyramid) that is above or below the surface that contains the base. (p. 465)

Pythagorean Theorem   The statement relating the lengths of the legs of a right triangle to the length of the hypotenuse:
$(\text{leg \#1})^2 + (\text{leg \#2})^2 = \text{hypotenuse}^2$. The Pythagorean Theorem is powerful because if you know the lengths of any two sides of a right triangle, you can use this relationship to find the length of the third side. (p. 425)

quadrants   The coordinate plane is divided by its axes into four quadrants. The quadrants are numbered as shown in the first diagram at right. When graphing data that has no negative values, sometimes a graph that shows only the first quadrant is used. (p. 11)

4-quadrant graph:

y-axis

II | I

x-axis

III | IV

1st-quadrant graph:

y-axis

x-axis

quadrilateral   A polygon with four sides. The shape at right is a quadrilateral.

quartile   Along with the median, the quartiles divide a set of data into four groups of the same size. Also see *box plot*.

quotient   The result of a division problem.

radical   An expression in the form $\sqrt{a}$, where $\sqrt{a}$ is the positive square root of a. For example, $\sqrt{49} = 7$. Also see *square root*. (p. 438)

radicand   The expression under a radical sign. For example, in the expression $3 + 2\sqrt{x-7}$, the radicand is $x - 7$. (p. 438)

radius (plural: radii)   A line segment drawn from the center of a circle to a point on the circle. (p. 128)

rate   A ratio comparing two quantities, often a comparison of time. For example, miles per hour. (p. 310)

ratio   A ratio compares two quantities by division. A ratio may be written using a colon, but is more often written as a fraction. For example, the comparison may be made of the ratio of female students in a particular school to the total number of students in the school. This ratio could be written as 1521:2906 or as the fraction shown at right. (p. 262)

$$\frac{1521 \text{ female students}}{2906 \text{ total students}}$$

rational numbers   Numbers that may be expressed in the form $\frac{a}{b}$, where a and b are integers and $b \neq 0$. For example, 0.75 is a rational number because 0.75 may be expressed in the form $\frac{3}{4}$. (p. 433)

ray   A ray is part of a line that starts at one point and extends without end in one direction. In the example at right, ray $\overrightarrow{AB}$ is part of $\overleftrightarrow{AB}$ that starts at A and contains all of the points of $\overleftrightarrow{AB}$ that are on the same side of A as point B, including A. Point A is the endpoint of $\overrightarrow{AB}$. (p. 396)

real numbers   Irrational numbers together with rational numbers form the set of the real numbers. For example, the following are all real numbers: $2.78, -13267, 0, \frac{3}{7}, \pi, \sqrt{2}$. All real numbers are represented on the number line. (p. 433)

reciprocal   The reciprocal of a nonzero number is its multiplicative inverse, that is, the reciprocal of x is $\frac{1}{x}$. For a number in the form $\frac{a}{b}$, where a and b are non-zero, the reciprocal is $\frac{b}{a}$. The product of a number and its reciprocal is 1. For example, the reciprocal of 12 is $\frac{1}{12}$, because $12 \cdot \frac{1}{12} = 1$. (p. 78)

reduce   To make smaller. (p. 262)

reflection   A transformation across a line that produces a mirror image of the original (pre-image) shape. The reflection is called the "image" of the original figure. The line is called a "line of reflection." See the example at right. Note that a reflection is also sometimes referred to as a "flip." (p. 233)

original   image

Line of reflection

relative frequency   A ratio or percent. If 60 people are asked, and 15 people prefer "red," the relative frequency of people preferring red is $\frac{15}{60} = 25\%$. (p. 325)

relative frequency table   A two-way table in which the percent of subjects in each combination of categories is displayed. (p. 325)

remote interior angles   If a triangle has an exterior angle, the remote interior angles are the two angles not adjacent to the exterior angle. Also called "non-adjacent interior angles." (p. 409)

remote interior
angles

exterior
angle

repeating decimal   A repeating decimal is a decimal that repeats the same sequence of digits forever from some point onward. For example, 4.56073073073... is a decimal for which the three digits 073 continue to repeat forever. Repeating decimals are always the decimal expansions of rational numbers. (p. 431)

Core Connections, Course 3

right angle An angle that measures 90°. A small square is used to note a right angle, as shown in the example at right.

right triangle A triangle that has one right angle. The side of a right triangle opposite the right angle is called the "hypotenuse," and the two sides adjacent to the right angle are called "legs." (p. 425)

rigid transformations Movements of figures that preserve their shape and size. Also called "rigid transformations." Examples of rigid motions are reflections, rotations, and translations. (p. 233)

rotation A transformation that turns all of the points in the original (pre-image) figure the same number of degrees around a fixed center point (such as the origin on a graph). The result is called the "image" of the original figure. The point that the shape is rotated about is called the "center of rotation." To define a rotation, you need to state the measure of turn (in degrees), the direction the shape is turned (such as clockwise or counter-clockwise), and the center of rotation. See the example at right. Note that a rotation is also sometimes referred to as a "turn." (p. 223)

rule A rule is an equation or inequality that represents the relationship between two numerical quantities. A rule is often used to represent the relationship between quantities in a table, a pattern, a real-world situation, or a graph. (p. 93)

same side interior angles Two angles between two lines and on the same side of a third line that intersects them (called a transversal). The shaded angles in the diagram at right are an example of a pair of same-side interior angles. Note that if the two lines that are cut by the transversal are parallel, then the two angles are supplementary (add up to 180°). (p. 401)

scale factor A ratio that compares the sizes of the parts of one figure or object to the sizes of the corresponding parts of a similar figure or object. In this course it is also referred to as the multiplier. (p. 262)

scale (on axes) The scale on an axis tells you what number each successive tick mark on the axis represents. A complete graph has the scale marked with numbers on each axis. Each axis should be scaled so that each interval represents the same amount. (p. 108)

scatterplot A way of displaying two-variable numerical data where two measurements are taken for each subject (like height and forearm length, or surface area of cardboard and volume of cereal held in a cereal box). To create a scatterplot, the two values for each subject are written as coordinate pairs and graphed on a pair of coordinate axes (each axis representing a variable). Also see *association*. (p. 196)

scientific notation A number is expressed in scientific notation when it is in the form $a \cdot 10^n$, where $1 \le a < 10$ and n is an integer. For example, the number 31,000 can be expressed in scientific notation as $3.1 \cdot 10^4$. (p. 367)

similar figures Similar figures have the same shape but are not necessarily the same size. For example the two triangles at right are similar. In similar figures, the measures of corresponding angles are equal and the ratio of the corresponding sides lengths are equal. (p. 245)

simple interest Interest paid on the principal alone. (p. 341)

simplify To simplify an expression is to write a less complicated expression with the same value. A simplified expression has no parentheses and no like terms. For example, the expression $3 - (2x + 7) - 4x$ may be simplified to $-4 - 6x$. When working with algebra tiles, a simplified expression uses the fewest possible tiles to represent the original expression. (p. 50)

slide *See* translation.

slope A ratio that describes how steep (or flat) a line is. Slope can be positive, negative, or even zero, but a straight line has only one slope. Slope is the ratio $\frac{\text{vertical change}}{\text{horizontal change}}$ or $\frac{\text{change in } y \text{ value}}{\text{change in } x \text{ value}}$, sometimes written $\frac{\Delta y}{\Delta x}$. When the equation of a line is written in $y = mx + b$ form, m is the slope of the line. Some texts refer to slope as the ratio of the "rise over the run." A line has positive slope if it slopes upward from left to right on a graph, negative slope if it slopes downward from left to right, zero slope if it is horizontal, and undefined slope if it is vertical. Slope is interpreted in context as the amount of change in the y-variable for an increase of one unit in the x-variable. (p. 310)

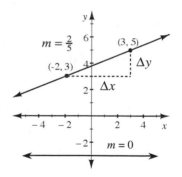

slope-intercept form A form of a linear equation: $y = mx + b$. In this form, m is the slope and the point $(0, b)$ is the y-intercept. *See* "$y = mx + b$." (p. 189)

solid A closed three-dimensional shape and all of its interior points. Examples include regions bounded by pyramids, cylinders, and spheres.

solution The number or numbers that when substituted into an equation or inequality make the equation or inequality true. For example, $x = 4$ is a solution to the equation $3x = 12$ because $3x$ equals 12 when $x = 4$. (p. 136)

solve To find all the solutions to an equation or an inequality. The solution(s) may be number(s), variable(s), or an expression.

sphere The set of all points in space that are the same distance from a fixed point. The fixed point is the center of the sphere and the distance is its radius. (p. 470)

Sphere

square (a number) To square a number means to multiply it by itself, or raise it to the second power. For example, 7 squared is 7^2 or $7 \cdot 7$ which is 49. (p. 438)

square root A number a is a square root of b if $a^2 = b$. For example, the number 9 has two square roots, 3 and –3. A negative number has no real square roots; a positive number has two; and zero has just one square root, namely, itself. Other roots, such as cube root, will be studied in other courses. Also see *radical*. (p. 438)

square units The units used to describe the measure of an area in the form of 1×1 unit squares.

standard form of a linear equation The standard form for a linear equation is $ax + by = c$, where a, b, and c are real numbers and a and b are not both zero. For example, the equation $2.5x - 3y = 12$ is in standard form. When you are given the equation of a line in standard form, it is often useful to write an equivalent equation in $y = mx + b$ form to find the line's slope and y-intercept. (p. 189)

stem-and-leaf plot A frequency distribution that arranges data so that all digits except the last digit in each piece of data are in the stem, the last digit of each piece of data are the leaves, and both stems and leaves are arranged in order from least to greatest. The example at right displays the data: 49, 52, 54, 58, 61, 61, 67, 68, 72, 73, 73, 73, 78, 82, 83, 108, 112, and 117.

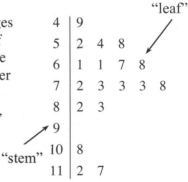

"leaf"

```
 4 | 9
 5 | 2  4  8
 6 | 1  1  7  8
 7 | 2  3  3  3  8
 8 | 2  3
 9 |
10 | 8
11 | 2  7
```

"stem"

stoplight icon The icon (shown at right) will appear periodically throughout the text. Problems that display this icon contain errors of some type. (p. 104)

straight angle An angle that measures 180°. This occurs when the rays of the angle point in opposite directions, forming a line. (p. 396)

180°

strength (of an association) A description of how much scatter there is in the data away from the line or curve of best fit.

substitution Replacing one symbol with a number, a variable, or another algebraic expression of the same value. Substitution does not change the value of the overall expression. For example, suppose that the expression $13x - 6$ must be evaluated for $x = 4$. Since x has the value 4, 4 may be substituted into the expression wherever x appears, giving the equivalent expression $13(4) - 6$. (p. 61)

supplementary angles Two angles a and b for which $a + b = 180°$. Each angle is called the supplement of the other. In the example at right, angles A and B are supplementary. Supplementary angles are often adjacent. For example, since $\angle LMN$ is a straight angle, then $\angle LMP$ and $\angle PMN$ are supplementary angles because $m\angle LMP + m\angle PMN = 180°$. (p. 396)

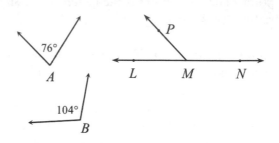

surface area The sum of all the area(s) of the surface(s) of a three-dimensional solid. For example, the surface area of a prism is the sum of the areas of its top and bottom bases, and its vertical surfaces (lateral faces). (p. 468)

system of equations A system of equations is a set of equations with the same variables. Solving a system of equations means finding one or more solutions that make each of the equations in the system true. A solution to a system of equations gives a point of intersection of the graphs of the equations in the system. There may be zero, one, or several solutions to a system of equations. For example, $(1.5, -3)$ is a solution to the system of equations at right; setting $x = 1.5$, $y = -3$ makes both of the equations true. Also, $(1.5, -3)$ is a point of intersection of the graphs of these two equations. (p. 196)

$$y = 2x - 6$$
$$y = -2x$$

table The tables used in this course represent numerical information by organizing it into columns and rows. The numbers may come from a graph, situation (pattern), or rule (equation). Many of the tables in this course are x-y tables like the one shown above right. (p. 124)

IN (x)	-2	4	1	6	-5
OUT (y)	-6	-2	-3	2	-9

term A term is a single number, variable, or the product of numbers and variables, such as -45, $1.2x$, and $3xy^2$. (p. 52)

terminating decimal A terminating decimal is a decimal that has only a finite number of non-zero digits, such as 4.067. Terminating decimals are a particular kind of repeating decimal for which the repeating portion is zeros, so the example could be written 4.0670000000... but it is not necessary to write the zeros at the end. (p. 5)

third quartile (Q3) The median of the upper half of an ordered set of data.

three-dimensional An object that has height, width, and depth.

tick mark A symbol that shows that a number line has been divided into intervals of equal length. See *number line*.

transformation This course studies four transformations: reflection, rotation, translation, and dilation. All of them preserve shape, and the first three preserve size. *See each term for its own definition*. (p. 233)

translation A transformation that preserves the size, shape, and orientation of a figure while sliding (moving) it to a new location. The result is called the "image" of the original figure. Note that a translation is sometimes referred to as a "slide." (p. 233)

original   image

transversal A line that intersects two or more other lines on a flat surface (plane). In this course, you often work with a transversal that intersects two parallel lines. (p. 391)

triangle A polygon with three sides.

Triangle Inequality In a triangle with side lengths a, b, and c, c must be less than the sum of a and b and greater than the difference of a and b. In the example at right, a is greater than b (that is, $a > b$), so the possible values for c are all numbers such that $c > a - b$ and $c < a + b$. (p. 420)

c
b a

Triangle Angle Sum Theorem The sum of the measures of the interior angles in any triangle is 180°. For example, in $\triangle ABC$ at right, $m\angle A + m\angle B + m\angle C = 180°$. (p. 405)

B
80°
40°   60°
A C

two-dimensional An object having length and width.

turn *See* rotation.

undefined slope The slope of a vertical line is undefined. (p. 310)

undoing In this course, "undoing" refers to a method of solving one-variable equations. In "undoing," you undo the last operation that was applied to an expression by applying its inverse operation. You then solve the resulting equation using various solution methods, including perhaps undoing again. For example, in the equation $4(x + 2) = 36$, the last operation that was applied to the left-hand side was a *multiplication* by 4. So to use "undoing," you *divide* both sides of the equation by 4, giving us $x + 2 = 9$. You then solve the equation $x + 2 = 9$ (perhaps by "undoing" again and subtracting 2 from both sides) to find that $x = 7$. (p. 35)

unit rate   A rate with a denominator of one when simplified. (p. 315)

variable   A symbol used to represent one or more numbers. In this course, letters of the English alphabet are used as variables. For example, in the expression $3x - (8.6xy + z)$, the variables are x, y, and z. (p. 52)

variable expression   See *expression*.

vertex (plural: vertices)   (1) For a two-dimensional geometric shape, a vertex is a point where two or more line segments or rays meet to form a "corner," such as in a polygon or angle. (2) For a three-dimensional polyhedron, a vertex is a point where the edges of the solid meet. (3) For a parabola it is the highest or lowest point on the parabola (depending on the parabola's orientation). (p. 109, 396)

vertical   At right angles to the horizon. On a coordinate graph, the y-axis runs vertically. (p. 310)

vertical angles   The two opposite (that is, non-adjacent) angles formed by two intersecting lines. "Vertical" is a relationship between pairs of angles, so one angle cannot be called vertical. Angles that form a vertical pair are always congruent. (p. 396)

vertical lines   Vertical lines run up and down in the same direction as the y-axis and are parallel to it. All vertical lines have equations of the form $x = a$, where a can be any number. For example, the graph at right shows the vertical line $x = 2$. The y-axis has the equation $x = 0$ because $x = 0$ everywhere on the y-axis. Vertical lines have undefined slope. (p. 310)

volume   A measurement of the size of the three-dimensional region enclosed within an object. Volume is expressed as the number of $1 \times 1 \times 1$ unit cubes (or parts of cubes) that fit inside a solid.

x-axis   The horizontal number line on a coordinate graph. See *axis*. (p. 11)

x-coordinate   In an ordered pair, (x, y), that represents a point in the coordinate plane, x is the value of the x-coordinate. That is, the distance from the y-axis that is needed to plot the point.

x-intercept(s) The point(s) where a graph intersects the x-axis. A graph may have several x-intercepts, no x-intercepts, or just one. You sometimes report the x-intercepts of a graph with coordinate pairs, but since the y-coordinate is always zero, you often just give the x-coordinates of x-intercepts. For example, you might say that the x-intercepts of the graph at right are $(0,0)$ and $(2,0)$, or you might just say that the x-intercepts are 0 and 2. (p. 124)

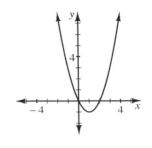

x → y table An $x \rightarrow y$ table, like the one at right, represents pairs of values of two related quantities. The input value (x) appears first, and the output value (y) appears second. For example, the $x \rightarrow y$ table at right tells us that the input value 10 is paired with the output value 18 for some rule. (p. 102)

IN (x)	OUT (y)
0	-2
-4	-10
10	18

y = mx + b When two quantities x and y have a linear relationship, that relationship can be represented with an equation in $y = mx + b$ form. The constant m is the slope, and b is the y-intercept of the graph. For example, the graph at right shows the line represented by the equation $y = 2x + 3$, which has a slope of 2 and a y-intercept of 3. This form of a linear equation is also called the slope-intercept form. (p. 162)

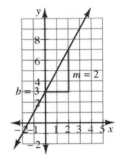

y-axis The vertical number line on a coordinate graph. See *axis*. (p. 11)

y-coordinate In an ordered pair, (x, y), that represents a point in the coordinate plane, y is the value of the y-coordinate. That is, the distance from the x-axis that is needed to plot the point.

y-intercept The point where a graph intersects the y-axis. A function has at most one y-intercept; a relation may have several. The y-intercept of a graph is important because it often represents the starting value of a quantity in a real-world situation. For example, on the graph of a tile pattern the y-intercept represents the number of tiles in Figure 0. You sometimes report the y-intercept of a graph with a coordinate pair, but since the x-coordinate is always zero, you often just give the y-coordinate of the y-intercept.

For example, you might say that the y-intercept of the graph at right is $(0, 2)$, or you might just say that the y-intercept is 2. When a linear equation is written in $y = mx + b$ form, b tells us the y-intercept of the graph. For example, the equation of the graph at right is $y = x + 2$ and its y-intercept is 2. (p. 124)

zero A number often used to represent "having none of a quantity." Zero is neither negative nor positive. Zero is the additive identity. (p. 59)

Index
Student Version

Many of the pages referenced here contain a definition or an example of the topic listed, often within the body of a Math Notes box. Others contain problems that develop or demonstrate the topic. It may be necessary to read the text on several pages to fully understand the topic. Also, some problems listed here are good examples of the topic and may not offer any explanation. The page numbers below reflect the pages in the Student Version. References to Math Notes boxes are bolded.

Core Connections, Course 3

Triangle Inequality, **419**
Turn
    rigid transformation, 223
    rotation, 226

U
Undoing
    division, 32, **35**
Unit rate, **315**
    Checkpoint 3, 141, 501
    of change, **310**

V
Variable, 47, **52**
    categorical, 324
    dependent, **113**, **378**
    independent, **113**, **378**
Vertex, 109
    angle, **396**
Vertical angles, **396**
Vertical line
    slope, **310**
Volume
    application, 474
    cone, 465, 472
    cylinder, 460, **463**
    pyramid, 465, **472**
    sphere, 470, 471, **475**

W
Web, multiple representations, 157, 168, 173
Weighing Pumpkins (PI-9), 531
What's My Number? (PI-11), 533
Which is the Fake? (PI-1), 525
Word problem
    writing rule, 200

X
$x \rightarrow y$ table
    from a pattern, 102
x-axis, **11**
x-intercept, 116, **124**
x-value, 14
xy-coordinate system, 14

Y
$y = mx + b$, 162, 293
y-axis, **11**
y-intercept, 116, **124**, 171, **189**
y-value, 14

Z
Zero, 59

Common Core State Standards for Mathematics

Mathematics | Grade 8

In Grade 8, instructional time should focus on three critical areas: (1) formulating and reasoning about expressions and equations, including modeling an association in bivariate data with a linear equation, and solving linear equations and systems of linear equations; (2) grasping the concept of a function and using functions to describe quantitative relationships; (3) analyzing two- and three-dimensional space and figures using distance, angle, similarity, and congruence, and understanding and applying the Pythagorean Theorem.

(1) Students use linear equations and systems of linear equations to represent, analyze, and solve a variety of problems. Students recognize equations for proportions ($y/x = m$ or $y = mx$) as special linear equations ($y = mx + b$), understanding that the constant of proportionality (m) is the slope, and the graphs are lines through the origin. They understand that the slope (m) of a line is a constant rate of change, so that if the input or x-coordinate changes by an amount A, the output or y-coordinate changes by the amount $m \cdot A$. Students also use a linear equation to describe the association between two quantities in bivariate data (such as arm span vs. height for students in a classroom). At this grade, fitting the model, and assessing its fit to the data are done informally. Interpreting the model in the context of the data requires students to express a relationship between the two quantities in question and to interpret components of the relationship (such as slope and y-intercept) in terms of the situation.

Students strategically choose and efficiently implement procedures to solve linear equations in one variable, understanding that when they use the properties of equality and the concept of logical equivalence, they maintain the solutions of the original equation. Students solve systems of two linear equations in two variables and relate the systems to pairs of lines in the plane; these intersect, are parallel, or are the same line. Students use linear equations, systems of linear equations, linear functions, and their understanding of slope of a line to analyze situations and solve problems.

(2) Students grasp the concept of a function as a rule that assigns to each input exactly one output. They understand that functions describe situations where one quantity determines another. They can translate among representations and partial representations of functions (noting that tabular and graphical representations may be partial representations), and they describe how aspects of the function are reflected in the different representations.

(3) Students use ideas about distance and angles, how they behave under translations, rotations, reflections, and dilations, and ideas about congruence and similarity to describe and analyze two-dimensional figures and to solve problems. Students show that the sum of the angles in a triangle is the angle formed by a straight line, and that various

Grade 8

configurations of lines give rise to similar triangles because of the angles created when a transversal cuts parallel lines. Students understand the statement of the Pythagorean Theorem and its converse, and can explain why the Pythagorean Theorem holds, for example, by decomposing a square in two different ways. They apply the Pythagorean Theorem to find distances between points on the coordinate plane, to find lengths, and to analyze polygons. Students complete their work on volume by solving problems involving cones, cylinders, and spheres.

Grade 8 Overview

The Number System

- Know that there are numbers that are not rational, and approximate them by rational numbers.

Expressions and Equations

- Work with radicals and integer exponents.

- Understand the connection between proportional relationships, lines, and linear equations.

- Analyze and solve linear equations and pairs of simultaneous linear equations.

Functions

- Define, evaluate, and compare functions.

- Use functions to model relationships between quantities.

Geometry

- Understand congruence and similarity using physical models, transparencies, or geometry software.

- Understand and apply the Pythagorean Theorem.

- Solve real-world and mathematical problems involving volume of cylinders, cones, and spheres.

Statistics and Probability

- Investigate patterns of association in bivariate data.

Mathematical Practices

1. Make sense of problems and persevere in solving them.

2. Reason abstractly and quantitatively.

3. Construct viable arguments and critique the reasoning of others.

4. Model with mathematics.

5. Use appropriate tools strategically.

6. Attend to precision.

7. Look for and make use of structure.

8. Look for and express regularity in repeated reasoning.

Grade 8

The Number System   8.NS

Know that there are numbers that are not rational, and approximate them by rational numbers.

1. Know that numbers that are not rational are called irrational. Understand informally that every number has a decimal expansion; for rational numbers show that the decimal expansion repeats eventually, and convert a decimal expansion which repeats eventually into a rational number.

2. Use rational approximations of irrational numbers to compare the size of irrational numbers, locate them approximately on a number line diagram, and estimate the value of expressions (e.g., $\pi2$). *For example, by truncating the decimal expansion of $\sqrt{2}$, show that $\sqrt{2}$ is between 1 and 2, then between 1.4 and 1.5, and explain how to continue on to get better approximations.*

Expressions and Equations   8.EE

Work with radicals and integer exponents.

1. Know and apply the properties of integer exponents to generate equivalent numerical expressions. *For example, $3^2 \times 3^{-5} = 3^{-3} = 1/3^3 = 1/27$.*

2. Use square root and cube root symbols to represent solutions to equations of the form $x^2 = p$ and $x^3 = p$, where p is a positive rational number. Evaluate square roots of small perfect squares and cube roots of small perfect cubes. Know that $\sqrt{2}$ is irrational.

3. Use numbers expressed in the form of a single digit times an integer power of 10 to estimate very large or very small quantities, and to express how many times as much one is than the other. *For example, estimate the population of the United States as 3×10^8 and the population of the world as 7×10^9, and determine that the world population is more than 20 times larger.*

4. Perform operations with numbers expressed in scientific notation, including problems where both decimal and scientific notation are used. Use scientific notation and choose units of appropriate size for measurements of very large or very small quantities (e.g., use millimeters per year for seafloor spreading). Interpret scientific notation that has been generated by technology.

Understand the connections between proportional relationships, lines, and linear equations.

5. Graph proportional relationships, interpreting the unit rate as the slope of the graph. Compare two different proportional relationships represented in different ways. *For example, compare a distance-time graph to a distance-time equation to determine which of two moving objects has greater speed.*

6. Use similar triangles to explain why the slope m is the same between any two distinct points on a non-vertical line in the coordinate plane; derive the equation $y = mx$ for a line through the origin and the equation $y = mx + b$ for a line intercepting the vertical axis at b.

Analyze and solve linear equations and pairs of simultaneous linear equations.

7. Solve linear equations in one variable.

   a. Give examples of linear equations in one variable with one solution, infinitely many solutions, or no solutions. Show which of these possibilities is the case by successively transforming the given equation into simpler forms, until an equivalent equation of the form $x = a$, $a = a$, or $a = b$ results (where a and b are different numbers).

   b. Solve linear equations with rational number coefficients, including equations whose solutions require expanding expressions using the distributive property and collecting like terms.

8. Analyze and solve pairs of simultaneous linear equations.

   a. Understand that solutions to a system of two linear equations in two variables correspond to points of intersection of their graphs, because points of intersection satisfy both equations simultaneously.

   b. Solve systems of two linear equations in two variables algebraically, and estimate solutions by graphing the equations. Solve simple cases by inspection. *For example, 3x + 2y = 5 and 3x + 2y = 6 have no solution because 3x + 2y cannot simultaneously be 5 and 6.*

   c. Solve real-world and mathematical problems leading to two linear equations in two variables. *For example, given coordinates for two pairs of points, determine whether the line through the first pair of points intersects the line through the second pair.*

Functions   8.F

Define, evaluate, and compare functions.

1. Understand that a function is a rule that assigns to each input exactly one output. The graph of a function is the set of ordered pairs consisting of an input and the corresponding output.[1]

2. Compare properties of two functions each represented in a different way (algebraically, graphically, numerically in tables, or by verbal descriptions). *For example, given a linear function represented by a table of values and a linear function represented by an algebraic expression, determine which function has the greater rate of change.*

3. Interpret the equation $y = mx + b$ as defining a linear function, whose graph is a straight line; give examples of functions that are not linear. *For example, the function $A = s^2$ giving the area of a square as a function of its side length is not linear because its graph contains the points (1,1), (2,4) and (3,9), which are not on a straight line.*

Use functions to model relationships between quantities.

4. Construct a function to model a linear relationship between two quantities. Determine the rate of change and initial value of the function from a description of a relationship or from two (x, y) values, including reading these from a table or from a graph. Interpret the rate of change and initial value of a linear function in terms of the situation it models, and in terms of its graph or a table of values.

5. Describe qualitatively the functional relationship between two quantities by analyzing a graph (e.g., where the function is increasing or decreasing, linear or nonlinear). Sketch a graph that exhibits the qualitative features of a function that has been described verbally.

Geometry   8.G

Understand congruence and similarity using physical models, transparencies, or geometry software.

1. Verify experimentally the properties of rotations, reflections, and translations:
   a. Lines are taken to lines, and line segments to line segments of the same length.
   b. Angles are taken to angles of the same measure.
   c. Parallel lines are taken to parallel lines.

2. Understand that a two-dimensional figure is congruent to another if the second can be obtained from the first by a sequence of rotations, reflections, and translations; given two congruent figures, describe a sequence that exhibits the congruence between them.

3. Describe the effect of dilations, translations, rotations, and reflections on two-dimensional figures using coordinates.

---

[1] Function notation is not required in Grade 8.

Common Core State Standards for Mathematics

4. Understand that a two-dimensional figure is similar to another if the second can be obtained from the first by a sequence of rotations, reflections, translations, and dilations; given two similar two-dimensional figures, describe a sequence that exhibits the similarity between them.

5. Use informal arguments to establish facts about the angle sum and exterior angle of triangles, about the angles created when parallel lines are cut by a transversal, and the angle-angle criterion for similarity of triangles. *For example, arrange three copies of the same triangle so that the sum of the three angles appears to form a line, and give an argument in terms of transversals why this is so.*

Understand and apply the Pythagorean Theorem.

6. Explain a proof of the Pythagorean Theorem and its converse.

7. Apply the Pythagorean Theorem to determine unknown side lengths in right triangles in real-world and mathematical problems in two and three dimensions.

8. Apply the Pythagorean Theorem to find the distance between two points in a coordinate system.

Solve real-world and mathematical problems involving volume of cylinders, cones, and spheres.

9. Know the formulas for the volumes of cones, cylinders, and spheres and use them to solve real-world and mathematical problems.

Statistics and Probability   8.SP

Investigate patterns of association in bivariate data.

1. Construct and interpret scatter plots for bivariate measurement data to investigate patterns of association between two quantities. Describe patterns such as clustering, outliers, positive or negative association, linear association, and nonlinear association.

2. Know that straight lines are widely used to model relationships between two quantitative variables. For scatter plots that suggest a linear association, informally fit a straight line, and informally assess the model fit by judging the closeness of the data points to the line.

3. Use the equation of a linear model to solve problems in the context of bivariate measurement data, interpreting the slope and intercept. *For example, in a linear model for a biology experiment, interpret a slope of 1.5 cm/hr as meaning that an additional hour of sunlight each day is associated with an additional 1.5 cm in mature plant height.*

4. Understand that patterns of association can also be seen in bivariate categorical data by displaying frequencies and relative frequencies in a two-way table. Construct and interpret a two-way table summarizing data on two categorical variables collected from the same subjects. Use relative frequencies calculated for rows or columns to describe possible association between the two variables. *For example, collect data from students in your class on whether or not they have a curfew on school nights and whether or not they have assigned chores at home. Is there evidence that those who have a curfew also tend to have chores?*